Fantastic Geometry

There is geometry in the humming of the strings;
There is music in the spacing of the spheres.

Pythagoras

*Welcher aber ... durch die Geometria sein Ding beweist
und die gründliche Wahrheit anzeigt, dem soll alle Welt glauben.
Denn da ist man gefangen.*

Whoever ... proves his point and demonstrates
the prime truth geometrically should be believed by all the world,
or there we are captured.

Albrecht Dürer

Fantastic Geometry

Polyhedra and the Artistic Imagination in the Renaissance

David Wade

THE SQUEEZE PRESS • MMXXII

for Gini

Any project of this kind is bound to involve a degree of emotional leave-of-absence and the imposition of one's own enthusiasm on other people. Fortunately I have been blessed throughout this undertaking by a highly supportive wife, family and friends, and this has seen me through. I am really grateful to all of you.

In particular I would like to thank Dr Heike Neumeister for her invaluable art-historical advice, and help with the translation of German texts. This would be a far lesser book without her assistance.

The project owes a great deal to John Martineau, who encouraged it in the first place and provided constructive criticism throughout, and to Les Wilkins and Daud Sutton who, between them, helped knock the raw material into shape.

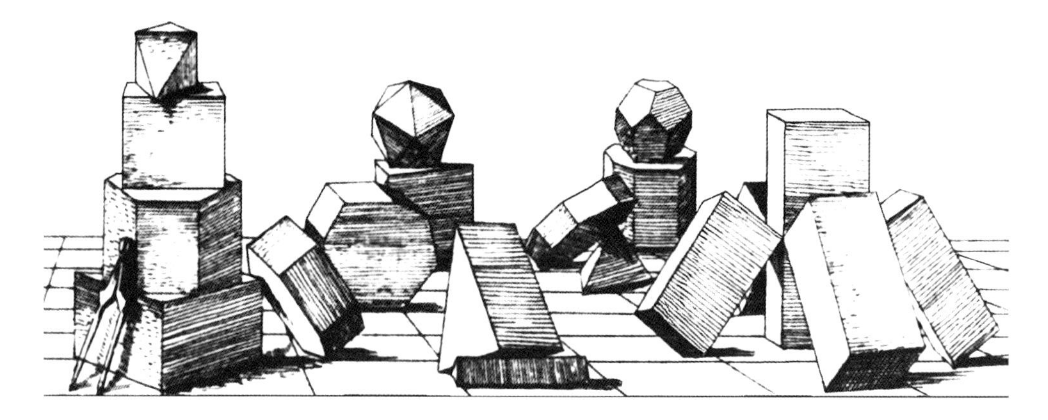

Contents

FANTASTIC
GEOMETRY
INTRODUCTION AND
BACKGROUND

A pen and watercolour drawing of a fantastical architectural setting with polyhedra and figures, two of whom are carrying measuring instruments. This is the largest surviving example of Lorenz Stoer's work. Although it appears to be a title page, its actual intended use is uncertain. Since the original is multichromatic it was clearly not intended for publication in this form; possibly it was an attempt to persuade a patron to fund some larger scheme.

Courtesy of Stätliche Graphische Sammlung, Munich.

Introduction

Mid-sixteenth century Germany saw the publication of a handful of books presenting a range of intriguing geometric drawings that were essentially unlike anything that had ever appeared before – or have been seen since. These images are the primary focus of this book, and perhaps the initial response that they evoke is of their strangely modern quality. They are perfectly accessible – we can appreciate them simply and directly on their own terms, but they also remain somewhat enigmatic. On learning of their date and provenance it is almost impossible not to speculate on the artist's motives in creating this fanciful, geometry-based imagery, and wonder how it was originally meant to be interpreted. And these questions lead naturally on to many others.

Most of the books in which these drawings appeared were published in the German city of Nuremberg, many within a very short period around the mid-1560s. What was so conducive to their production in this particular place and time? Even the fact that they appeared as illustrations in well-bound, marketable books is interesting, considering that the whole business of printing and publishing was in its infancy at this time. Finally, there is the term 'perspective' which features in the title of these volumes; what exactly does this signify? These books do not, on the face of it, appear to be expounding on this subject in any serious way.

Unfortunately, in pursuit of answers to these questions we get very little information from the books that are the main focus of this enquiry, or from the scant biographies of the artists involved. It is known that two of them were goldsmiths, and that they became notable citizens of the city of Nuremberg. We have a fair idea of the origins and dates of birth and death of Wenzel Jamnitzer, Lorenz Stoer and Johannes Lencker, and that of their various publications, but not much more. Of two later artists we have practically no information whatsoever. Skilled master-craftsmen and reputable citizens that they were, none of them attracted detailed biographies of the kind that Vasari compiled for the Italian fine artists, so little is known of the detail of their lives and thoughts. However, the limited textual references within these books give an indication of the source of the inspiration for their drawings. It transpires that the inspiration for this imaginative, collective fascination with regular geometric figures goes very far back indeed, ultimately to Classical antiquity. This is an art that was inspired by the values, attitudes and beliefs of the Pythagorean–Platonic tradition.

In this respect at least, our artist-authors were very much of their time. The great intellectual movement of the Renaissance, of which they were part, was a period when very big names indeed were caught up in an enthusiasm for these Platonic notions of an ideal geometry. This newly rediscovered idea, that fundamental truths of the universe might be based on mathematics, particularly of geometry, was a concept that was to prove extraordinarily productive in both the artistic and scientific spheres throughout the Renaissance. The list is impressive – Piero della Francesca, Paolo Uccello, Leonardo da Vinci and Albrecht Dürer all produced dissertations on the regular 'Platonic' solids. In addition, Johannes Kepler and Galileo Galilei, among many other notable figures, were deeply influenced by Platonism in their own scientific investigations.

In fact, Platonism had exerted a leavening effect on the arts before, in Europe and beyond, sometimes in subtle and imperceptible ways. It seems that wherever Platonic notions associating the contemplation of geometry with the transcendental have taken hold, that this has been reflected in aesthetic expression. The Platonic ideal of art as an imitation of eternal beauty exerted a sustained influence in the Byzantine and Islamic spheres, and was made gloriously manifest in the stained glass cathedral windows of Western Europe. The art that is the focus of this book, by comparison, is rather more secular and vague in its artistic intentions, but this scarcely detracts from the appeal of its refined geometricism.

Because of the paucity of any detailed contemporary accounts of the aesthetic intentions or philosophical beliefs of Wenzel Jamnitzer and the other artists featured here, I have felt it necessary to establish the context in which their remarkable graphic imagery came about. This requires a brief summary, firstly of Platonism itself, then of its influence on Renaissance thought, and finally how this was modified in its transition northwards to Germany. This progression is laid out in the first three chapters of this book.

There is another important motivating aspect of this art, one that is incorporated in the titles of each of the books involved, that of 'perspective'. It is evident that the problems of creating a convincing representation of three dimensions onto a two-dimensional surface exerted a particular and sustained fascination for Renaissance artists. This preoccupation reflected the abiding spirit of the time, common to both the arts and sciences, which might be characterised as a drive to explore and grasp reality. Comprehension and measurement of every aspect of the land below and the skies above became an integral part of this enterprise. Vision was extended with lenses; knowledge by the printed word; the sense of space by geographical and astronomical exploration; the sense of ratiocination by developments in mathematics. And a natural association was made between these concerns and those most rational of objects – geometric solids. Polyhedra, as well as being part of the practical discipline of geometry, acquired symbolic value as artistic motifs.

In common with all artistic movements, this one ran its course, ending in the early years of the seventeenth century. The vehicle on which it travelled, the Perspective Treatise (of which we will hear much more), went on to carry the grander visions of the Baroque, a style that eventually eclipsed this earlier tradition.

The primary objective here though is not a forensic art-historical examination of the subject, but to focus the spotlight on this brief flowering of fantastic geometry. In the past the graphic work of Jamnitzer and his followers have tended to be overlooked or, when noticed at all, to be regarded as a minor adjunct of German Mannerism. But their work may be due for a re-evaluation, not least because it still has the potential to engage and inspire. Its abstract, scale-transcending quality would seem to have a particular relevance to certain movements in contemporary sculpture for instance, and it may be that this art form has had to wait until the twenty-first century to realise its potential fully.

At a time when art might be characterised as being in a state of free-floating uncertainty, and when Euclidean geometry itself has been superseded in mainstream maths, the pure forms of this geometry-based art project a timeless quality, and because of this it can always provide the inspiration for further artistic invention.

The exploration of this timeless quality is the underlying intention of this book.

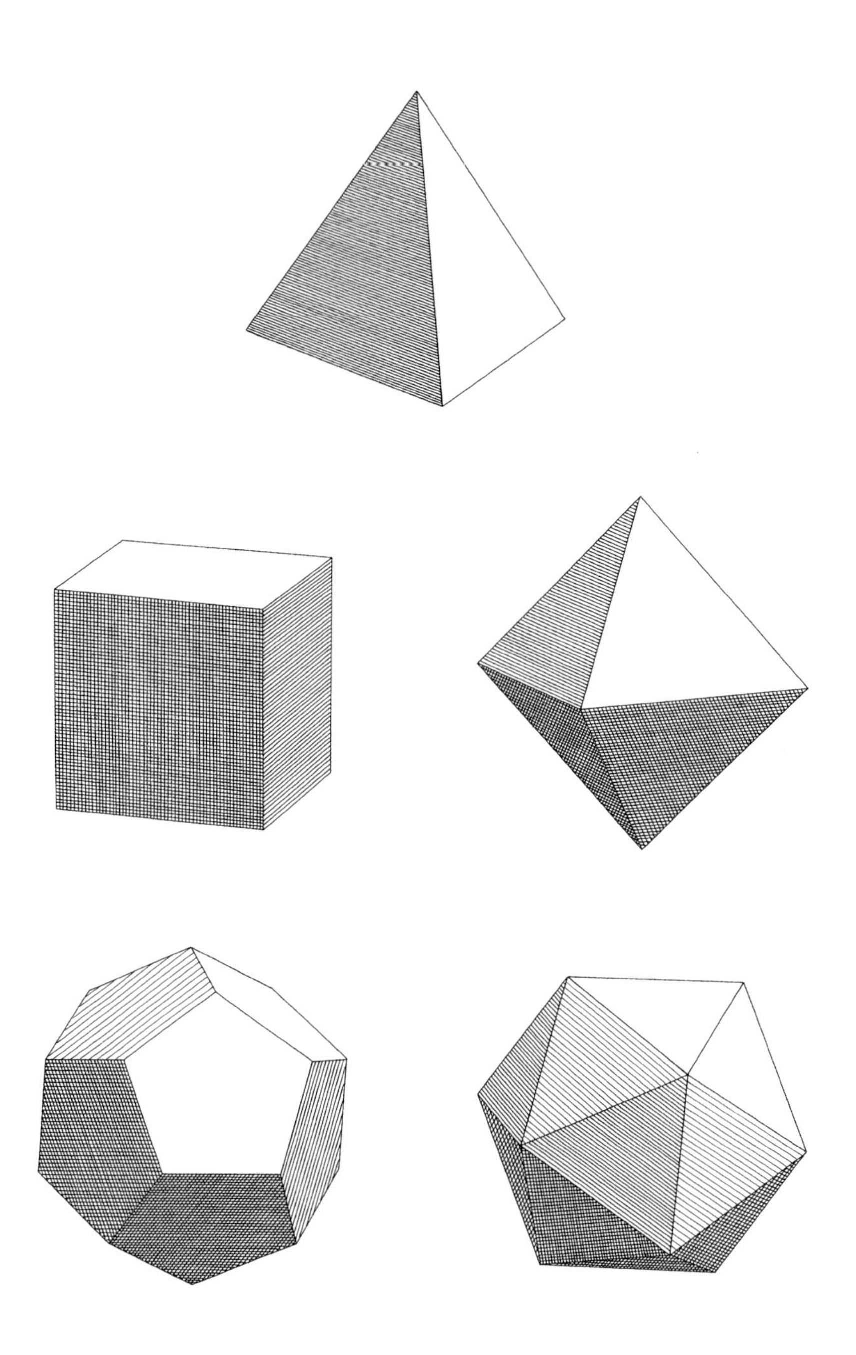

The five Platonic solids —
tetrahedron, cube, octahedron, dodecahedron and icosahedron.

I

The classical origins of a compelling idea

Pythagoras, Plato and their heritage

The potent idea that 'number is all', that mathematics underlies and is therefore the key to understanding the world, is usually attributed to the pre-Socratic philosopher Pythagorus. Pythagorus is a legendary and somewhat shadowy figure, about whom myths tended to accumulate – but he almost certainly did exist. He is believed to have been born on the island of Samos, and to have settled in southern Italy around 531 BC, where he established a semi-religious school of philosophy. Although the details of the earlier beliefs of the Pythagoreans are not known, it seems that they were much concerned with the study of music and mathematics. Certainly their most enduring legacy lay in the discoveries that they made in these fields. According to Aristotle they came to believe that numbers and proportions were the primary elements of nature, and focused their attention on instances where these were most apparent – in the ratios of the musical scales, for instance. They were also very interested in geometric figures, to which, as well as to numbers and ratios, they attributed mystical properties. In fact they seem to have believed that numbers and forms had a life and existence of their own, separate from the world, and they developed an elaborate cosmology in which certain of these were identified with gods. Their speculations in the field of geometry were therefore bound up with a contemplation of the transcendent, constituting – as they saw it – a form of prayer.

Aristotle later criticised the Pythagoreans for being number-obsessed, and clearly found many of their explanations far too contrived. Like numerologists through the ages they were rather prone to bend the facts to fit their ideas – 'If anything was lacking to complete their theories they quickly supplied it'. But despite the eccentricities of some of their cosmological views there was a great deal of substance in their theories. Importantly, for the future of western thought, their ideas retained their appeal. The school that was founded by Pythagoras endured for more

A medieval woodcut depicting the Pythagorean discovery that musical notes can be expressed in mathematical terms, beginning with the realisation that that the harmonious sounds coming from blacksmiths anvils is due to their regular proportions – 1:2, 2:3, 3:4 and so on.

than a millennium, and many of its precepts were later taken up by Plato and incorporated into his own philosophical views.

The influence of this stream of thought is most obvious in one of the most important of his Dialogues, the 'Timaeus', written in 360 BC. Following Pythagorean teaching, Plato differentiates the physical, which is subject to change and decay, from the eternal, which consists of pure, changeless forms. The physical world is, however, derived from the eternal (although the details of precisely how this occurs are somewhat hazy),

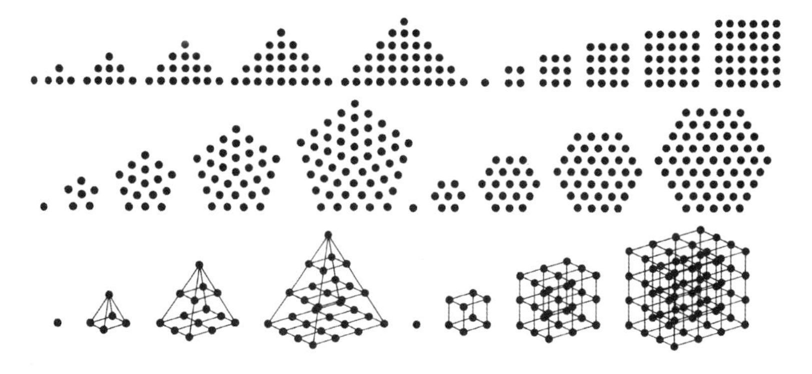

Pythagorean figures. Numbers were originally regarded by the Pythagoreans as patterns of dots which formed characteristic figures. Beginning with simple polygonal groups they progressed to tetrahedral, cubic and other three-dimensional series.

and is ultimately made up of elementary particles. These are of four kinds, corresponding to the four elements of the Classical world, earth, air, fire and water. The elements, in turn, were identified with the first four regular solids: thus, earth = cube; air = octahedron; fire = tetrahedron; water = icosahedron. The fifth of these regular figures (which came to be known as the Platonic solids), the dodecahedron, was associated with the cosmos. In time Plato's theories became so thoroughly bound up with the Pythagorean precepts that he had inherited that it was difficult to distinguish between them. But the notion that geometrical forms were possessed of a timeless perfection, and that they were our best chance for a greater understanding of the true nature of the cosmos, was a very persistent and creative one for both the arts and the sciences.

In 320 BC Aristaeus the elder, a mathematician who was clearly influenced by Plato, wrote a *Comparison of the Five Regular Solids*, in which he established that 'the same circle circumscribes both the pentagon of the dodecahedron and the triangle of the icosahedron when both are inscribed in the same sphere'. This work inspired his near-contemporary, Euclid, who investigated the whole range of plane and solid geometry in the same systematic way, culminating in his *Elements*, the first comprehensive and logical system of geometry – and one that endured until the twentieth century. In the final book (Book XIII) of the *Elements* Euclid explains, in eighteen propositions, how to inscribe the five regular solids within a sphere. To later commentators this was taken as evidence that he meant his influential work as a sort of testament

Examples of Euclid's Elements *in Arabic translation.*

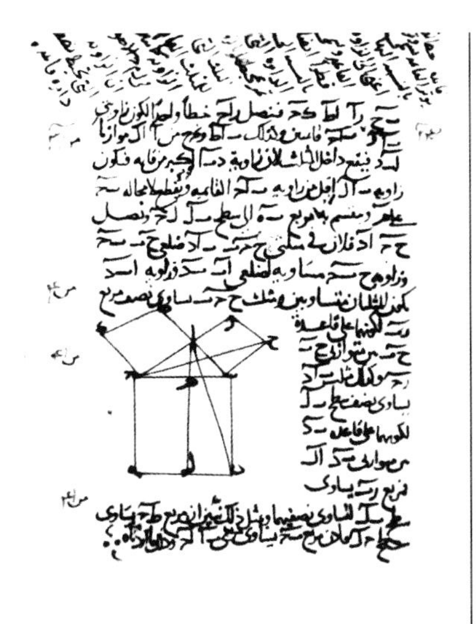

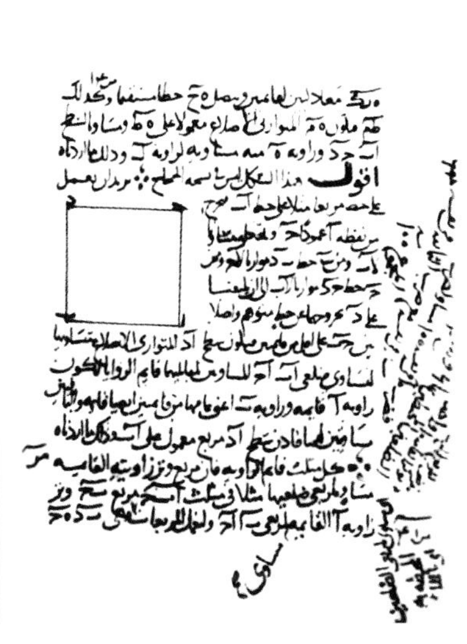

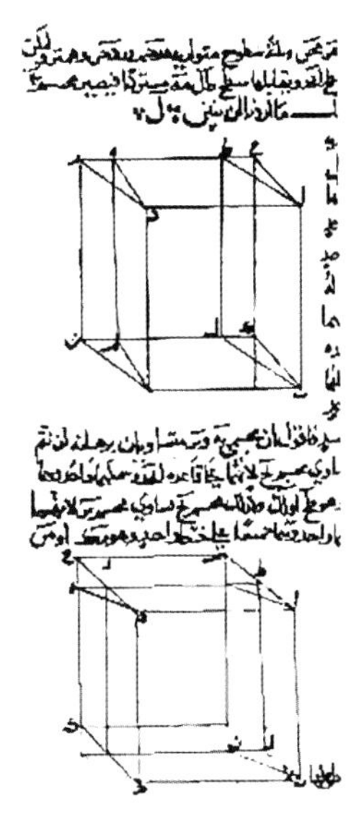

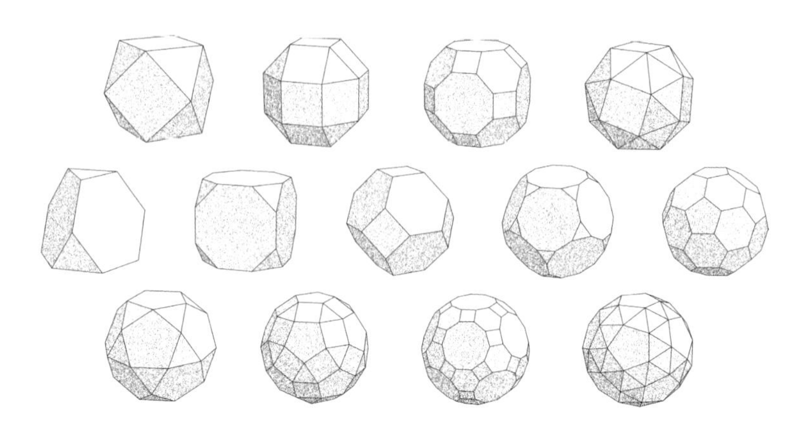

The thirteen Archimedean solids. The middle row are simple truncations of the five Platonic solids. The rows above and below are further forms related to the cube and octahedron (top), and the dodecahedron and icosahedron (bottom).

to their cosmological importance. The *Elements* was certainly one of the most influential textbooks ever written, and several of the greatest mathematicians of the Classical world made amendments and further advances on it.

The subject of polyhedra was of particular interest to Archimedes (287–212 BC), who thoroughly investigated truncated versions of the regular solids and in so doing discovered, and gave his name to, the thirteen *semi-regular* solids. Apollonius of Perga (262–180 BC), famous for his treatment of conics, also wrote a treatise on the ratios between the dimensions of the icosahedron and dodecahedron These discoveries were improved on by Hypsicles of Alexandria (190–120 BC), in a work that later became known as Book XV of Euclid's *Elements*. In the late-Classical period speculation in mathematics and physics tended towards more practical applications rather than the purely theoretical, even so, Hero of Alexandria (*fl.* 150 AD) dealt with the measurement and relative volumes and sizes of polyhedra, and as late as the fourth century AD these matters were still engaging the interest of Pappus of Alexandria. But the Classical world was fast approaching a crisis of confidence.

The Byzantine and Islamic tenures of Classical Greek knowledge

In the fifth century AD the internal and external problems that had long been disturbing the Classical world reached a critical period which saw the division of the Roman Empire, and ultimately the collapse of the empire's west and the official adoption of Christianity in its east. But despite these momentous, and sometimes catastrophic, events there was a determination among some brave scholars to preserve ancient classical knowledge. In the event much was saved, and Euclid, among others, was never entirely forgotten. The Roman philosopher Boethius (480–524 AD) for instance, living in the precarious conditions following the fall of Rome, dedicated his life to this cause, translating both Euclid and Ptolemy from Greek to Latin. Boethius regarded himself as a Platonist as well as a Christian and, in keeping with the spirit of the Platonic tradition, wrote tracts that associated geometry with music theory and astronomy, among which were dissertations on the regular solids. His philosophical views became a major influence on the western medieval church, a beacon of rational thought during the dark ages.

In the Christian east, Byzantium was to remain a bastion of Greek civilisation for centuries to come. Classical science and literature continued to be taught and, particularly in comparison with the barbaric west, high levels of literacy and numeracy were maintained. Euclid's *Elements* remained familiar as a basic text, retaining its Platonic metaphysical associations; however these, along with other Classical philosophies, were incorporated into a Christian framework. In this setting geometry was seen as a means for a deeper understanding of God. The Byzantines, in a continuation of the early Christian neoplatonic stream, were more concerned with such matters as the relation of the divine with the physical world. Little original work was added to the technical aspects of the older texts at this time, but they were at least preserved. Constantinople became renowned for its humanist scholars who were regarded as 'the librarians of the world'.

The Byzantine Empire, although it lasted for over a thousand years, was frequently under threat by external forces, from Latins, Persians, various Barbarian tribes, and the forces of Islam – to which it finally succumbed in 1453. The extraordinary rise of Islam in the eighth century had already robbed Byzantium of great swathes of its territory, but this initially nomadic incursion rapidly developed into a formidable, and rival, cultural entity. These early Muslim conquests of much of the Byzantine Middle East introduced them to levels of culture and wealth that almost amounted to a second Revelation, and made an enormous impact on their own development as a civilisation. When they, in turn, had to administer a huge empire, they turned to Greek sources for knowledge of every kind.

The urgent requirement for the resources that only a high culture could provide saw the establishment of a Muslim state-sponsored translation movement and the beginnings of a sustained enthusiasm for available Classical texts. An atmosphere was generated in which scholarship was encouraged, and Classical knowledge was soaked up like a sponge, giving rise to a thoroughgoing cultural reawakening which, in the second half of the eighth century, led to the translation into Arabic of the major corpus of surviving Greek medical and scientific works (including those by Plato, Aristotle, Galen, Euclid, Archimedes and Ptolemy). The enormous transfer of knowledge into this new, confident cultural setting had a catalytic effect, kindling a genuine interest in scientific subjects. Initially there was a continuation of Greek traditions of scholarship, but very soon an independent Islamic science emerged, producing valid criticisms and original extensions to this ancient knowledge.

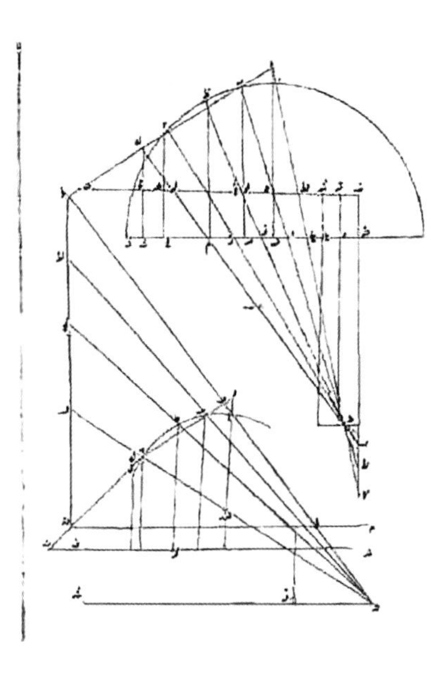

The Platonist Apollonius's Book V *on Conic Sections, in Arabic translation.*

The Islamic intellectual resurgence was responsible for many important advances in mathematics (including geometry), optics and medicine, knowledge that was then spread throughout the Islamic world, even to distant Spain. As we shall see, the preservation, adaptation and subsequent transmission of this Classical heritage, together with that of Byzantium, was to have enormous consequences for western science.

Platonism

Platonism is based in the first place on Plato's own writings, most of which survive, and on his and his followers teachings in the many succeeding schools of philosophy. This meant that although there undoubtedly was a 'Platonic' tradition, over time this did not amount to a consistent, coherent set of ideas. In fact Platonism (and Neoplatonism) came to mean rather different things at different periods.

The Academy that Plato founded in 387 BC was destroyed by Roman forces in the First Mithridatic War (86 BC), and even by this time various distinct philosophies had been taught there, veering first towards Skepticism, then to Stoicism. The Academy was later refounded in Athens where it tended towards eclecticism, adopting what was felt to be the most reasonable aspects of the different competing philosophies. It was finally closed by the Christian Byzantine Emperor Justinian in 529, in an act of repression that has been described as 'the end of antiquity'. In the nine hundred years between this time and the beginnings of the Renaissance in western Europe, Platonism survived in three distinct cultural traditions – in the Byzantine Empire, in the Islamic world and, to a far more limited extent, in western Europe.

The nub of Plato's thought is based on the notion of the independent existence of abstract concepts, and that the phenomenal world is merely a pale imitation, or approximation of, the world of ideas, which is eternal and perfect.

Plato felt that these ideas or forms were not directly available to the senses, but could be determined only by a turning away from the 'shadow-world' of sense impressions towards an inner consciousness, and that this process could unveil the secrets of the universe. Geometry was involved in much of this. Plato, like Pythagoras before him, was fascinated by the pure, precise relations that operated between geometric figures, particularly the solids, and came to identify these figures with notions of other-worldly perfection. His school, the Academy, famously displayed a sign that proclaimed 'Let none ignorant of geometry enter my door', and in his dialogue Timaeus *(in which he lays out his cosmological speculations) he declares that 'God ever geometrises', and that 'Geometry existed before the Creation'.*

In The Republic *Plato asserts that 'Geometry draws the soul towards truth and creates the spirit of philosophy', and in* Philebus *he has his teacher Socrates explaining the particular relation between geometry and beauty: 'By beauty of shape I want you here to understand not what the multitude generally means by this expression, like the beauty of living things or of paintings resembling them, but something alternatively rectilinear and circular, and the surfaces and solids which one can produce from the rectilinear and circular, with compass, set-square and rule. Because these things are not, like the others, conditionally beautiful, but are beautiful in themselves.'*

In his dialogue Timaeus, *Plato identified the four elements of air, earth, fire and water with his four of his five 'basic solids', which were in turn derived from two 'basic' right-angled triangles. The fifth and culminating solid in this scheme, the dodecahedron, represented the cosmos.*

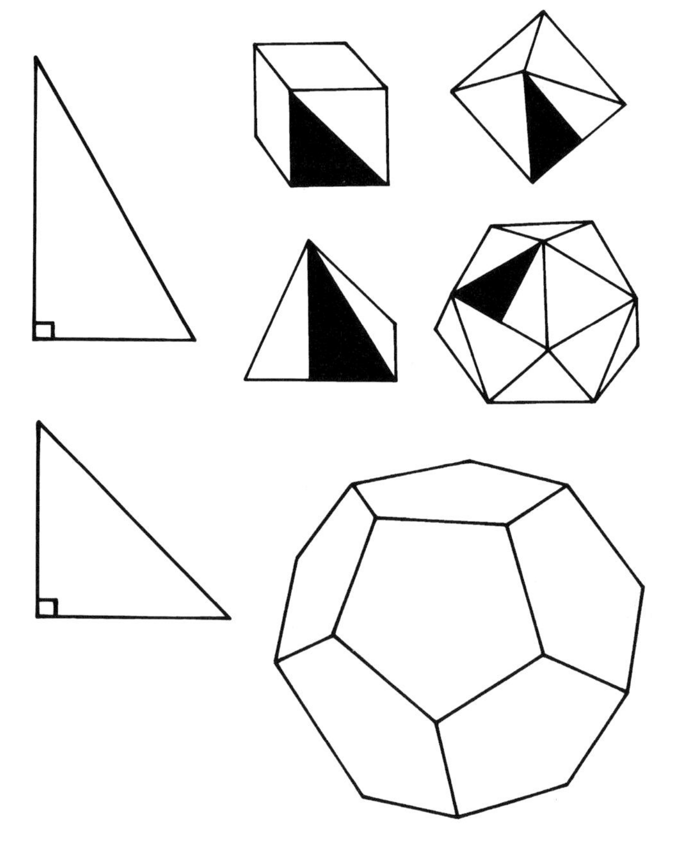

2

The revival of the Latin west

Translation and the transmission of ideas

The great reawakening of science and art that we now know as the Renaissance was inspired and fuelled by translated texts of classical antiquity. Plato's philosophical works, and those of his Neoplatonic followers, were at the centre of this great transfer of knowledge. The Classical heritage had not been entirely forgotten in the earlier Medieval west, but such knowledge that there was of its texts tended to be incomplete and second-hand. Greek was known to only a very few scholars, and Latin translations were few and difficult to obtain. This changed in the later medieval period with a growing awareness of, and receptivity to, Classical texts from both Byzantine and Islamic sources.

Arabic translations of Greek works were available as early as the twelfth century, following the Christian conquest of Toledo. Under the rule of the Caliphate Toledo had enjoyed a golden age, famous for its tolerance and the coexistence of its Jewish, Christian and Muslim inhabitants. After its fall to the Christian King Alfonso VI it managed to survive as a centre of cultural exchange, supporting many schools of translation; this attracted determined scholars from many parts of Western Europe. Sicily was another important point of contact with Islamic culture, and the Crusades, for all their brutality, also created an awareness of the higher civilised values of the Islamic world. In fact the chief stimulus for scientific, as well as cultural advancement generally at this time, were personal contacts with representatives of this tradition. These contacts led to important Latin versions of Arabic translations of Greek originals. In the thirteenth century, for instance, Campanus of Novara,[1] who had travelled to Muslim countries to broaden his knowledge, put together a reasonable Latin version of Euclid's *Elements*.[2] By the later middle ages these glimpses of a lost world of scholarship generated a positive hunger for authentic texts, and these early acquisitions laid the groundwork for the Renaissance. But events in the east were soon to make a far greater volume of material available.

From around 1400, as a result of the disturbances caused by Turkish incursions into Byzantine territory, previously unknown Greek manuscripts began appearing in Italy. When Constantinople finally fell to the Turks in 1453 many scholars fled to Italy bringing great quantities of manuscripts with them. The scholars, with their priceless volumes, were well received, particularly in Florence, where some went on to become intellectual celebrities. The bulk of the surviving Greek literature, which included classics of philosophy, mathematics, poetry and drama, suddenly became available. The influx of this wealth of knowledge generated a positive enthusiasm for translation, which in turn promoted the discussion and dissemination of ideas – in much the same way that had happened in ninth century Baghdad. Florence, with its leading figure the Neoplatonist philosopher Marsilio Ficino (1433–99), became the centre of this great humanist movement. In 1462 Cosimo de'Medici, the *de facto* ruler of Florence, founded an Academy for the study of Plato. Ficino was appointed as its head and was provided with all 36 of Plato's dialogues in Greek, which he translated into Latin within seven years. He later translated and annotated the works of all the major Neoplatonists. Ficino's contribution to scholarship and humanism was incalculable. Many of the great changes that are associated with the Renaissance began in Florence in the earlier fifteenth century, and the city continued to be at the forefront of advances in both the arts and sciences.

Figuring the Platonic solids

Classical perceptions of the relevance of mathematics to the study of both nature and art were probably the single most important principle to have been revived during the Renaissance. It testifies to the potency of this concept that some of its greatest and most gifted personalities took it up, many of whom were directly involved with a reexamination of the Platonic solids. The list includes Regiomontanus, Piero della Francesca and Leonardo da Vinci, all of whom were true polymaths, in an age when such brilliance could span the disciplines of science and art.

Regiomontanus (1436–1476) is of that breed that Joseph Needham referred to as the last of the magicians and the first of the scientists, in somewhat the same category as the Elizabethan, John Dee. But his mathematics was sound, and he is now seen as the most important astronomer of the fifteenth century, a pivotal figure who set the agenda for the revolution in astronomy wrought by Copernicus, Kepler, Galileo and Newton. He also made many important contributions to the study of geometry and trigonometry, and was involved in reforming the calendar for Pope Sixtus.

Regiomontanus was born in fairly humble circumstances as Johannes Müller, the son of a miller, near the small town of Konigsberg,[3] in present-day Bavaria. His prodigious talents were recognised early, and he entered university at the age of eleven. In common with other scholars who were dependent on patronage at that time he travelled, studied and taught widely, on both sides of the Alps. While still a young man Regiomontanus went to Italy where he learned Greek, and was much involved in the translation and publication of new editions of ancient texts, by Apollonius and Archimedes among others. He lectured in Venice, Padua and in Hungary, but later moved to Nuremberg, attracted by its reputation both as a centre for the manufacture of scientific instruments and of the new technology of printing.[4]

Here he wrote a treatise on geometry, based on Archimedes' work *On the Sphere and Cylinder*, which included a section on the Platonic and other solid figures, in which he demonstrated their systematic transformation from one to the other. His work in this field laid the foundation for later geometers, including his pupil Martin Behaim (who built the first terrestrial globe), and the great Renaissance artist Piero della Francesca. Famously, his work influenced Columbus in the planning of his great voyage of discovery. Unfortunately, on his return to Rome in 1476, this brilliant polymath fell victim to the plague and died at the relatively early age of forty.

Although best known for his paintings, Piero della Francesca (1415–1492) was also a mathematician with a particular interest in geometry, which increased in his later years. In fact the historian Vasari described him as 'the greatest geometer of his time', and he produced three books on the subject – *Libellous de Quinque Corporibus Regularibus* (a notebook on the five regular solids); *Trattato d'Abaco* (dealing with algebra and the measurement of polygons and polyhedra); and *De*

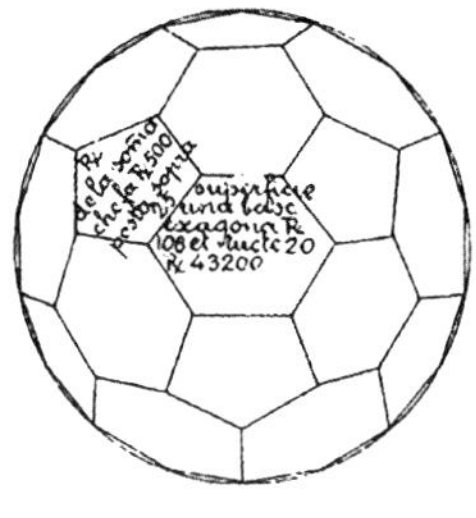

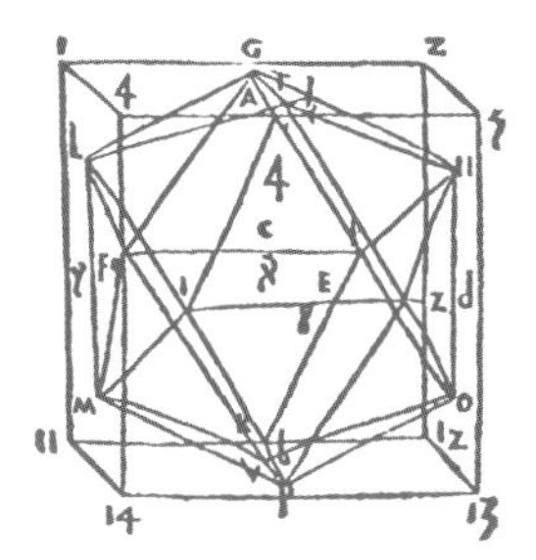

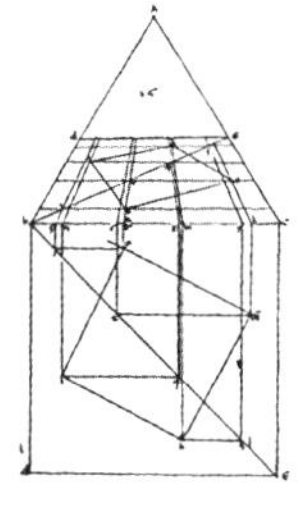

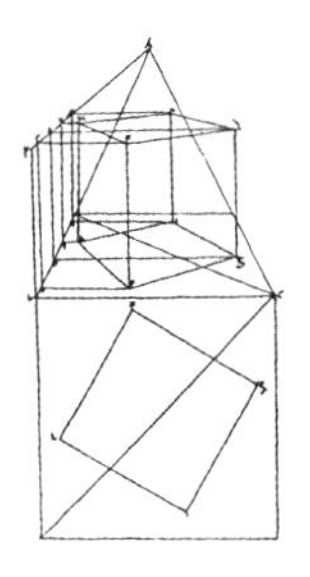

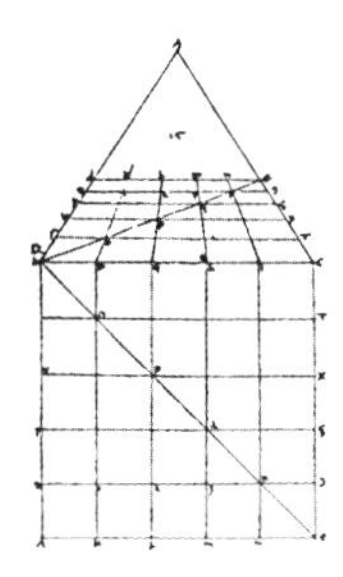

A truncated icosahedron, (above), an icosahedron inscribed in a cube, and perpective diagrams from Piero della Francesco's Libellous de Quinque Corporibus Regularibus. *Piero was known as a mathematician as well as a painter.*

Prospectiva Pigendi (a rigorous examination of the problems of optics and perspective). None of these were printed in his own lifetime, but were placed, as manuscripts, in the library of his patron the Duke of Urbino (where he had actually begun his own study of classical mathematics). Piero is also known to have owned translations of the work of Archimedes and Euclid. Being used to the hands-on approach of a working artist, he shows a spatial as well as an abstract mathematical interest in the regular and semi-regular polyhedra. It seems very likely that he made models of these figures to assist his measurement and comparison of their respective volumes, and was the first to draw the Platonic solids as they should appear in perspective. Piero is recognised as a strong influence on the Franciscan monk Luca Pacioli and on Leonardo da Vinci, whose contributions we will be dealing with shortly.

A surviving fragment of Uccello's floor mosaic from the Basilica di San Marco, showing a small stellated dodecahedron.

A drawing of a stellated sphere.

It is worth mentioning here Paolo Uccello (1397–1475), the Florentine painter who also had a reputation as a mathematician, though little is known of this aspect of his work. It is known that in 1425 Paolo went to Venice to work on mosaics for the façade of the Basilica di San Marco. Unfortunately these no longer exist, apart from one intriguing panel that shows a small stellated dodecahedron, a figure that came to be associated with Johannes Kepler (and which indeed bears his name), two hundred years before it was rediscovered by the astronomer. Various drawings by Uccello of geometric subjects have also survived, including a perspective sketch of a *mazzocchio*, and a curious stellated sphere, both of which frequently appear as motifs in the work of later artists. Taken together, these figures indicate a sound working knowledge of solid geometry, and of the principles of perspective.

Luca Pacioli (1446–1517) came from the same small town as Piero della Francesca, who was later to tutor the younger man in mathematics. Piero introduced his pupil to the Duke of Urbino and both used his library, which was reputed to be the finest in Europe at the time. In 1494 Pacioli, who had become a Franciscan monk and a travelling scholar, produced his *Summa*, a summary of mathematics that was printed in Venice using the new Gutenberg method.

This work came to the notice of Leonardo da Vinci (1452–1519) who, after meeting with Pacioli, brought him to Milan, where he was to stay for three fruitful years (1496–9). During this time Pacioli wrote *De Divina Proportione*, a book based on Plato's philosophical speculations, Euclid's geometry and Christian theology, all of which he related to the golden proportion in a grand cosmological scheme.[5] Leonardo worked with Pacioli on this book, contributing many illustrations, mainly consisting of a series of forty skeletised and solid versions of polyhedra. The *Divine Proportion* was published in Venice in 1509, and enjoyed immediate success.

Leonardo had begun dedicating much of his time to geometry during his early forties. It is known that he was familiar with the five regular and thirteen semi-regular solids, since they appear in the collection of drawings known as the *Codice Atlantico*. By the time he had finished working with Pacioli he had become so enthralled with mathematics that he neglected his painting – a contemporary observer noted at the time that 'the sight of a brush puts him out of temper'. In fact his notebooks reveal that he made a close study of Euclid's *Elements* over a ten-year period, and later became preoccupied with theories of proportion and various intractable geometrical problems.[6] Despite his enthusiasm Leonardo's knowledge of geometry remained fairly basic, but his illustrations for Pacioli's work were rightly described by the author as 'extraordinary and most beautiful figures'. On the basis of their accuracy it seems very likely that he made these drawings from actual models of polyhedra, and that he may have used optical aids, including a perspectival window.

It is clear from his fascination with the subject that for Leonardo, as for Pacioli, solid figures had a sublime quality; understanding their forms and the relations between them was to penetrate to the very foundation of reality, and amounted to form of meditation. The vision of Pythagorus and his followers lived on – the universe could only really be explained in geometric terms.

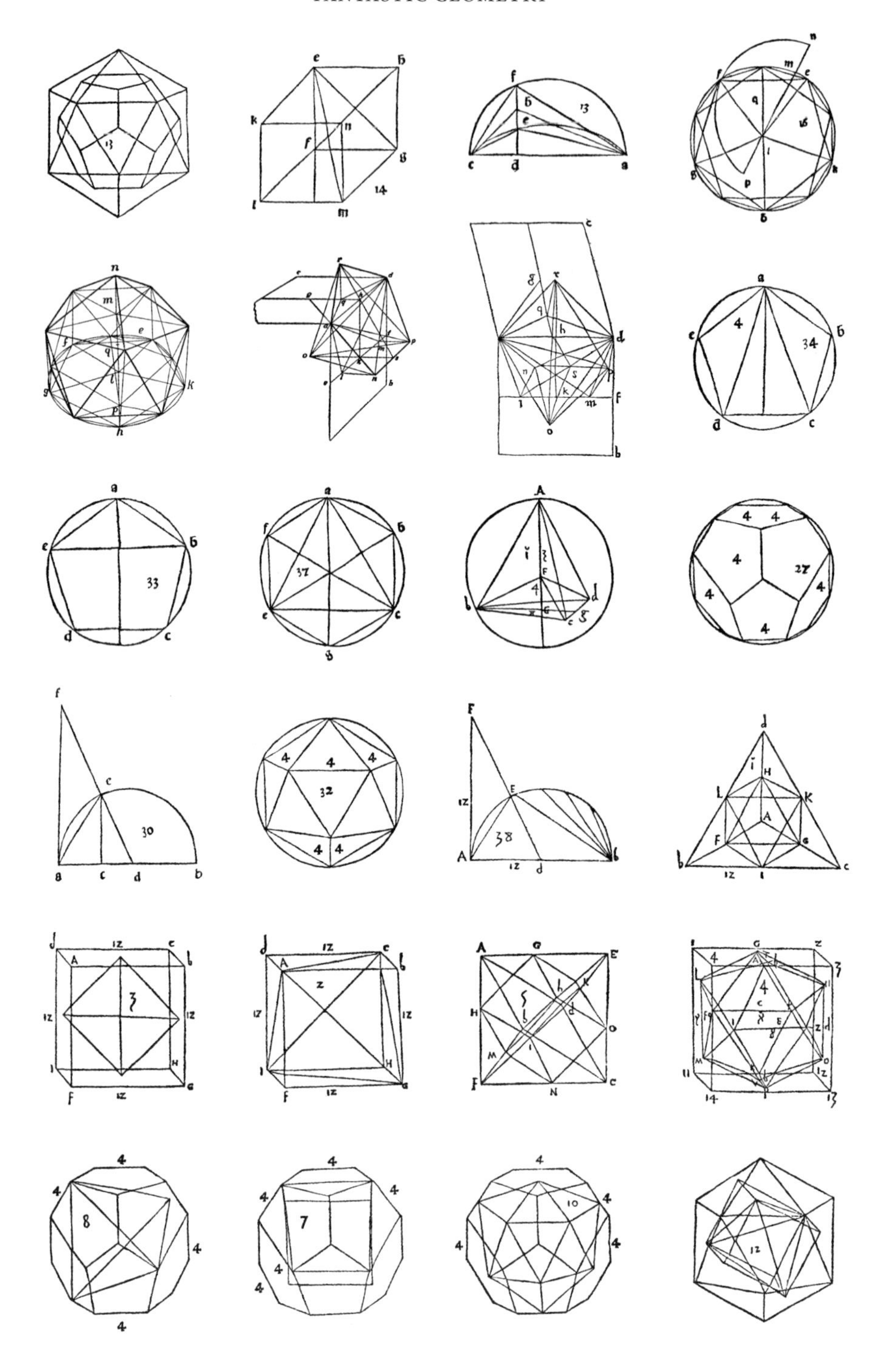

A selection of Leonardo's geometrical diagrams for Luca Pacioli's De Divina Proportione.

New ways of seeing – developments in geometry, optics and perspective during the Renaissance

Among the more important texts that had been translated from Arabic in the medieval period was the seven-volume 'Book of Optics' *(Kitab al-Manazir)* by Ibn al-Haytham, *c.*935–1039). This work, the most outstanding of many on the subject produced in the Islamic world, was brought into Latin in the late twelfth or early thirteenth century, probably by Gerard of Cremona. Because of its rigorous treatment of the subject, it is now regarded as one of the most influential books in the whole of science. Ibn al-Haytham was a polymath who is credited with at least ninety-two books on a wide variety of subjects. His theories on optics were based on a series of experiments with lenses, mirrors, refraction and reflection, as a result of which he came to be regarded as the 'father of modern optics'. His work in this area, which was originally based on that of Ptolemy, greatly surpassed that of his ancient predecessor, and he became the leading authority in optics for over five hundred years. Ibn al-Haytham's methods, in which he constructed devices and tested the results obtained from them, also introduced a new approach to scientific enquiry which was enormously influential in itself. His *magnus opus* on optics was later used as a sourcebook by Roger Bacon, Johannes Kepler, Isaac Newton and Rene Descartes in their own theories.

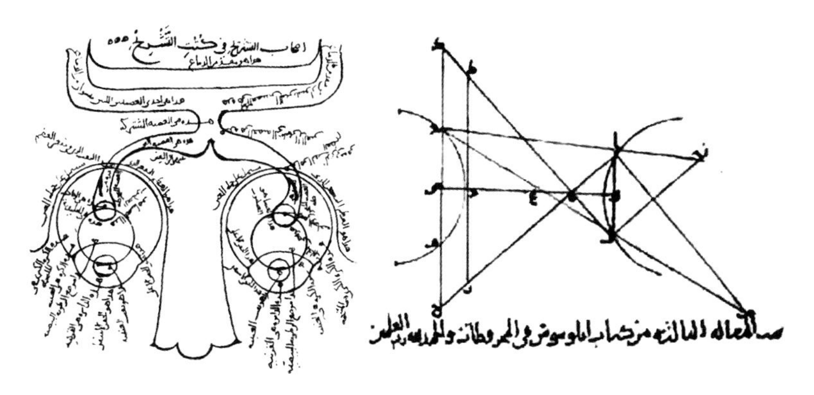

Diagram of the eye, and of the 'visual pyramid', from Ibn al-Haytham's Kitab al-Manazir (Book of Optics)*. Ibn al Haytham's geometrical conception of place as geometrical extension, from which light projected conically to the eye (makhrut al-shu'a'), provided a proper basis for the idea of perspective.*

Developments in optics, in all its aspects, were a central concern during the Renaissance for both the arts and sciences. The aims of enquiry included both a better understanding of the physiology of vision and with the physics of light, an area of study which was bound up with the recent technical improvement of lenses, mirrors and other devices. By the later Middle Ages there had already been remarkable advances

Al-Haytham's Kitab al-Manazir *(*Book of Optics*) was printed in Latin translation by Friedrich Risner in 1572, as* Opticae Thesaurus: Alhazeni Arabis. *Originally written between 1011 and 1021, when the author was under house arrest in Cairo, this book laid the foundation of the modern understanding of optics. Among many other revelations it presented the correct process of vision for the first time, and explained the mechanics of the camera obscura. It influenced many early-modern European scientists, including Kepler, Huygens and Descartes .*

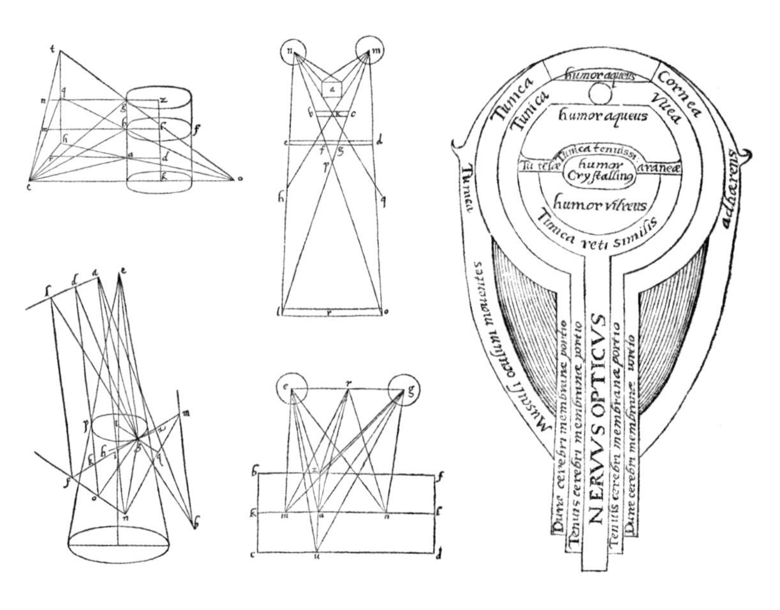

in Europe in this area. It can come as a surprise to learn that eyeglasses first appeared in Florence towards the end of the thirteenth century, and that by the fifteenth century these, and magnifying lenses, were relatively familiar items.[7] In recent years it has become clear that many Renaissance artists (including Dürer, Van Eyck, Holbein and Carravagio) used optical devices as aids in their work. The theory behind the *camera obscura*, for instance, was fairly well understood by the fifteenth century (in fact the first analogy between this device and the workings of the eye had been made by Ibn al-Haytham in his *Kitab al-Manazir*).[8] As well as an intriguing and useful tool for artists, this contrivance was of considerable interest from a scientific viewpoint to both Leonardo da Vinci and Johannes Kepler, both of whom referred to it in their own writings on optics.

Man using eye-glasses, from the Liber Chronicarum *(*The Nuremberg Chronicle*).*

The particular attention given to the study of optics during the Renaissance, and the advances in science and the arts that resulted, cannot be exaggerated. It was at the forefront of experimentation in an age of intellectual discovery, culminating in the appearance of telescopes and microscopes in the late sixteenth century. These developments quite literally introduced new ways of seeing, taking human perception far beyond the limits of the medieval imagination. When, for example, Galileo viewed the obvious imperfections on the surface of the moon with his newly invented telescope, the entrenched medieval distinctions between the 'sublunary' and 'superlunary', and the entire cosmological system associated with this, were utterly discredited.[9] Advances in optics, together with the invention of the printing press, were pivotal to the emergence of the modern era; together, they were responsible for a thorough transformation of the human psyche. In the artistic field this perceptual phase-change was reflected in the growing desire for more realistic representation, and an enthusiasm for the techniques of linear perspective.

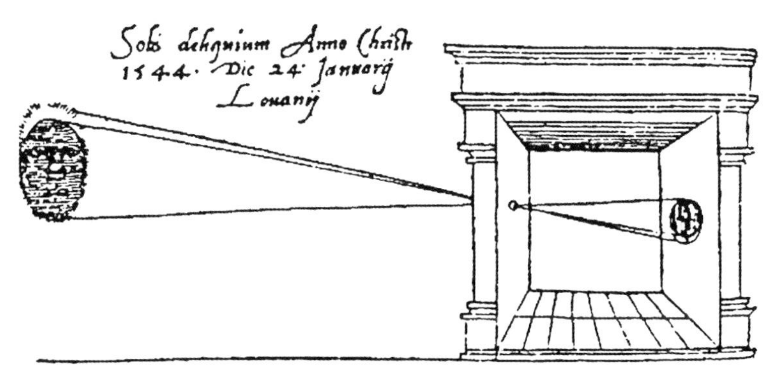

Camera Obscura, Reinerus Gemma Frisiua, *1544. Frisius used a darkened room to study the solar eclipse of 1544.*

Florence and Perspective

The term *perspectiva*, as it was used during the Renaissance, was defined more broadly than it is today. It was the Latin version of the Greek *οπτικά* (optics), and applied both to the physical aspects of light and the physiological aspects of vision, as well as to the problems involved in the representation of spatial depth. Ibn al-Haytham's *Kitab al-Manazir,* which dealt with all of these matters, had been in circulation in manuscript form in Latin translation since the thirteenth century, and became available in an Italian version as *Deli Aspecti* in the following century. Al-Haytham (whose name was Latinised into Alhazen) had conducted numerous experiments into the visibility of spatial depth, and his discoveries came to exert a profound and well documented influence on the course of European art. *Deli Aspecti* was known to the Florentine sculptor and architect Lorenzo Ghiberti (1378–1455) who, according to his biographer, quoted from it 'verbally and at length'. Ghiberti has long been recognised as one of the most important of the early users of perspective, and he introduced the concept to his pupils, who employed the techniques to even greater effect. Among these were the painter Paolo Uccello, who had worked in Ghiberti's studio, and the sculptor Donatello (*c.*1386–1466).

The first actual paintings known to have employed the novel techniques of geometric linear perspective were made by the Florentine architect Filipo Brunelleschi (1377–1446), a contemporary of Ghiberti. Brunelleschi appears to have used perspective in his architectural drawings to demonstrate to clients how his buildings would look on completion. He is also known to have produced two experimental panels, one of which, famously, was meant to be viewed in a mirror through a hole drilled in its centre to compare with its actual subject, the Florentine Baptistry. With these compelling examples Brunelleschi established one of the basic precepts of perspective, the notion that converging lines should meet at a single vanishing point on the picture plane, and that all the components of a painting should get smaller, in all directions, with their increasing distance from the eye. Others in Florence quickly picked up on this new theory.

Shortly after Brunelleschi had produced his groundbreaking perspective paintings (which unfortunately have not survived), his fellow architect Leon Battista Alberti (1404–72) wrote a treatise, *Della Pittura* (1436), specifically aimed at artists. This work described the new methods of using perspective in some detail. Alberti was well equipped

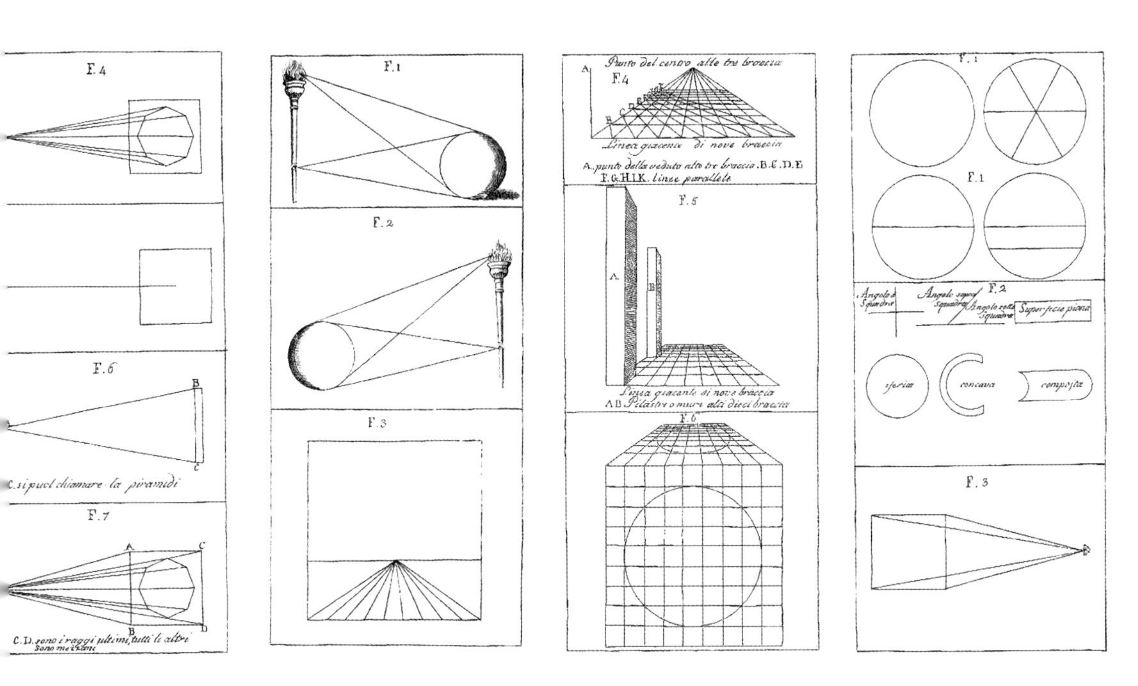

Perspective diagrams from Battista Alberti's Della Pittura, *1436.*

to impart this knowledge, having been trained in science of optics in the school of Padua under the influence of Blasius of Parma (*c.*1374–1416), who himself had studied and taught al-Haytham's *Optics*. It is clear that Alberti's aims in *Della Pittura* were not merely to improve the techniques of painting by placing them on a more rational footing, but also to raise the professional status of artists above that of a mere craft, the role that they had occupied in the Middle Ages.

In the continuing chain of transmission, Alberti's pupil, Piero della Francesca, went on to elaborate on his masters treatise in one of his own, *De Prospectiva Pigendi*, which he illustrated with a series of diagrams and perspective drawings. It is clear that Piero had come to regard the difficulties of realistic portrayal in terms of a solvable mathematical problem. This approach was very influential, as was the inclusion of perspective views of geometric figures in his book. His emphasis on the Platonic solids in this work effectively established their role as part of the repertoire of perspective treatises thereafter.

The plan and elevation constructions involving orthogonal lines (or 'visual rays'), used by both Uccello and Piero della Francesca, were particularly applicable for the portrayal of complex geometrical or architectural forms. The links between perspective and architectural planning were, as we have seen, already there with Brunelleschi, but the enthusiasm for perspective as a more realistic depiction of space in paintings, so characteristic of emerging early-modern attitudes, went together with requirements for accurate measurement of space in a more general way. As a result perspective came to be associated with developments in the field of surveying, map-making, and the instruments involved with these activities.

Alhazen's cone of vision (makhrut al-shu'a') corresponded with the idea of a pyramid of vision, offering a model that can be more easily projected in the orthogonal drawings needed for the geometric construction of perspective. An illustration from Egnatio Danti's Two Rules of Practical Perspective *(1583). Danti (1536–86) was a mathematician and astronomer.*

This worldly, rationalising movement was also linked to a revival of interest in the buildings of the Classical past. The emergence from the cloistered outlook of the middle ages lead to a positive enthusiasm for the legacy of the ancient past in every available aspect. In this spirit Brunelleschi and Donatello undertook an extended survey of architecture in Rome, which included measuring the dome of the Pantheon. Their ambitious undertaking was for practical as much as nostalgic reasons; Brunelleschi went on to build his masterpiece, the Duomo, for the Santa Maria del Fiore, a dome that was even larger than that of the Pantheon's. For his part, Donatello, after his thorough investigation of classical forms, introduced a new freedom and intensity into sculpture that was equally influential. According to Vasari, the author of *Lives of the Artists*, taken together 'these works were the means of arousing the minds of other craftsmen, who went on to devote themselves to this process with great zeal'. The 'process' he was referring to was, of course, the revival of Classicism.

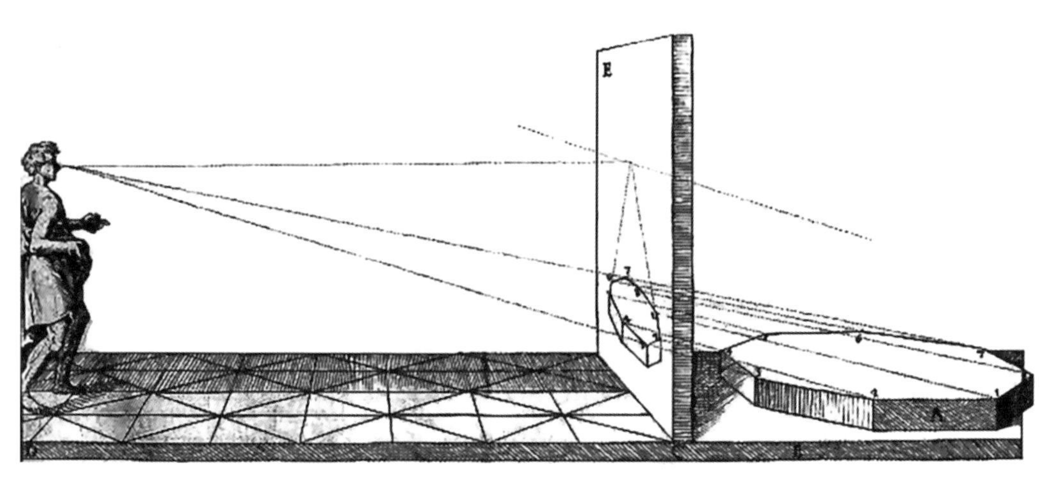

Three dimensions into two: the methods and instruments of perspective

The first mention of linear perspective in the written word appears in Leon Battista Alberti's treatise Della Pittura (On Painting, *1435). In this he observes that 'a painting is the intersection of a visual pyramid at a given distance', as if the view through an open window were to be intercepted by a 'veil' across it. There is a clear indication here of Alberti's familiarity with Alhazen's theories ('He who looks at a picture in the way that I have described will see a cross-section of the visual pyramid') – and the first suggestion that artists might use a* reticolato, *or reticulated frame, as a drawing aid. He also puts forward a method of composing paintings that involved a defining horizontal line and the laying out of a base, rather like a stage, on which the buildings, objects and figures would be placed – the whole ordered by a grid of orthogonal lines to give scale to the various elements in the picture. This is, of course, the now familiar 'one-point construction', which introduced the revolutionary idea of a vanishing point. It is clear from* Della Pittura *that, for Alberti, a knowledge of geometry was absolutely essential to the mastery of painting.*

Alberti's successor Piero della Francesca also emphasised the importance of geometry in comprehending the methods of perspective. In his own work De Prospectiva Pigendi, *he too refers to the use of an 'intersection', which almost certainly meant a perspectival window of some kind (in fact these devices later became known as 'Alberti windows'). These new concepts spread very quickly. The use of the horizon line, the vanishing point and proportional foreshortening must have been fairly well established by the time Leonardo da Vinci encountered Alberti's system of perspective, very likely while he was still an apprentice in Verrocchio's studio in the early 1500s.*

Leonardo himself became very involved in this subject. There are many references to it in the collection of thoughts and notes that became known as the Trattato della Pittura. *There is a reference here to perspective as 'nothing other than seeing a place or objects behind a pane of glass, on the surface of which the objects are to be drawn'. It would seem that he experimented with a perspective window, in conjunction with a surveyor's rod, to create diminishing perspective, and recommended these devices as a method of training the eye. He also followed Alberti's suggestion of the use of colouring techniques, together with the appropriate, geometric, construction of shadows, to strengthen the illusion of depth. Leonardo's systematic approach to painting lead to his uncovering of the inverse size/distance law, by which an object's apparent size is halved at twice the calculated distance, and reduced to a third when the distanced is trebled, etc.*

For a while the methods of perspective remained the domain of Florence, but they were soon taken up by the other major centres in Italy, and by the early sixteenth century they had become a standard part of artistic training throughout Europe. Albrecht Dürer encountered the concepts and methods of linear perspective during his first visit to Italy in 1494 and introduced them to other artists on his return to Nuremburg. His enduring fascination with these problems, particularly with the use of perspectival frames, is clear from the number of drawings that he made featuring various versions of this device. Dürer's objectives in using the Alberti windows were essentially the same as that of the Italian Renaissance painters. The art of painting (and its practitioners) would be elevated by placing it on a rigorous, rational basis; only in this way could it become a worthy instrument for the study of nature and, by extension, for revealing the underlying order of the world.

The devices used to attain the required degree of realistic representation, which typically involved reticulated frames, adjustable taut threads and pointers attached to uprights, seem antiquated and overschematic from the modern viewpoint, but they are an indication of the determination, characteristic of this period, to overcome the deceitful habits of the eye.

The artist-authors who followed in Dürer's footsteps were equally caught up in this consuming interest of the time, of the methodological problems of realistic representation. Their books were, in large part, a demonstration of this rationalising approach, and many of them used technical devices to assist them in their drawings. They were undoubtedly successful in their representation of complex subjects. It is precisely this which gives them such a modern appearance. For these artists the clarity of representation which they desired, and frequently achieved, was completely in accord with the Platonic purity of their subject matter.

Notes and references

1. Campanus of Novara (*c.*1220–96), mathematician and astronomer, compiled a Latin edition of Euclid's *Elements* that became the most frequently used version right up to the sixteenth century (it was printed by Ratdolt in 1482). Campanus is also known for his *equatorium*, an early astronomical instrument used to determine the positions of the moon, sun and planets.

2. A printed version of an Italian translation of Euclid's *Elements* was brought out in 1543; an edition in the German vernacular appeared in 1558.

3. Not to be mistaken for the much larger town of the same name in East Prussia.

4. 'Quite recently I have made observations in the city of Nuremberg ... for I have chosen it as my permanent home not only on account of the availability of instruments, particularly the astronomical instruments on which the entire science was based, but also on account of the great ease of all sorts of communication with learned men living everywhere, since this place is regarded as the centre of Europe because of the journeys of the merchants.' Regiomontanus, 1471; from a letter to a friend.

5. The historian Vasari, although he was writing some fifty years later, was rather scathing of Pacioli, accusing him plagiarism, saying that he had lifted much of this work from Piero della Francesca, without giving the artist-mathematician full credit for it.

6. Leonardo spent a great deal of time on such problems as 'squaring the circle' (which is impossible), and 'doubling the cube'. He supplied his own proof of Pythagorus' Theorum, and made interesting observations on conical sections and surface areas.

7. The evolution of lenses, particularly those useful as eye-glasses, is somewhat obscure. Ibn al-Haytham makes reference to concave lenses and magnifying glasses in his *Book of Optics*, translated in the thirteenth century. Useful glass lenses appeared in Italy in the following century.

8. The *camera obscura* effect, created by light passing through a small aperture into a darkened room, had been noticed throughout history. There had also been many attempts at a scientific explanation for the phenomena, even in the Ancient world – notably by Mo-Ti in fifth century China and Aristotle in fourth century BC Greece.

9. Medieval speculation had combined Platonism with Aristotolianism to create a cosmological scheme that divided the universe into two distinct realms, the imperfect sublunary region (beneath the moon), and the celestial superlunary. Under the medieval church this view hardened into a rigid, unquestionable dogma.

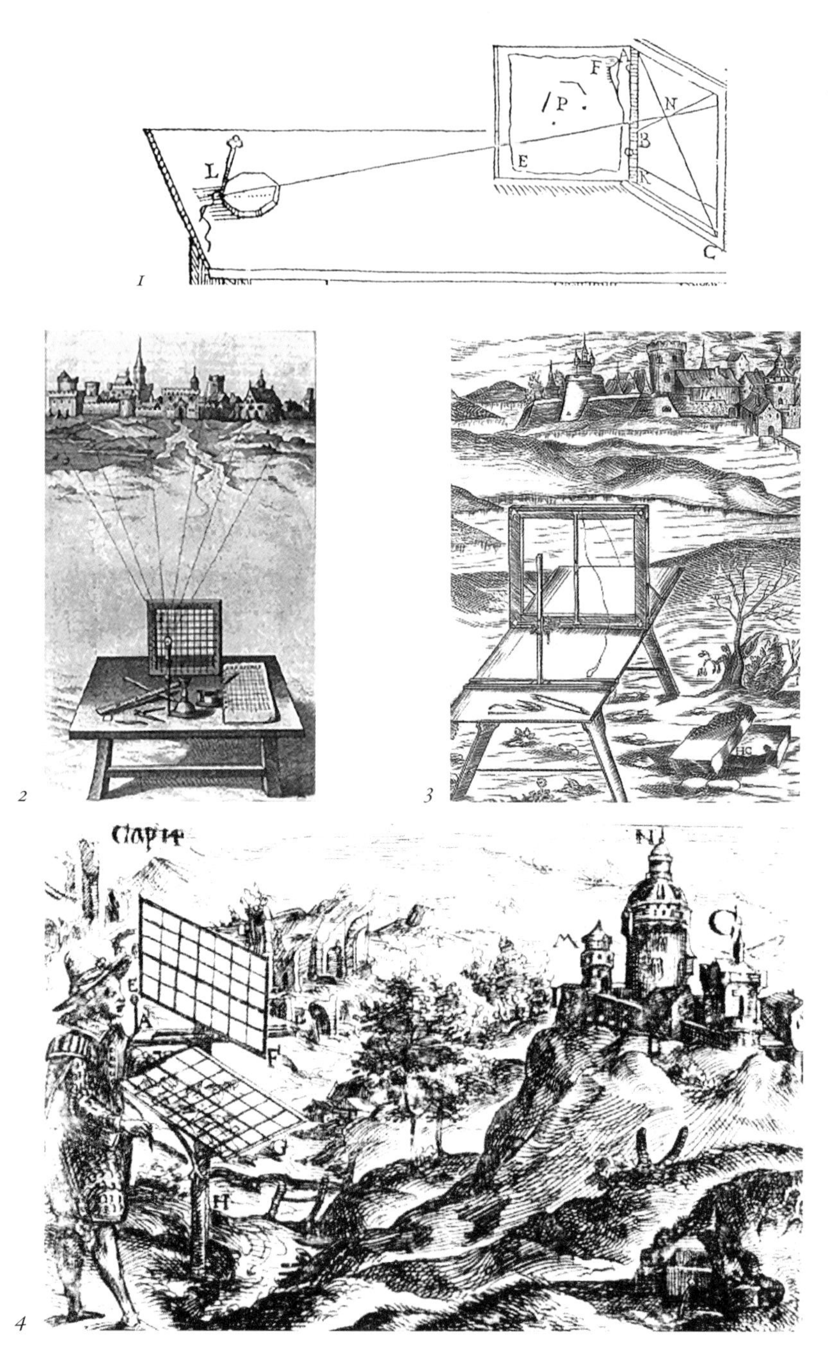

1. Vignola's version of Dürer's perspective frame. *2. An Alberti Frame.*
3. Detail from Faulhaber's Neue Geometrische und Perspectivische Inventiones.
4. From Hulsius' Tractatus Primus.

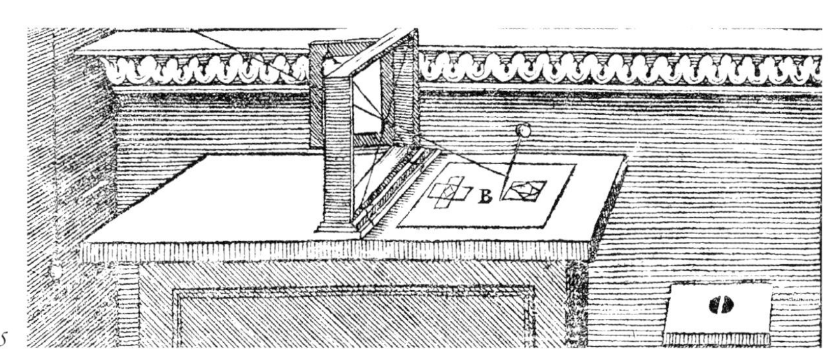

5

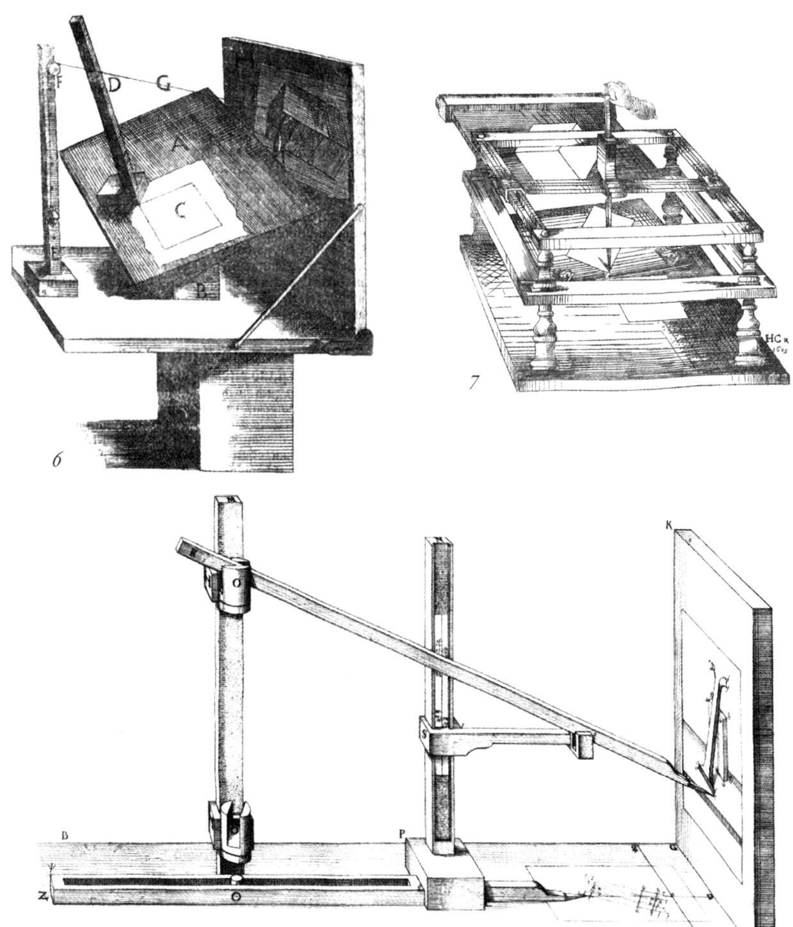

6

7

8

5. *Detail from Pfinzing's* Extract der Geometriae und Perspectivae. 6. *Peter Halt's portable perspective drawing board; from* Drei Wichtige neue Kunststuck in underschiedlichen Perspectivischen Instrumentum inventiert und erfunden. 7. *Faulhaber's perspective mechanism.* 8. *Lucas Brunn's perspective instrument; the apotheosis of Wenzel Jamnizer's system.*

Three of Dürer's drawings from his Underweysung der Messung *of 1525,demonstrating his enduring fascination with perspectival frames. In his 'Draughtsmen Drawing a Lute', (top) the ring in the wall becomes the viewing point and a thread delineates the visual rays. While the draughtsman directs this thread/ray to the selected points on the lute, his assistant notes the points where the thread passes through the frame, and transfers these to a hinged drawing board. The other drawings are 'Jacob de Keyser's invention' (middle) and 'The Draughtsman's Net' (bottom).*

3

Geometry and perspective in the Northern Renaissance

Although civilised life on both sides of the Alps was moved by deep cultural changes during the Renaissance, there were marked contrasts of tone in the ways in which it affected the major centres. This divergence was largely attributable to national differences – of language, climate and the existing forms of civil society. In Italy, as we have seen, there was a revival of the values of classical antiquity, which inspired a new interest in Latin and Greek. But the most profound effect of Italian humanist ideas on Northern Europe was to act as a catalyst for religious reform, culminating in the upheavals of the Protestant Reformation – one of the consequences of which was a rejection of Latin for scientific, philosophical and intellectual discourse and the adoption of vernacular languages. However, radical influences flowed in both directions; the invention of printing, which originated in Germany, was rapidly taken up in Renaissance Italy,[1] and this innovation greatly facilitated the spread of new ideas wherever it was adopted.

Northern artists travelled to Italy and were deeply impressed by developments there, but the stimulus that they received was ultimately more significant for its invigorating effect on Northern art rather than as a direct stylistic influence. Renaissance art in the north came to be characterised by a new emphasis on precise observation, realism and naturalism. Typically, when the interest in the regular solids spread to Germany, there was rather more emphasis on their practical aspects – how they might be useful in art and how they might explain the physical world. But the philosophical implications of Platonism, the study of the Platonic solids, and the impact of perspective in all its aspects, were to be as influential here as they had been in Italy.

In southern Germany there was also a strengthening of the association between the methods of linear perspective and advances in surveying, mapmaking and astronomy. This was facilitated by the manufacturing traditions (particularly in Nuremberg) that were able to produce the quality of instruments, scientific and otherwise, that were required by these new disciplines. The new industry of printing and publishing, which had also flourished in this area, played an equally important role in this broad movement. Many of the greatest figures of the Northern Renaissance, most of who were notable for the extraordinary range of their accomplishments, were involved in one way or another in these developments.

Ratdolt's Euclid

The publication of Euclid's *Elements*, in Venice in 1482, is an important benchmark in the history of the regular solids, and in the production of printed books generally. The *Elementorium Geometricum*, to give it its full Latin title, was the masterwork of a master printer – Erhard Ratdolt. Ratdolt, the son of an Augsberg sculptor, moved to Venice for the opportunities it provided in the new field of quality printing.

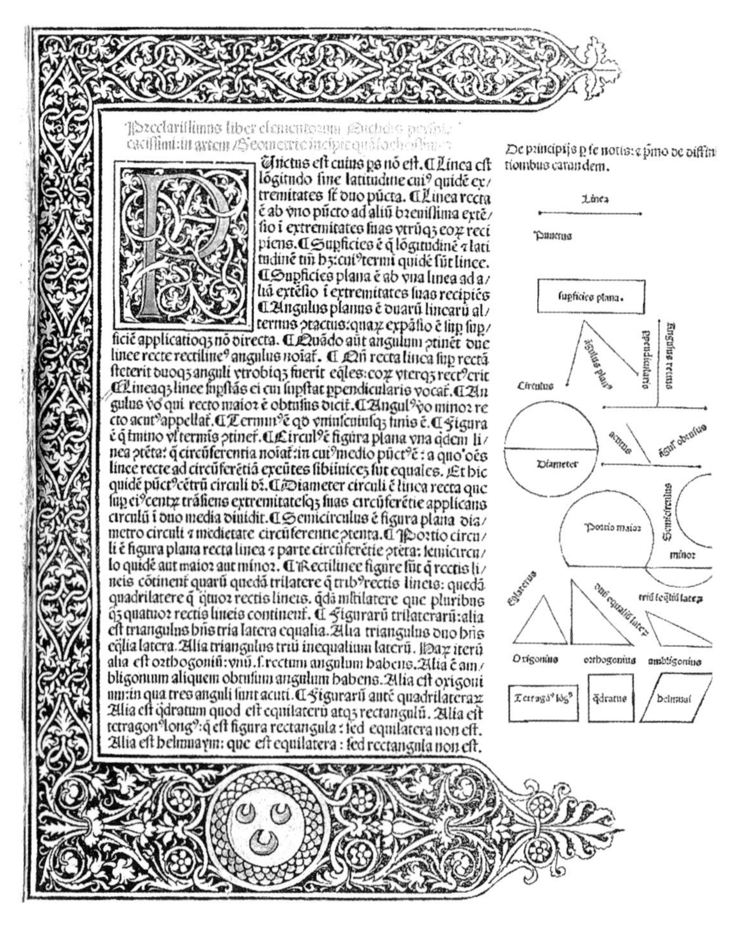

Erhard Ratdolt, a pupil of Regiomantus, produced the first printed edition of Euclid's Elements *in 1482; this magnificent book features a large number of mathematical diagrams crafted by Ratdolt himself.*

The printing trade in Venice at this time, during the second half of the fifteenth century, was dominated by Germans – there were around thirty of them in the city – but Radolt's productions were to prove exceptional, not least for their typographic decoration, which he virtually invented. He produced a *Kalendario*[2] for Regiomontanus in 1482, which featured the first title page of any book, and his *Elements* was the first printed book to be illustrated with mathematical figures, some six hundred in all, for which he devised a novel method of plate-making.[3] Ratdolt also designed type, and managed to print using gold-leaf; a very talented and original craftsman.

The *Elements* was adapted from a medieval translation by either Campanus or Adelard of Bath, both of whom have claims on the achievement, and had both travelled to the Islamic world.[4] Ratdolt's beautiful publication, just twenty-seven years after Gutenberg had built his first printing press, was an immediate success, and enormously influential. Most importantly, it introduced the very notion of theoretical geometry to the receptive cultural milieu of the early Renaissance. Dürer, who visited and stayed in Venice, was among many who were deeply impressed by this work which, together with Pacioli's *De Divina Proportione*, inspired his own substantial books on the subject.

Dürer – artist, humanist and geometer

Albrecht Dürer (1471–1528), the most important and influential artist of the Northern Renaissance, was born in Nuremberg, the third child in what was to become a very large family. His father was a goldsmith and expected his son to follow him in this trade, but Dürer's artistic gifts became apparent at a very early age, and he was apprenticed to the studio of the painter Michael Wolgemut at the age of fifteen. Such was his prodigious talent that by his mid twenties he had become a famous and established artist.

Dürer was to make two memorable trips to Italy. The first of these, when he was twenty-three, took him to Venice. The art that he saw, and the artists that he met, made a great impression on him. He returned to Nuremberg brimming with the new ideas of perspective and proportion he had encountered there, and he became a prime mover in the movement towards a greater accuracy and acuity in representational art that was to sweep across Europe. He made a second Italian trip in 1506–7, again to Venice. By this time he was more interested in learning about mathematics from Italian sources than in its art. As he had grown older, Dürer had developed a great enthusiasm for geometry. In common with Leonardo,

Typical pages of Dürer's exploration of two-dimensional geometry, from the second book of his Underweysung der Messung, *a textbook of descriptive geometry intended 'for artists and craftsmen'. The fourth book of this work deals with three-dimensional forms and the construction of polyhedra. It provides nets of the regular and semi-regular solids and encourages the reader to construct them.*

and influenced as the latter was by Piero della Francesca and Luca Pacioli, Dürer became a proponent for a disciplined approach to art, in particular, one that emphasized the role of geometry.[5] He had planned to produce a textbook dealing with every aspect of art quite early on in his career, but this never materialised. Towards the end of his life however, in 1525 and 1528, he produced two substantial treatises intended for artists and craftsmen. The first of these, *Underweysung der Messung* (*Instructions in Measurement*, Nuremberg, 1525) is of particular interest here.

This was an ambitious textbook in four substantial chapters. It is largely concerned with descriptive geometry, and is accompanied by some hundred and fifty illustrations. Written in vernacular German, it was obviously intended for practical rather than theoretical use, although there are frequent references to Euclid. Beginning with the definitions of points, lines and angles, it works comprehensively through such matters as conic sections, the construction of polygons, and the calculation of areas. It then goes on to the building of architectonic forms, including columns, towers, etc. There is also an extended section dedicated to the 'correct shaping of letters', or typography, possibly inspired by similar passages in Pacioli's *De Divina Proportione*. The whole of the final chapter concerns the construction of regular and irregular solids, in which Dürer provides the appropriate plans and instructions to help build these polyhedral forms. Dürer's books on geometry and proportion were, in essence, an attempt to combine the abstract concepts of classical geometry with the traditional geometrical knowledge that had long been practised in the various crafts. His aim seems to have been to put the arts and crafts on a sounder, more mathematically-based foundation, and to ennoble them in the process. Interestingly, and as an indicator of its influence at the time, the *Underweyung der Messung* was cited by both Kepler and Galileo in their own published works.

In his Underweysung der Messung *Dürer deals with the proper forming of the Latin alphabet.*

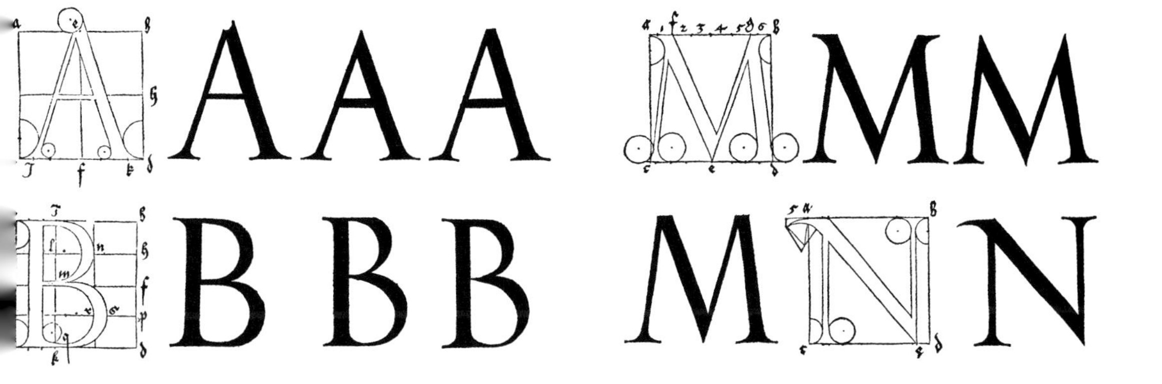

As well as being very influential Dürer's *Underweysung der Messung* and *Vier Bucher von Menschlicher Proportion* (*Four Books on Human Proportion*, Nuremberg, 1528) were commercially successful, and both were translated and reprinted many times. In fact they became sought-after volumes with an appeal that obviously went far beyond the artist-craftsmen to whom they were ostensibly intended. In effect, Dürer had established a literary genre. After his death many more treatises on geometry and perspective appeared in Germany and elsewhere. Most of these were produced by artist-craftsmen with backgrounds in various trades, practically all of them referred back to Dürer's book on geometry, and most included polyhedra in one form or another.

There was, of course, a financial aspect to the production of these treatises. A new class of bourgeoisie had emerged with money to spend on such prestige items as well-produced books and prints. This meant that the emerging medium of printing enabled artists, engravers and woodcutters to make a living at a time when, as a result of the upheavals caused by the Protestant Reformation, art and craft workshops were deprived of income from Church commissions. These artist-craftsmen proved themselves highly adaptable to the new circumstances; the degree of sophistication that was reached in printing techniques, and sheer quantities of print production can be surprising. Dürer's pupil Erhard Schon, for example, is credited with producing over two hundred woodcut prints, and some 1,200 illustrations for 116 books. Schon was exceptionally versatile and prolific, illustrating everything from religious broadsheet propaganda to satirical poetry, but in 1538 he too turned his hand to an artist's manual on design and perspective. There were many other Nuremberg artists that were to take up this idea, and these successors of Dürer, as we shall see in the next chapter, produced a variety of responses to his seminal work.

The 'geometric type' (typus geometriae) from a popular encyclopedia, the Margarita Philosophica, *published in Freiberg in 1503. The master geometer's desk displays various geometrical figures and his tools, while assistants perform tasks involving his geometrical skills.*

Early-modern polymaths, perspective and geometry

The great revival of interest in geometry, and the developments in perspective/optics that took place in early Renaissance Italy were duplicated when it moved north of the Alps, and as had been the case in Italy, the stature of those involved in these subjects is an indication of how important they were regarded. This period was a time of extraordinary intellectual advances – in science and technology, in geographical exploration, and in astronomical speculation. The Northern Renaissance had its own galaxy of brilliant individuals that made major contributions in these fields, very often across a whole range of disciplines. At this time the towns of southern Germany were among the great centres of this intellectual ferment and many brilliant scholars either came from, or chose to live in, the likes of Nuremberg, Augsburg, Ulm and Ingolstadt.

Petrus Apianus (the Latinized version of Peter Bienewitz), 1496–1552, a renowned mathematician and geographer, was one such. Having completed his studies in Leipzig and Vienna he went on to settle in Ingolstadt in Bavaria, where he set up a print shop in 1527. Over the next twenty-five years he published a remarkable series of high quality and much sought after books on such diverse subjects as mathematics, astronomy, geography and cartography. He had an early success with a book on arithmetic that was intended for the practical requirements of trades people and merchants, and written in the vernacular.[6] Other, more luxurious, books on cosmography and astronomy followed; *Cosmographicus Liber, Quadrans Apiani Astronomicus,* and the magnificent *Astronomicus Caesareum,* were regarded as masterpieces and went into many editions. He also found

Petrus Apianus' Instrument Buch, *the first printed treatise on astronomy and surveying. The frontispiece of this work uses two regular polyhedra emblematically, as an indication of scientific seriousness.*

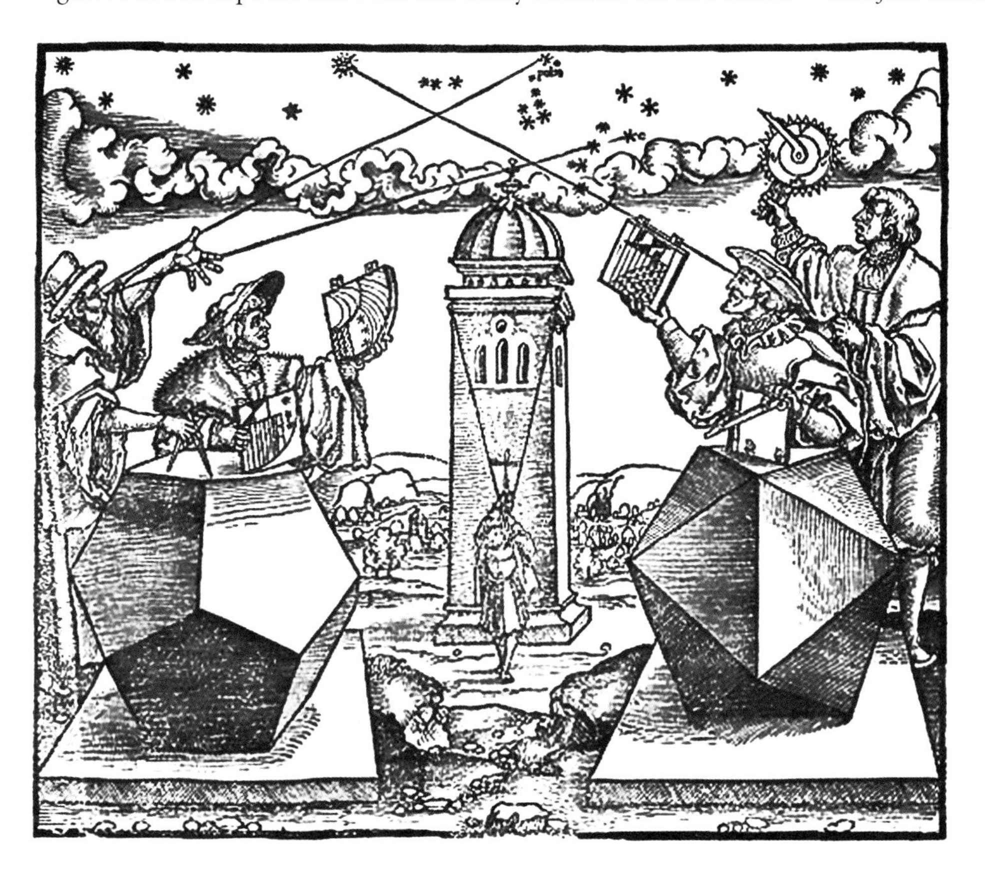

In his astronomical masterpiece Cosmographicus Liber, *Apianus features a variety of regular geometrical figures as emblemata in a charming series of illuminated capitals.*

time to write an '*Instrument Book*' (*Instrument Buch*, 1533) which was the first general treatise on astronomy and surveying. The title page of this last book is particularly interesting in the present context, as it shows a group using quadrants and other instruments (some of which were devised by Apianus himself), but it also prominently features two polyhedra, a dodecahedron and an icosahedron. His preoccupation with the Platonic solids is also indicated in the *Cosmographicus Liber*, where they appear among a charming series of illustrated capitals.

Another distinguished mathematician, Johann Neudorffer (1497–1563), was born in Nuremberg. Like Apianus, he too devised and published tables of commercial arithmetic, and was a teacher of geometry, but achieved his greatest fame as a calligrapher and biographer. Dürer employed Neudorffer for the lettering on his 'Apostles' panels, and he was a pioneer typographer, credited with the invention of the Fraktur script. Neudorffer is portrayed in a contemporary print as sharing a table with Wenzel Jamnitzer; the two famous sons of the city, geometricians both, are shown with the implements of their trades before them and the town itself looming behind. A caduceus, the symbol of commerce (and of printing) hovers above; an armillary sphere, symbolic of science and astronomy, stands in the foreground. Johann Neudorffer also appears in a famous portrait by Nicholas Neufchatel, in which he is explaining the properties of a dodecahedron to a young pupil.

A detail from the famous portrait of Johann Neudorffer by Nicholas Neufchatel, in which he is explaining the properties of the dodecahedron to a young pupil.

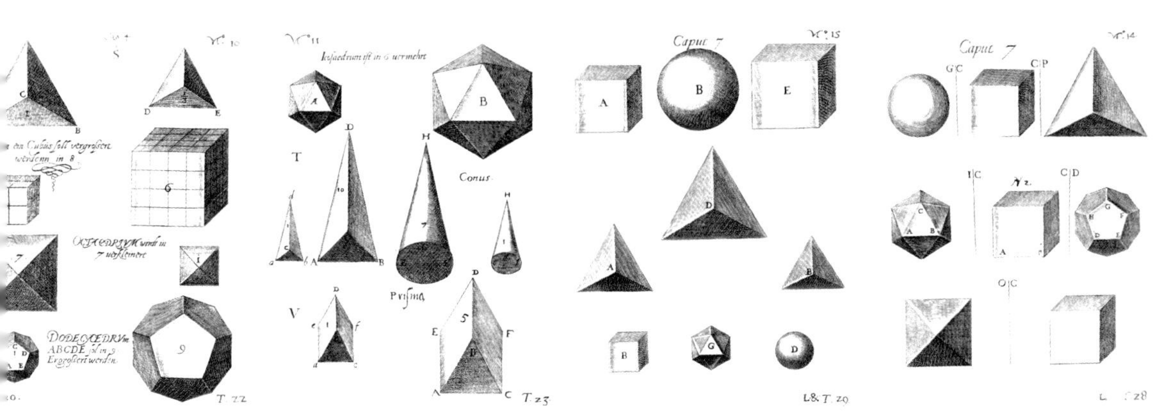

Pages from Hulsius's Tractatus Primus Instrumentum Mechanicorum, *dealing with solid geometry.*

The extraordinarily talented Levinus Hulsius (1546–1606) was born in Ghent, but moved to Nuremberg in 1583, apparently as a result of his Protestant beliefs. As a linguist he was able to earn a living by teaching languages, but became involved in the manufacture and dealing in geometrical instruments. In common with many of the other talented individuals mentioned above, he ventured into printing and publishing. In 1602 he acquired the printing-plates of Tycho Brahe's *Astronomiae Instauratae Mechanica*, and brought out a further edition of that important work. He also wrote a number of treatises on the construction of geometrical instruments, including the *Tractatus Primus Instrumentorum Mechanicorum* in 1605, which has a section on geometrical solids. As a lexicographer Hulsius was responsible for compiling and publishing several dictionaries (including French–German and Italian–German). This remarkable man was also active in publishing the most recent accounts of navigations from farflung parts of the world, together with maps based on information that he had garnered from sea captains in Antwerp.

In the sixteenth scientific instruments of all kinds were highly valued, and were often seen as objects worthy of collection. They were sometimes presented as prestige gifts to the various courts, and many such gifts were retained in the princely collections known as *Kunstkammers* (chambers of arts). Some of these *Kunstkammer* were mere accumulations of curiosities, others were far more serious, dedicated collections. The most famous example of the latter was housed at the Dresden Court in Saxony, which was regarded as one of the best of its kind in the whole of Europe. It held an extensive collection of objects of scientific interest, including tools and technical instruments, many of which had been commissioned. This was a sort of prototype science museum, and attracted some very illustrious visitors, including Johannes Kepler, who is known to have

Two plates from Johann Faulhaber's Neue Geometrische und Perspectivische Inventiones, *which demonstrate the range of his interests. In the first the artist-craftsman is working with a perspectival frame; a book of geometric figures is open on the table and a set of Platonic solids hang from the wall. Through the window on the left are scenes involving the sciences of ballistics, surveying and agriculture. The right-hand window shows an astronomer and an armillary sphere. The lower plate shows a draughtsman demonstrating a plan of a fortified city to a soldier with the aid of a perspectival frame.*

visited this *Kunstkammer* around 1600. Kepler witnessed a demonstration of a *camera obscura* here, which made a great impression on him, and also saw a model of a dodecahedron, which is said to have inspired his meditation on symmetry, the *Strena*.

The curator of this establishment from 1620 onwards was the court mathematician Lucas Brunn (1572–1628), an outstanding figure in his own right. Brunn had come to Dresden from Nuremberg where, as a professor of mathematics, he had published a treatise on perspective, the *Praxis Perpectivae* of 1613, which was influenced by Hans Lencker's *Perpectiva Literaria*.[7] He was also a maker of astronomical instruments and, since he was thoroughly familiar with the most recent developments in optics, was an obvious candidate for the post of curator to the *Kunstkammer*. The Elector of Saxony, Rudoph II, was personally interested in the subject, having conducted his own experiments with lenses and mirrors. In the finest tradition of the Renaissance polymaths, Brunn produced a German edition of Euclid in 1625, in the preface of which he declared that 'geometry and the study of proportion form a lofty and necessary art', and praised the Saxon Electors for their patronage of the *Kunstkammer*. The inventory of the library of this enlightened institution shows that it held the works of Dürer, Jamnitzer, Lencker, Lautensack and Hirschvogel, and many other volumes on perspective and geometry.

Whatever scientific advances were being made in this period, enlightenment in the modern sense was rarely fully-fledged, and in many senses the emergence from the medieval past was far from complete.[8] This mixture of post-medieval and modern attitudes is embodied in the mathematician Johann Faulhaber (1589–1635). Faulhaber is an important figure in mathematics; he pioneered the use of logarithms, wrote treatises on algebra, collaborated with Kepler and influenced Descartes. But he also held a number of arcane, not to say peculiar, ideas, mostly numerological and cabbalistic, which frequently caused him to fall foul of the religious authorities. Faulhaber came from a family of weavers, but his talent for mathematics showed at an early age and by the time he was twenty he was teaching in his own school. In common with so many of the gifted scientific minds of that time he was able to apply his talents to highly practical ends. He advised on the fortifications on his home town, Ulm, for which this was a desperately fraught period, and designed and made surveying instruments, particularly those with military applications. Faulhaber achieved great prestige in this field, and became much sought after as a fortifications engineer throughout the region. Amidst all this activity he still found time to produce a series of books dealing with his mathematical work, his inventions and his mystical beliefs. These include the *Neue Geometrische und Perspectivische Inventiones* of 1610, which includes a number of plates demonstrating Faulhaber's abiding interest in geometry and perspective, and indicate that he made his own perspectival frames and polyhedral models, since there is a set of the Platonic solids suspended from the wall of his workshop in one of these prints.

Kepler – celestial mathematician

Johannes Kepler (1571–1630) was born in modest circumstances in a small town in Swabia, southern Germany. Another brilliant and precocious talent, his talent for mathematics was first realised at his local school, which led to his acceptance into a seminary and eventually to the university at Tubingen. At Tubingen Kepler encountered the extraordinarily radical Copernican model of a sun-centred planetary system, which he rapidly accepted.

His life-long mission thereafter was to investigate the physical nature of the planets, their relationships with each other, and the mathematical character of their orbits around the sun. His first ideas on this ambitious project were published in the *Mysterium Cosmographicum* (*The Mystery of The Cosmos*, 1596). Written in his early twenties, it is now famous as the first published assertion of the Copernican heliocentric theory. Kepler proposed a geometric scheme for the orbits of the six then-known planets. He was influenced throughout his career by the Platonic notion that an archetypal world of forms and ideas lay behind the world of physical appearances. These ideas, combined with his commitment to Protestant theology, led him to the belief that geometry was 'co-eternal with the divine mind'. In the *Mysterium* he lays out what he believed to be the order of this divine geometry.

Kepler's first attempts at uncovering a geometric schema to account for the observable orbits of the planets involved various arrangements of polygons within circumscribing circles. When this attempt proved unsatisfactory he turned to arrangements of 'nested' polyhedra, one within another, to find a convincing model of the geometry underlying the universe, but ultimately the data could not be made to fit the theory and this imaginative scheme also failed.

In 1610 Galileo published his discovery of Jupiter's moons, an event that greatly impressed Kepler and inspired him in his own study of the properties of lenses, published as *Dioptrice* in 1611, in which he presented his idea for a more advanced type of telescope using two convex lenses, a

HARMONICIS LIB. V. 181

ëdris irregularibus, quibus tegitur Cubus intus. Huic ſuccedit Icoſaë-

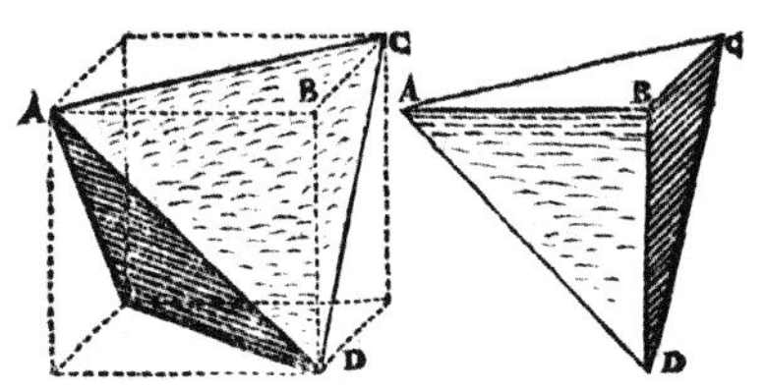

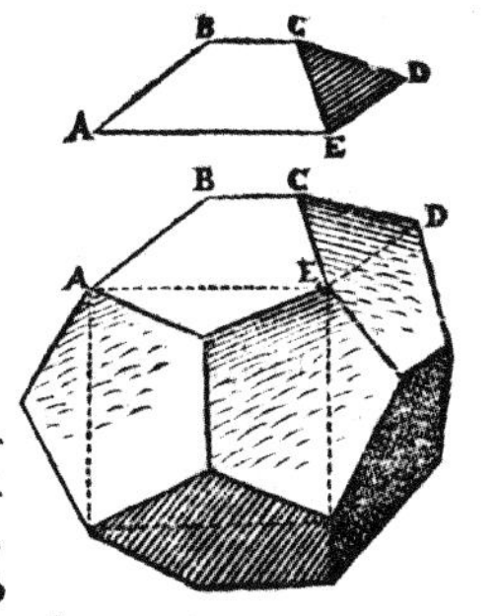

dron 4. ob ſimilitudinem, ultima ſecundariarum, angulo ſolido plurilineari utentium. Intimum eſt Octoëdron 5. Cubi ſimile, & prima figura ſecundariarum, cui ideò primus locus interiorum debetur, quippe inſcriptili: uti cubo circumſcriptili primus exteriorum.

Sunt autem notabilia duo veluti conjugia harum figurarum, ex

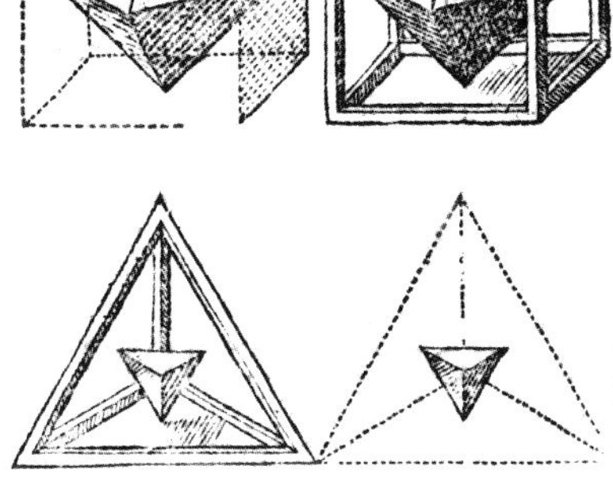

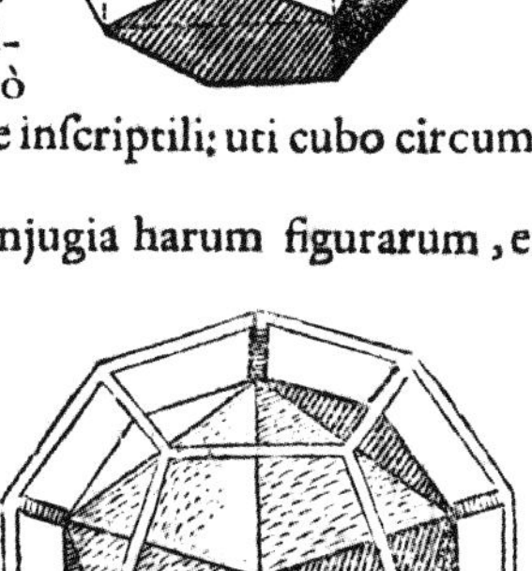

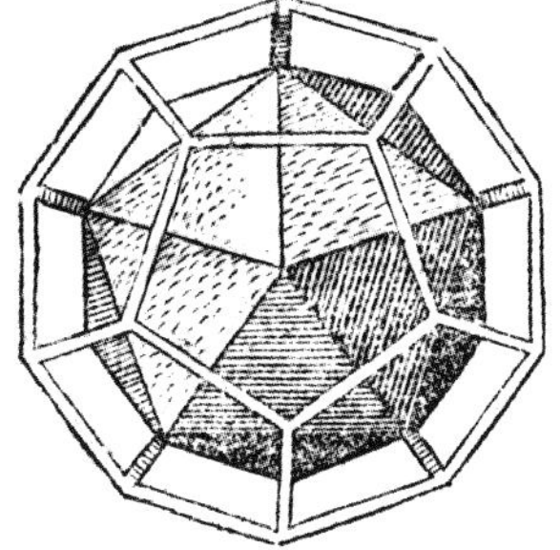

diverſis combinata claſſibus: Mares, Cubus & Dodecaëdron ex primarijs; fœminæ, Octoëdron & Icoſiëdron ex ſecundarijs; qui-

Regular three-dimensional arrangements from Kepler's Harmonices Mundi, *1619. Kepler firmly believed that the secret of universal order could be found in geometry, that 'geometry was co-eternal with the divine mind'.*

completely successful design which soon gained universal acceptance. Also in 1611 Kepler produced a charming essay entitled 'On Hexagonal Snow' ('Strena Seu de Niva Sexangula'), in which a meditation on the hexagonal symmetry of snow-crystals led him to consider different arrangements of two- and three-dimensional close packing, both in nature and in mathematical theory. Out of this came an explanation of the structure of honeybee cells and the speculation that a hexagonal arrangement of spheres would fill space in the most efficient way – a conjecture that, surprisingly, had to wait till the twenty-first century for verification.

Of particular relevance in this context, Kepler made a systematic study of polyhedra, placing them into classes for the first time, and proving that these classes were complete – he was the first to do this for the thirteen convex uniform polyhedra, the so-called Archimedean solids. Two important polyhedra, the small stellated dodecahedron and the great

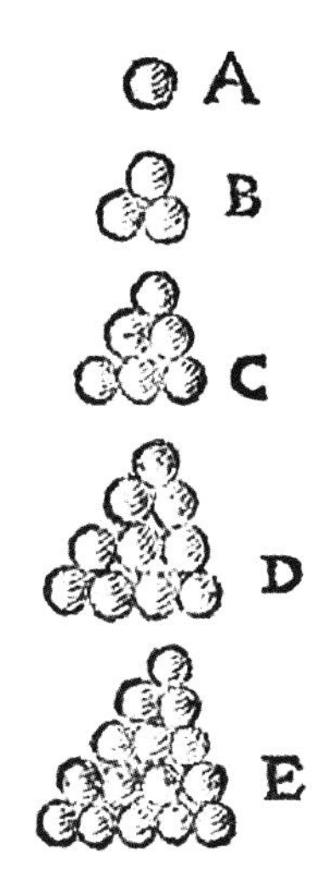

Diagram from the 'Strena Seu de Nive Sexangula' of 1611, in which Kepler investigates the close close-packing of spheres and relates this to the formation of crystals, including the six-sided snowflake.

stellated dodecahedron, bear his name (although they had actually been depicted previously by both Uccello and Jamnitzer), and he gave them a mathematical description, realising that technically speaking they were *regular* polyhedra. He also discovered the rhombic dodecahedron and rhombic triacontahedron.

Kepler was truly modern and a true scientist. He was inspired by an ideal Platonic vision, and never entirely abandoned the idea of an orderly universe. Though he continued to search for geometrical and numerological relationships among the planets and elsewhere, in the end these were only acceptable if they conformed to the observable phenomena. In his *Harmonices Mundi* (*The Harmony of the World*, 1619), he finally presented his laws of planetary motion, which in broad outline still stand today. At the age of fifty he returned to the *Mysterium*, publishing a greatly extended version in 1621.

Kepler was another to whom the expression 'last of the magicians, first of scientists' applies; he was a visionary, but a very practical one. Always guided by Platonic notions of a perfectly structured, geometrically harmonic universe, he pursued this path to an almost obsessive degree. His mathematics placed the Copernican heliocentric theory on an unassailable footing, and through this work alone he truly opened doors to our modern understanding of the workings of the universe.

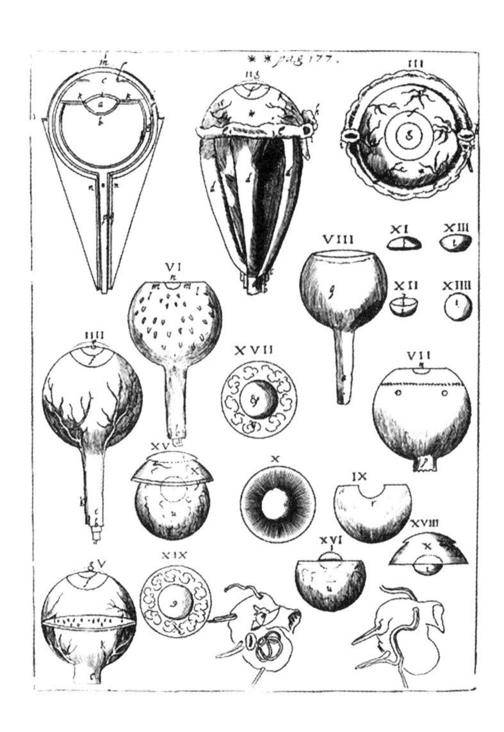

Kepler's illustration depicting the structure of the eye which, he realised, functioned in the same way as a camera obscura *(a term that he invented). From the* Astronomiae Pars Optica, *1604.*

From Jost Amman's Das Standebuch (Book of Trades)*, published in 1568. Among its 114 woodcuts, which have accompanying verses by Hans Sachs, are these images depicting various aspects of the printing trade.*

PRINTING AND PUBLISHING IN THE RENAISSANCE

From its invention in Germany around the mid-fifteenth century, the printing press and the whole business of printed publication expanded at an extraordinary rate. Estimates vary, but by any measure the statistics are quite remarkable. Within just fifty years, by 1500, there were as many as a thousand print-shops in capitals throughout Europe, and these had produced something in the region of 40,000 editions, and up to twenty million books. The capacity of this new technology to create hundreds, even thousands, of identical texts provided an unprecedented stimulus to intellectual life, one that greatly facilitated study and debate. Texts were no longer an exclusive medium to be used by scholars for other scholars, but were available to all who could read and had the wherewithal to purchase the printed word. Books, pamphlets and prints soon became familiar, and in some cases eminently collectable items. Printing became an entirely new kind of occupation, the print-shop a new centre of intellectual exchange.

The range of topics covered in these early years of printing is equally surprising. The very earliest publications dealt mainly with religious subjects; Gutenberg's Bible *was, of course, a very early production of the genre, but very soon books on every imaginable subject were available. There were maps and travel books; scientific texts and medical manuals; treatises on warfare and fortification; on nature and cookery; almanacs and sheet music; even pornography. Books were popular, particularly among the new monied mercantile classes, and they could be profitable to the entrepreneurs who were involved in their production. Cities like Nuremberg, Venice and Antwerp became notable centres of their production.*

There was a negative side to the use of the new medium. Both sides of the Catholic–Protestant schism used printed material to promote their cause, occasionally resulting in sensational and violent propaganda. In general, however, the right to publish freely, without having to submit to state or church authorities, exerted a liberating influence and led to an unprecedented diffusion of ideas.

Printing presses were typically financed by private patrons, often with an eye for profit, but anyone with the means, or the cause, could set up their own press. Regiomontanus established a printing house in Nuremberg in 1471 to publish his own scientific ideas and those of others, making him the first scientific publisher; this was a noble precedent. Tycho Brahe printed his own works, as did Johannes Kepler, and Galileo's conflict with the church was precipitated by the publication of his own controversial scientific discoveries. Kepler commented that 'the number of authors whose writings are printed is now greater than the number of all the authors over the past thousand years'. Moreover, these Renaissance authors had the nerve to contradict and overthrow long-held beliefs; printing became a powerful liberating and democratising influence. In 1543 the Nuremberg printer Johannes Petreius produced one of the most radical and influential books of all time, Nicolas Copernicus's De Revolutionibus Orbium Coelestium *(*On the Revolutions of the Celestial Spheres*). Although it was notoriously slow to gain acceptance, this 200-page book, with an initial print run of around 400 copies, managed to bring about one of the most profound changes in human thought in all of human history.*

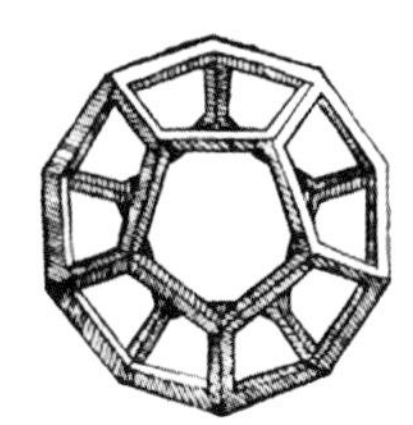

Notes and references

1. The availability of paper from around 1400 was the first stage in the printing revolution, Gutenburg's use of a press and reuseable type in the 1450s the next great step. Gutenberg's innovation caught on very fast, spreading from Mainz to Nuremberg by the 1460s, and to Italy around the same time.

2. Calendars and almanacs were some of the most popular and useful forms of early printed material. Ratdolt's *Kalendario*, based on Regiomontanus' calculations, which provided accurate information on the phases of the moon and the positions of the planets, was far superior to previous productions.

3. Ratdolt's plates for the many diagrams in his version of Euclid's *Elements* used the ingenious method of setting wires into plaster blocks.

4. Although the religious divisions between Islam and Christianity were manifested in their respective geographical spheres of influence, there were always points of contact, through both trade and war. Islamic knowledge, far superior in the fields of science and medicine to that of medieval Europe at this time, was enthusiastically sought after by such scholars as Stefan of Pise, Leonardo Fibonacci, Robert of Chester and Gerard of Cremona – the last of whom translated no fewer than eighty-seven books from Arabic into Latin.

5. In this way Dürer is contributing to the widely-held Renaissance view epitomised by the Latin phrase *ars sine scientia nihil est,* 'art without (scientific) knowledge is nothing', originally attributed to the fourteenth-century French architect Jean Mignot.

6. Interestingly, Apianus's book on arithmetic is one of the objects shown on the table of Hans Holbein's famous painting *The Ambassadors.*

7. Hans Lencker had also been involved in the Dresden *Kunstkammer*, as a tutor to the Elector.

8. It is worth remembering that although the Renaissance is associated with the rise of humanism, this period was also the heyday of the European witch-craze. Kepler's mother was a victim of this hysterical movement, and was only saved from burning at the stake through Kepler's energetic efforts in her defence.

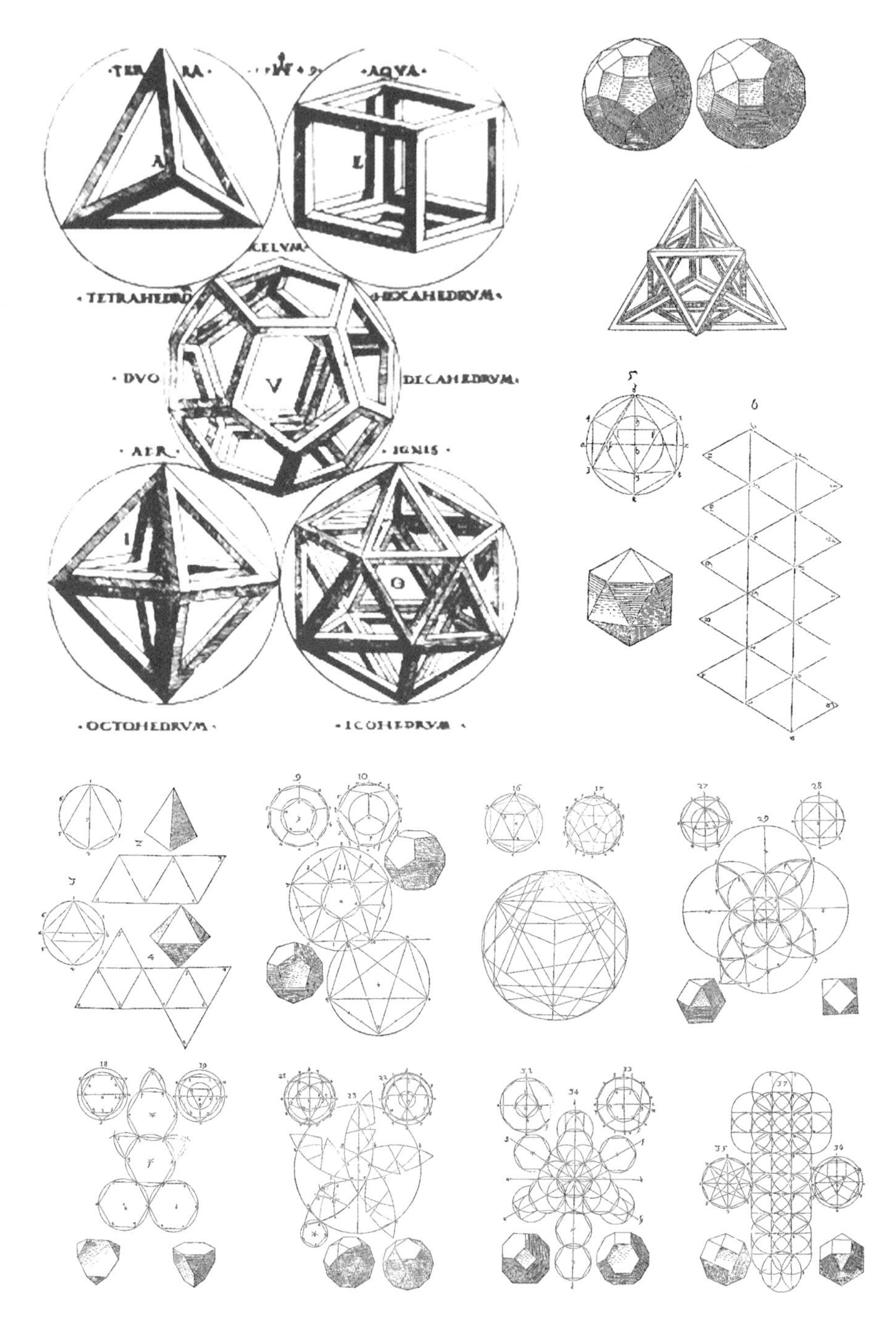

Title page and diagrams from Augustin Hirschvogel's
Ein Aigentliche und Grundliche Anweysung in die Geometria, *Nuremberg, 1543.*

4
Geometrical treatises in Germany in the 1500s

Instruction manuals after Dürer

The success of Dürer's books,[1] which ran to several editions, led others to follow his example and produce 'instruction manuals for artists' of their own. Dürer's works set the tone and the subject matter for this new genre, and although many are interesting in their own ways, none that followed were quite as ambitious or comprehensive, in a purely didactic sense, as the original. Dürer's books included sections on plane geometry, on polyhedra, on proportional canons of the human body, on architectonic forms, on typography, and of course on the principles of perspective. His successors tended to select just one or two of these themes, but there are marked differences in the ways they handle them. Although they all present themselves as teaching manuals, and many include basic primers on geometry, there are a variety of different approaches, and some of the more interesting use the form to demonstrate their own particular skills and imagination.

As indicated in the introduction to this book, little is known about any of these post-Dürer artist-authors. Many of them, like the master himself, seem to have been native to Nuremberg, or at least came to live there, and most had a background in one or other of the crafts. Jamnitzer, Lautensack and Lencker were goldsmiths (as was Dürer's own father), Hirschvogel was originally a glass painter, Stoer a master carpenter. Their books all tend to focus on the geometrical aspects of art, in which they combine older, craft usage of geometry with a more academic and theoretical kind, including theories on perspective – and they all wrote in the German vernacular.

The background to these all of these productions was the popularity and commercial success of books and prints at this time. Competitive pressures within this thriving market had led to improving standards of production, with illustrations in particular achieving very high levels of accuracy and clarity. The printing revolution was making a profound impact on art itself, with many artists achieving international recognition through the medium of engraved and woodcut prints. Dürer was in the forefront of this elevation of print into an art form. In his forties he decided to concentrate on printmaking, and created the brilliant series that ensured his, and the form's, reputation – and made him fairly wealthy in the process. Dürer's preoccupation with the role of geometry in providing a scientific and theoretical foundation to the *artes liberal* was equally influential.

Largely as a result of this influence a certain fashion for geometry developed in early sixteenth century Germany, a style that accorded with the new rationalising mood of the Renaissance. In fact the concept of properly measuring and accurately representing the physical world had taken hold in many quarters. This was a period that saw great advances in such diverse areas as astronomy, surveying, cartography, optical lens making, and the manufacture of scientific instruments of all kinds. There were many interconnections between science, art and the crafts in this broad movement, and to engage with it, if only by purchasing one of the many available treatises on geometry and perspective, was to be associated with the new spirit of enquiry that seemed intent on uncovering the hidden structure of the world; the modern magic of science.

The Popularisers: Rodler, Hirschvogel and Lautensack

Among the earlier authors to emulate Dürer was his one-time student Hieronymus Rodler. Just three years after Dürer's death, in 1531, Rodler produced a booklet with the declared aim of making Dürer's ideas more comprehensible. This short work focuses on the use of perspective in drawing; woodcuts show simple drawings of interiors and exteriors of a working craft environment to illustrate his theory but, uncharacteristically, there is no mention of plane or solid geometry, and there are no examples of regular figures at all. Far from Dürer's sophisticated approach, Rodler's work conveys an almost naïve simplicity.

By contrast, Augustine Hirschvogel (1503–53) produced a very serious treatise entitled *Ein aigentliche und grundliche Anweysung in die Geometria* (*An Original and Thorough Instruction in Geometry*, Nuremberg, 1543), which was primarily concerned with polyhedra. His book actually improved on Dürer's in this respect by showing the constructions of an extended range of solid figures, together with alternate perspective views – he investigates the semi-regular Archimedean as well as the regular Platonic solids. This was a thoroughly workmanlike manual, and is clearly intended to be a practical aid to all those engaged in the crafts or architectural trades (see page 48 for examples of his work).

Perspective drawings from Hieronymus Rodler's Eyn schön nützlich Büchlein, *1531.*

Hirschvogel was born in Nuremberg into a family of glass painters, and his career, in which he became a mathematician and cartographer as well as a famous printmaker, epitomises the possibilities for artistic and social mobility of his time. When Nuremberg adopted the Protestant Reformation the demand for stained glass came to an end and the Hirschvogel workshop, of necessity, had to seek commissions in other areas. The talented Augustin first applied his talents to cartography, at which he excelled , and he was soon producing maps of Austria for the Imperial Court of Vienna. He also became known for his *Views of Vienna*, which included a city plan in which he employed perspective, and the method of triangulation, which he devised himself. In his use of mathematics, accurate surveying and perspective for these representations of the city Hirschvogel is part of a tradition that traces directly back to Dürer, who recommends the use of scientific instruments for just this purpose in his *Underweysung*.

Heinrich Lautensack, who produced an *Instruction on the use of Compass and Straightedge in Perspective and Proportion*, (*Des Circles und Richtscheyts*, Augsburg, 1564), continued this move towards more accurate standards of representation. His manual adopts the agenda set by Dürer. It provides a primer on linear geometry and methods for the construction of regular and semi-regular solids, deals with the theory of perspective, and proposes systems of proportion for the human body and horses. Like Rodler's and Hirschvogel's books of the two previous decades it is a worthy, serious production, if a little dull, and was clearly intended as a guide for artists and craftsmen and nothing more. But a series of volumes were about to appear that were to use the geometrical/ perspective treatise format in more imaginative ways.

A portrait by Jost Amman of Wentzel Jamnitzer with his perspectival machine.

The Creatives: Wenzel Jamnitzer, Johannes Lencker, Lorenz Stoer, and Anon

With this group of author–artists we finally arrive at the short-lived phase of visual creativeness that forms the primary focus of this book. It seems very likely that each of this group knew, or at the very least, was familiar with, each others work – and they would certainly have known the more prosaic geometric perspective treatises of the recent past. But their productions are of a different order of artistic imagination. There was nothing in any previous manual as original as their inventive drawings, and although these authors exerted a certain influence, there was nothing quite as interesting in anything that followed. This brief flowering of creativity came from an art-fellowship that seems scarcely to have been aware of its own existence. Although the ostensible purpose of their books was didactic, namely, to demonstrate methods of geometry and perspective, there is little attempt in any of them to convey an actual theory of perspective, relying instead on the 'evidence' of their own drawings, which are far more imaginative than in any previous treatises. It is hard to avoid the conclusion that this group are, artistically speaking, playing with this genre. They seem to be tapping in to the wider appeal for this form that had been generated by their predecessors, and the books they produced were certainly popular. They were translated, reprinted and, in Jamnitzer's case, repeatedly pirated.

Wenzel Jamnitzer (1508–85) lays claim to be the founding figure of this group. His work is the most assured and schematised, and he was the best known in his own time, but biographical details are rather limited. He originally came to Nuremberg from Vienna, and acquired citizenship in 1534. By the time he turned his attention to *Perspectiva Corporum Regularium* in 1568, he had chalked up a long, successful career as a goldsmith. He was, in fact, the leading goldsmith of his day, and the family workshop that he headed had made precious objects for any number of European royal courts, including four Habsburg emperors. He became known as the 'German Cellini', and attained the position of Master of the Mint in Nuremberg, making him a very notable figure in the town. Jamnitzer was also known to have been interested in scientific problems, to have made scientific instruments, and to have published on these matters. But the *Perspectiva* is in a different category; although it reflects both his craft skills and his scientific interests, it is essentially a work of pure geometric fantasy.

It is intriguing to speculate on Jamnitzer's conscious intentions in this book. It is clear that he was fully aware of Platonic notions of the 'elemental' symbolism associated with the regular solids, and he explicitly based his figures on the thirteenth book of Euclid and on Plato's *Timaeus*, but he seems to have had his own cosmological ideas of their correspondence with the physical world. As far as can be determined (since he never managed to complete his Introduction), he intended the scheme in the *Perspectiva* to present some sort of 'metaphorical alphabet' in which the five regular solids corresponded to the five Greek vowels, and the variations of the solids corresponded to the twenty-four letters of that alphabet. This 'method never before employed', as he described it, would result in the 'avoidance of all superfluity and, in contrast to the old-fashioned way of teaching, no line or point will be drawn needlessly'. There is a clear resonance here to Plato's notion of the five regular solids as the basis of the phenomenal world, but it is a thoroughly idiosyncratic interpretation in which he seems to have envisioned the generation of endless solid figures of various shapes and sizes as a metaphor for the creation of the physical world

He finishes his book with a series of twenty 'skeletised' versions of regular figures, twelve spherical variations, eight conical fantasies and, finally, four geometric toroidal *mazzocchio* shapes set amidst a clutter of other geometric figures. Quite how these drawings are meant to fit into his scheme is not explained, but one suspects that they are simply effusions of Jamnitzer's extraordinary imagination.

The engravings for *Perspectiva Corporun Regularium* were cut by Jost Amman, an incredibly talented and prolific engraver with a long association with Jamnitzer. Amman came to Nuremberg from Zurich in 1560, where he served an apprenticeship in Jamnitzer's workshop (his initials appear on eleven of the engravings in the *Perspectiva*). He went on to become a well-known illustrator in his own right, with more than fifty books to his credit. Amazingly, at the same time that Amman was engraving Jamnitzer's opus he was working on another volume, *Das Standebuch* (*The Book of Trades*, Nuremberg, 1568), an extensive survey of contemporary crafts and occupations that featured no fewer than 106 engravings (see page 45). This appeared in the same year as the *Perspectiva*. Jost Amman's extraordinary productivity is indicated by the assertion made by of one of his pupils that his work over a particular four-year period would have filled a hay wagon.

Johannes Lencker (1523–85), was a near-contemporary of Jamnitzer, and had much else in common with him. He too was a well-known goldsmith and a notable citizen of Nuremberg and, like Jamnitzer, played a prominent role in its civil life. He is also known to have been involved in devising measuring and drawing instruments, including those he employed in creating his treatise *Perspectiva Literaria* of 1567. Unfortunately beyond these bare facts little more is known about him.

The *Perspectiva Literaria* is as curious and idiosyncratic an 'instruction manual' as Jamnitzer's opus, consisting in the main of three-dimensional, perspective drawings of the letters of the entire alphabet, strewn about in a variety of positions. By using lettering in his geometrical–perspective treatise Lenker is to some extant following both Pacioli in *De Divina Proportione* and Dürer in his *Underweysung der Messung*. But his description of these images as 'primary visual evidence', without further elaboration, seems somewhat disingenuous. As with Jamnitzer's geometric inventions, there is a sense here of artistic divertissement as much as genuine instruction, although he does claim in his introduction to the *Perspectiva Literaria* that it should 'teach by certain rules how to form each object on a flat surface ... so that it would appear proportionally exact'.

Lenker completes his *Perspectiva Literaria* with a marvellously imaginative series of drawings of architectonic and polyhedral forms, including an embellished *Nautilus* shell (see pages 210–15). Some of

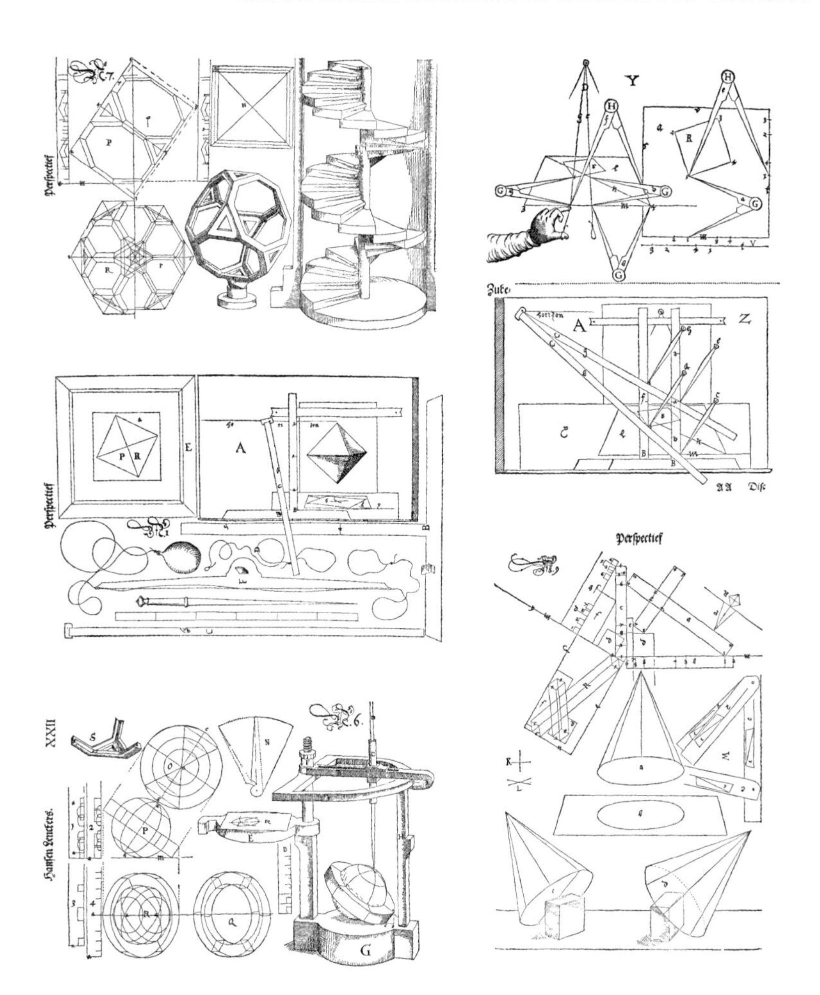

Perspectival images together with drawing and surveying instruments from Johannes Lenkers's Perspectiva *of 1571, according to James Elkins all part of 'his complex understanding of perspective'.*

these are similar enough to Jamnitzer's drawings to indicate a close familiarity, although Lenckers 1567 book actually came out in the year before Jamnitzer's *Perspectiva Corporum Regularium* of 1568. Whatever the intentions of this work, and whatever was going on in the minds of those involved in the production of each of these collections of geometrically-based drawings, it is clear that there is a distinct sharing of style and visual ideas, even if they did not amount to a 'school'.

A few years later, in 1571, Lencker produced a new book, simply called *Perspectiva*, which provided more explicit instructions on the use of perspective than the earlier work. In it Lencker makes a distinction between the 'high, beautiful and subtle art' of perspective as a philosophical theory and his own more practical approach to the subject. He makes it clear that he is concerned only with correct proportional representation. This volume also presents an interesting series of sketches depicting what one imagines is a fairly comprehensive survey of the instruments used in surveying and drawing at the time.

The third known Nuremberg artist to have published a geometric perspective book, which appeared in the same year as those of Lencker and Jamnitzer, is Lorenz Stoer. However, Stoer's *Geometria et Perspectiva* cannot be considered as a teaching aid by any stretch of the imagination since it is quite short, consisting of just eleven drawings, and has no text at all. It is, though, a most intriguing work. It features a series of geometric solids, some regular, balanced one on top of the other, set among various landscapes of overgrown, half-ruined buildings. Sometimes these geometrical and architectonic forms are accompanied by strange, trellised scrollwork.[3] On his title page Stoer suggests that these drawings might be useful as patterns for *intarsia* (marquetry panels), although no examples of *intarsia* have survived to indicate that these particular drawings were ever used for this purpose. Devoid of human or animal figures, they convey a rather melancholy, almost post-apocalyptic atmosphere – the 'eternal' qualities of the solid figures are emphasised by the ruined, abandoned appearance of the cityscapes. Could this in part be a reflection of the devastating effects of the plague, and the fears of further visitations? Nuremberg and Augsburg had both suffered from a series of outbreaks of this dread disease throughout the sixteenth century, the most recent in 1563, just three years before this book was published. The drawings certainly have a haunted feeling about them, but the Renaissance had seen a revival of interest in classical ruins; they had began to be surveyed and measured, and were included in other perspective treatises, so Stoer's use of this subject matter is far from unique.[4]

Stoer also produced two remarkable folios of a series of geometric figures. Because they were in colour it is unlikely that these ever were intended to be published; one contains 33 paintings,[5] the other 336.[6] These delicate watercolours are clearly a labour of love. Several of the drawings in the latter collection have dates, indicating that they were produced over a thirty-year period from 1562 to the end of the century. Bound together around 1600, they present an extraordinarily beautiful collection of inventive geometric forms, and are the remarkable evidence of a sustained enthusiasm of a refined geometricism.

There is one further artist whose work obviously belongs with this group. The drawings by this person, which were never published, are very much in the geometric style of Jamnitzer, Lencker and Stoer, but whereas there is at least some information about the lives of these three,

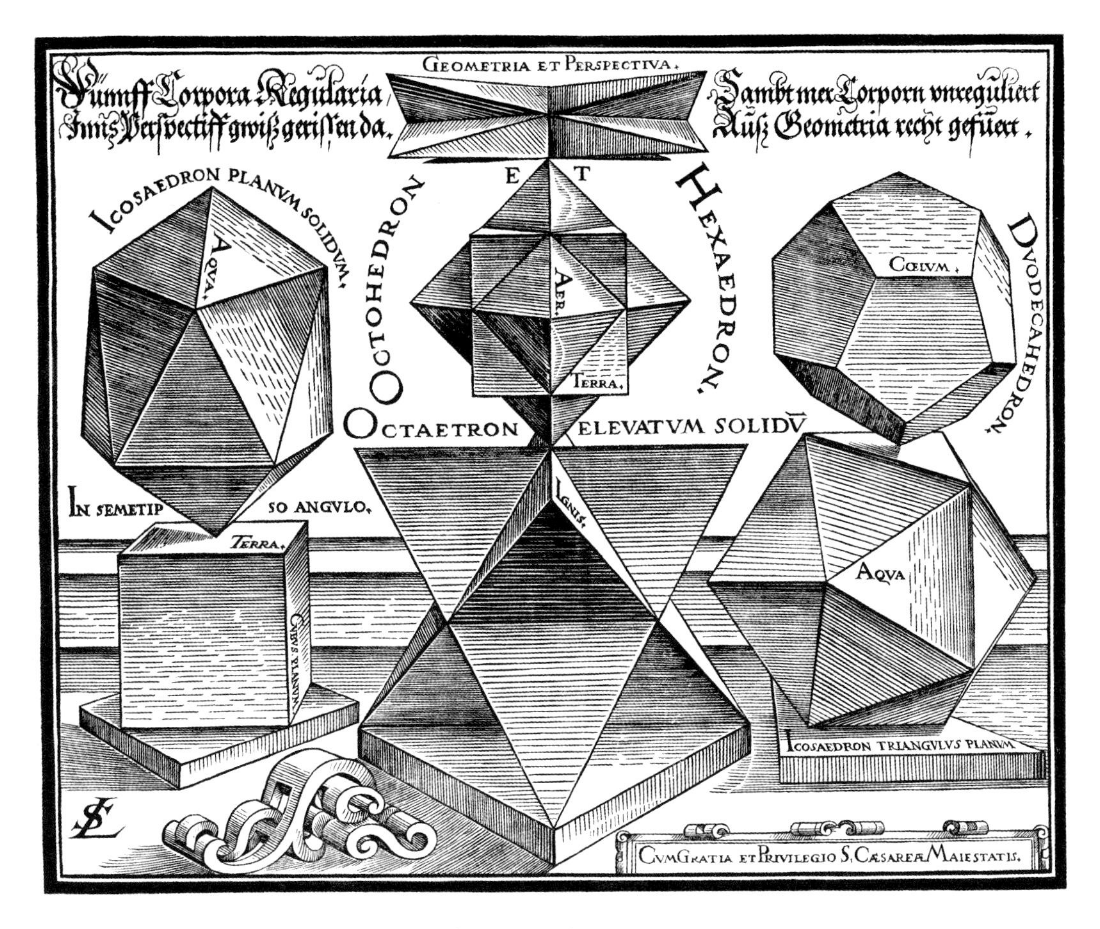

Woodcut title page from Lorenz Stoer's Geometria et Perspectiva.

nothing whatsoever is known of this final contributor. The anonymous folio in which these drawings appear, dated as 1565–1600, contains images that are clearly derived from both Jamnitzer and Lencker, but have a softer style of their own.[7] There are 36 drawings in all, beginning with the regular solids and moving on to a series of variations, finishing with 'skeletised' polyhedra and some curious architectonic figures. An endearing and distinctive feature of these watercolours is the inclusion of small creatures alongside the geometric figures.

The purpose, if any, of these drawings is as obscure as their originator. They are in the perspective–geometrical treatise tradition followed by Jamnitzer and the others, but the instructive intention seems even less convincing than in the productions of the rest of this group. Two of the drawings have headings that indicate that they may have been intended as a title-page for some proposed book, but most appear to have been drawn in the spirit of Stoer's folios – from a sustained fascination with geometrical figures and the sheer satisfaction of analysing and drawing them. It is possible that, like Stoer's 'ruin' drawings, there may have been hopes that some might serve as patterns for *intarsia*, but if so they seem to have been no more successful in this than were Stoer's own work.

For a variety of reasons there will always be uncertainties about this brief flowering of geometric art and the group of artists that produced it. In the first place, as we have seen, the lives of the artists are themselves obscure. In addition none of them, apparently, had a great deal to say about their work. To compound these deficits, a great deal of information and material evidence may have been lost in the turmoil of war and pestilence that descended on their homeland during and shortly after their time.

We do know that, sadly, both Jamnitzer and Lencker were victims of the plague that hit Nuremberg in 1585. The city had, in fact, seen repeated outbreaks of this disease since the first massive epidemic in 1437–50. War, religious turmoil, and sporadic recurrences of the plague were part of the background of Germany at that time.[8] It is difficult for us to imagine the devastation and disruption of ordinary life that these unwelcome events must have created. One of the significant side-effects must have been periodic suspensions of trade and travel. For our artist-craftsmen such interruptions may have presented a serious threat to their livelihood, but it could also have left them with time on their hands. Could this have been a factor in the creation of at least some of these drawings? There are many precedents of artistic creativity under conditions of enforced isolation and temporary exile. Boccaccio's *Decameron* was written while he and a group of friends were seeking refuge from the plague in a villa outside Florence, and Dürer's first trip to Italy was prompted by a similar motive, to escape the plague that had struck Nuremberg in 1498.

A curious, stacking figure by an anonymous artist who was clearly influenced by Jamnitzer and Stoer.

Later contributions: Pfinzing and Halt

Whatever the particular circumstances that gave rise to this short-lived genre, it has qualities that make it unique in art, but by the end of the sixteenth century the vogue for geometric invention seems largely to have run its course. Geometric perspective treatises after this time still included geometric figures to demonstrate their theories, but in general they are far less adventurous. The volume by Pfinzing, *Extract der Geometriae und Perspective*, is typical in this respect.

Paul Pfinzing was born into a Nuremberg patrician family in 1554, and is best known as a cartographer, a field in which he was a pioneer. From around 1583 his printshop produced a series of very highly regarded maps of Nuremberg, and in 1598 he published a treatise of his own, in a limited edition 'for friends'. The intention of Pfinzing's book is more clearly didactic than those of the four previous artists. It refers to the geometry of the regular solids, and has a series of odd geometric constructs in association with the technical instruments used to produce perspective drawings of them. Although the overall effect is slightly incongruous,

Illustrations from Paul Pfinzing's Extract der Geometriae und Perspective, *featuring the technical instruments used to produce perspective drawings.*

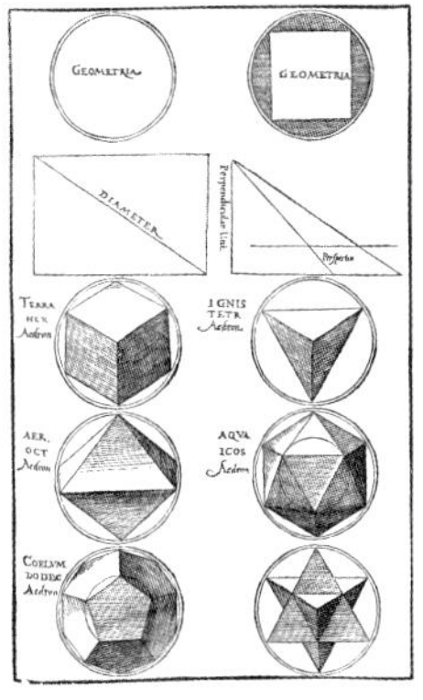

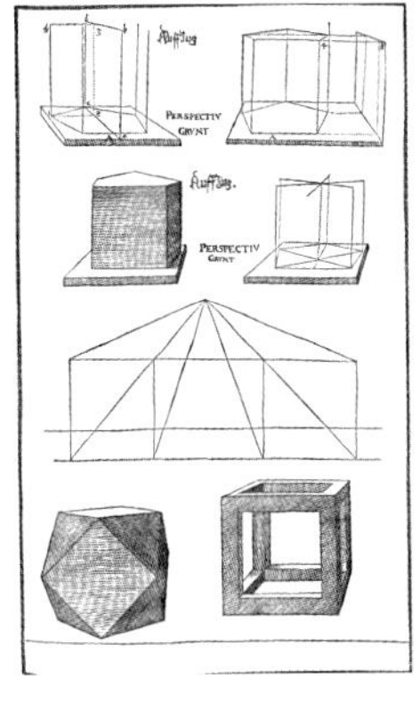

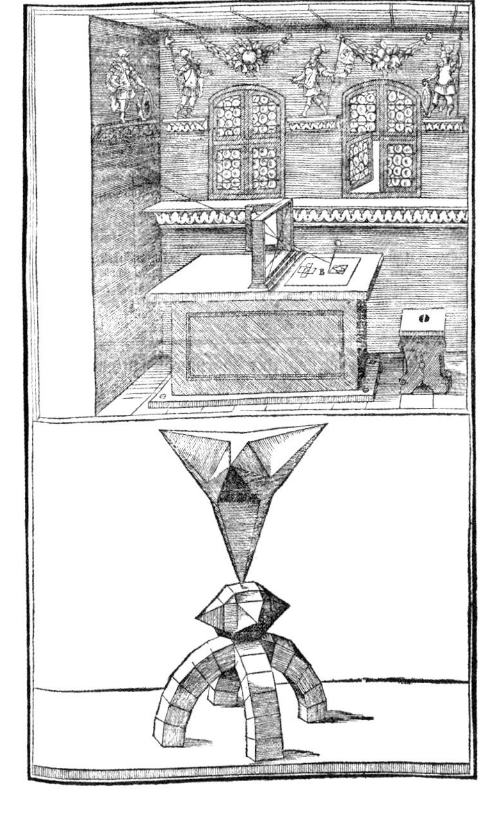

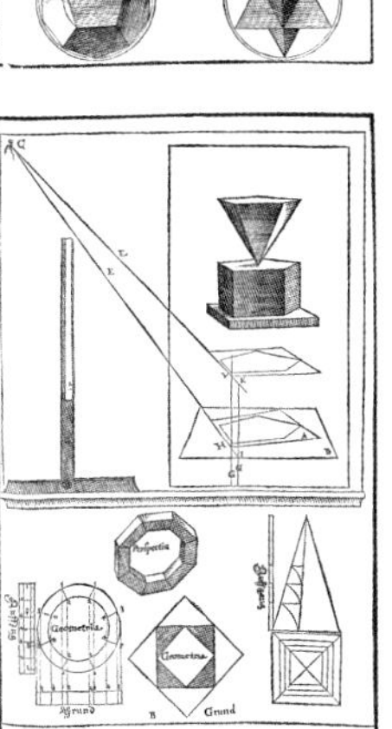

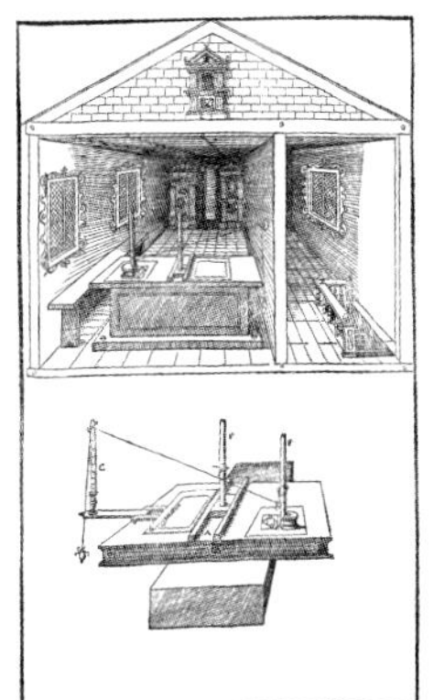

enough was thought of the book for it to be republished in 1616, after Pfinzing's death.

Thereafter, among German authors at least, the tradition of fanciful 'perspectival' geometry seems almost to have ended. But there is one last, intriguing, venture into this tradition. In 1625 the stonemason Peter Halt produced a book entitled *Perspectivische Reiss Kunst* (*The Perspectival Art of Drawing*, Augsburg) which was ostensibly aimed at craftsmen – stonemasons, carpenters and woodworkers. His drawings are clearly influenced by Lorenz Stoer, who he may have known personally. Much of his book is concerned with the construction of geometric figures, both on the plane and extended into three dimensions. Halt used a 'perspectograph' of his own devising as an aid to his drawings, a gadget which resembles the one made by Lucas Brunn (both devices were based on Jamnitzer's model),[9] but he also emphasizes the role of artistic imagination. On the theoretical side Halt offers a synthesis of Jamnitzer's Platonic notions of polyhedral forms as the basic 'building blocks' of reality with Lencker's emphasis on the alphabet. In this scheme the five vowels are identified with the five regular solids, which he proudly shows on his title page. Using a somewhat contrived analogy, he explains that a familiarity with the basic regular polyhedra is as essential to the creation of three-dimensional forms in any medium, as are a knowledge of the vowels to the comprehension of language – a proposal that accords with the Pythagorean–Platonic notions of Jamnitzer and his followers. Peter Halts drawings are not quite as confident or imaginative as Jamnitzer's, but they are very much in this tradition of fanciful geometry and have a certain originality of their own.

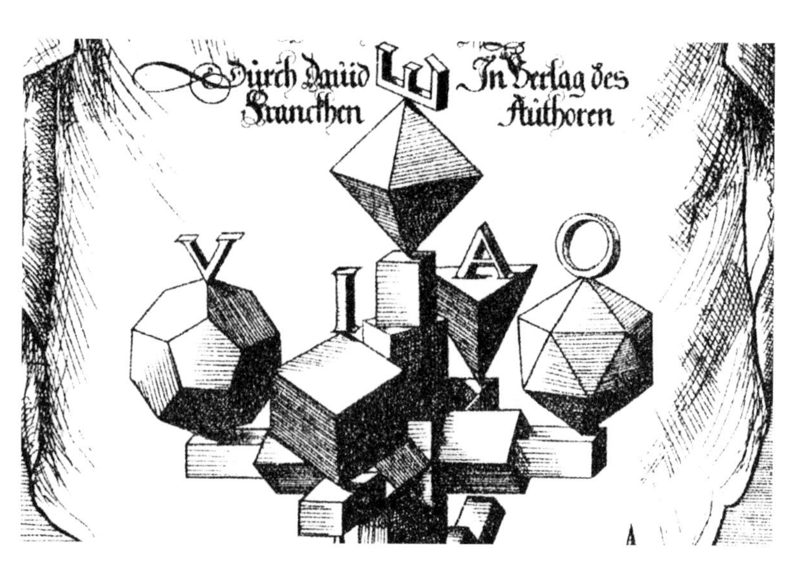

Detail of the title-page of Peter Halt's Perspectivische Reiss Kunst, *in which he identifies the five regular Platonic solids with the five vowels.*

So, nearly sixty years after the publication of Jamnitzer's P*erspectiva Corporum Regularium*, and almost exactly a hundred years after Dürer's *Underweysung der Messung*, Peter Halt's work brings an end to this somewhat overlooked genre of geometricism in German art. In art-historical terms this style enjoyed a brief flowering, but looking at these forms from the vantage of our post-modern present it seems likely that their abstract, sculptural quality probably makes more artistic sense now than at any time since they were produced. My personal opinion, as a sculptor, is that it has a great deal to offer the twenty-first century art world.

A characteristic drawing by the stonemason Peter Halt, from his Perspectivische Reiss Kunst, *Augsberg, 1625.*

This engraving shows Wenzel Jamnitzer and the mathematician Johann Neudorffer at a table, with the city of Nuremberg in the background. Both are prominent citizens, and each in his different way is involved with geometrical figures. With Neudorffer, as a classical scholar, the emphasis is on the academic aspects of this study, whereas Jamnitzer, the practical master-craftsmen, is using his invention of a perspectograph to delve into the artistic possibilities of geometry.

NUREMBERG – EARLY-MODERN CENTRE OF ENTERPRISE AND CULTURE

Natural resource and location are the ultimate determinants of any town or region. Nuremberg in the late medieval period was not particularly well endowed with the former, but it was located at the crossroads of several trade routes. These realities marked its character from the beginning; it owed its existence, and later prosperity, to its enterprise. The later medieval period saw the emergence of a range of new trades and industries in what was now an imperial free city. By the end of the Middle Ages, at the dawn of the Modern era, it was the foremost producer in Europe of finished metal products, including wire, household utensils, weapons and armour. In essence it was at the forefront of the early Industrial Revolution. The demand for its products led to a sense of economic confidence, and

Nuremberg became a vibrant and innovative manufacturing centre with strong links to other important European cities – particularly with Venice, which was an important trading partner.

With its growing capacity to adopt novel technologies, it was inevitable that Nuremberg would become involved with the recently invented process of printing. In 1470 Anton Koberger, a Nuremberg patrician, started a printing house that rapidly became the most successful in Germany. Others followed, and Nuremberg soon became a leading centre of printing and book production. It was also renowned for other 'high-tech' and luxury commodities, including scientific instruments – which were the reason that Regiomantanus and other important figures chose to pursue their scientific investigations here. Albrecht Dürer was the most famous son of the town, and spent much of his creative life in Nuremberg, but many other important figures are associated with it. Martin Behaim, the creator of the first terrestrial globe in 1492, was born and worked in the town, as was Peter Helein, who manufactured the world's first pocket watch in 1504. It is indicative of the spirit of the time and place that the text that shattered the medieval worldview, Nicolas Copernicus's iconoclastic De Revolutioibus Orbium Celestium, *in which he proposed a heliocentric model of the universe, was published in here in 1543.*

Nuremberg was a principle centre of German humanism, the intellectual movement associated with the revival of classical knowledge, and on the religious front it played a prominent part in the Protestant Reformation, which was accepted by the town in 1525. In the arts the city also had an important role as the focus of the movement known as German mannerism.

Yet in the end it was Nuremberg's vitality and its multiplicity of concerns – as a trade hub, a centre of innovation and a focus of religious, philosophical and artistic ideas– which ultimately led to its demise. Its geographic centrality, with traders and visitors constantly passing through the city, meant that it was particularly susceptible to visitations of the plague. There were outbreaks every few years between the middle and late sixteenth century that led to the deaths of thousands of its citizens (two of the artists featured here, Jamnitzer and Lencker, were victims of this disease in the 1585 outbreak). These devastating events were later compounded by the social ravages of intensive religious strife. Nuremberg was thoroughly involved in the Thirty Years War (1618–48), which had a particularly devastating effect on the town, after which it went into a something of a decline from which it only really recovered in the nineteenth century.

NOTES AND REFERENCES

1. *Unterweisung der Messung* (*Instructions on Measurement*), 1525; *Vier Bucher zu Menschlicher Proportion* (*Four Books on Human Proportion*), 1528.

2. It is likely that the woodcuts for this short book were made in the workshop of Hans Rogel, an Augsburg printer and publisher, after Stoer had moved there, some time around 1557.

3. These ornamental forms, known as *rollwerk*, which prefigure Baroque *rocaille*, seem to have originated in France and the low countries. They would probably have been seen by Stoer in prints from these countries, but were greatly exaggerated by him.

4. The Renaissance tradition of interest in ruins went back to Brunelleschi and Donatello, for whom it was associated with the classical revival. This linkage continued with the architect Sebastiano Serlio, who included views of ruins in his work on perspective. But there was also a tradition of idealised ruins, particularly among printmakers from the low countries.

5. Now kept in the Herzog August Bibliothek in Wolfenbuttel.

6. Now kept in the University Library at Munich.

7. These are also kept in the Herzog August Bibliothek in Wolfenbuttel.

8. The plague was persistent throughout Germany in the sixteenth century; Nuremberg was hit by the plague in 1405, 1435, 1437, 1482, 1494, 1520, 1534, 1552, 1556, 1562 and 1563. Nearby Augsburg was even more seriously affected, with more than twenty outbreaks during the sixteenth century

9. Halt produced a booklet, *Drei Wichtige newe Kuntststuck in underschidlichen Perspectivischen Instrumentum inventiert und erfunden,* Augsburg, 1626, which contained a description of this device and another of his inventions for perspective drawing.

5
Dissemination and Decline of a Sub-Genre

The geometric perspective treatise in Italy

Artistic influences flowed freely during the Renaissance. Aesthetic tastes and technical developments that originated on one side of the Alps were, sooner or later, taken across to the other, and these influences tended to follow long-established trade routes. Venice, whose merchants had been operating there since the 1300s, had close commercial and cultural ties with Nuremberg. It was therefore quite natural that book production, which had originated and flourished in Nuremberg, should have established itself earlier and more successfully in Venice than elsewhere in Italy. Even as early as the 1500s there were dozens of Nuremberg printers working in Venice, producing books on all manner of topics. However, Italian authors were slower than their German counterparts in the field of perspective theory. After Luca Pacioli and Leonardo's *De Divina Proportione* in 1509, no Italian works on this subject using three-dimensional regular figures appeared until Daniel Barbaro's *La Pratica della Perspettiva* in 1569.

Daniel Barbaro (1513–70) was an aristocratic philosopher and mathematician, most famous for his translation and commentary of Vitruvius. His perspective book attempts a thorough, comprehensive account of the subject, dealing with each of various aspects that had been covered by earlier German theorists, including a substantial section on the regular and semi-regular solids for which he provides 'nets' and perspective views. He includes descriptions and drawings of some stellated figures, and the stock geometric perspective treatise item of a *mazzocchio*,[1] plus variants. Barbaro's book is serious and didactic in tone, with an emphasis on mathematical explanations, but he does allow himself one flight of geometric fantasy with a curious armoured sphere, possibly inspired by a drawing by Uccello (see page 16).

After this, interest seems again to have waned. Geometrical bodies did not appear in print form in Italy until nearly thirty years later,

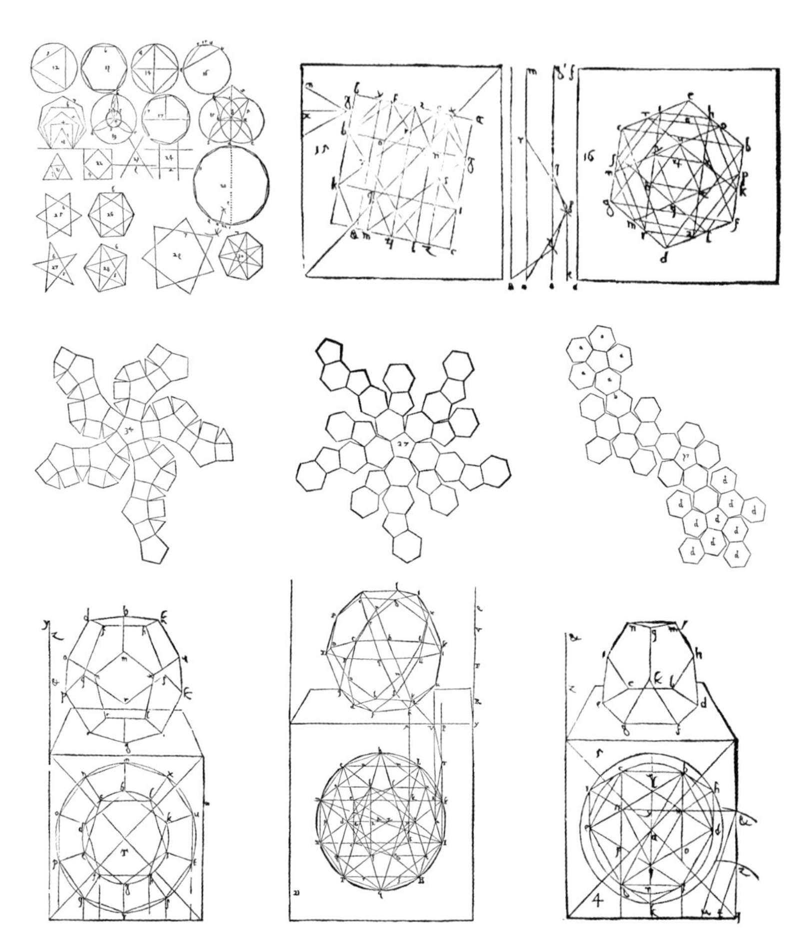

Constructions of two- and three-dimensional figures, from Danielle Barbaro's La Practica della Perspettiva, *Venice, 1596.*

with Pietro Accolti (1570–1642), who was also an architect, who used geometrical figures in his *Prospettiva Pratica* (*Practical Perspective*, Florence, 1625), though this workmanlike production is heavy on theory and the illustrations are purely of didactic interest. Mario Bettini (1582–1657), an Italian Jesuit philosopher, mathematician and astronomer, was responsible for several important mathematical works, including *Aerarium Philosophiae Mathematicae* (*A Treasury of Mathematical Philosophy*, Rome, 1648), which is essentially an encyclopaedia of mathematical curiosities. In this work, various regular figures and their nets are presented in an attractive format, but again the intention is purely didactic.

Lorenzo Sirigatti's (*d.* 1625) *La Pratica di Prospettiva* (*The Practice of Perspective*, Venice, 1596), in contrast with Barbaro's, is light on the theory of perspective, but presents a series of finely-drawn solid and skeletised regular figures, and a number of intriguing variations of

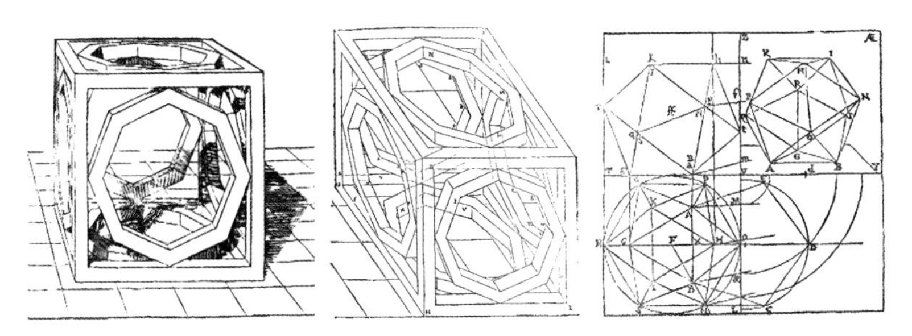

Drawings from Pietro Accolti's Prospettiva Pratica, *Florence, 1625.*

spherical bodies and *mazzocchio*. Many of these latter figures have the same spiky, armoured appearance as Barbaro's sphere. Sirigatti ends his collection with two assemblages of geometric shapes, very much in the style of Jamnitzer and Stoer, but these are almost the final throes of the sub-genre of fantastic geometry in Italy.

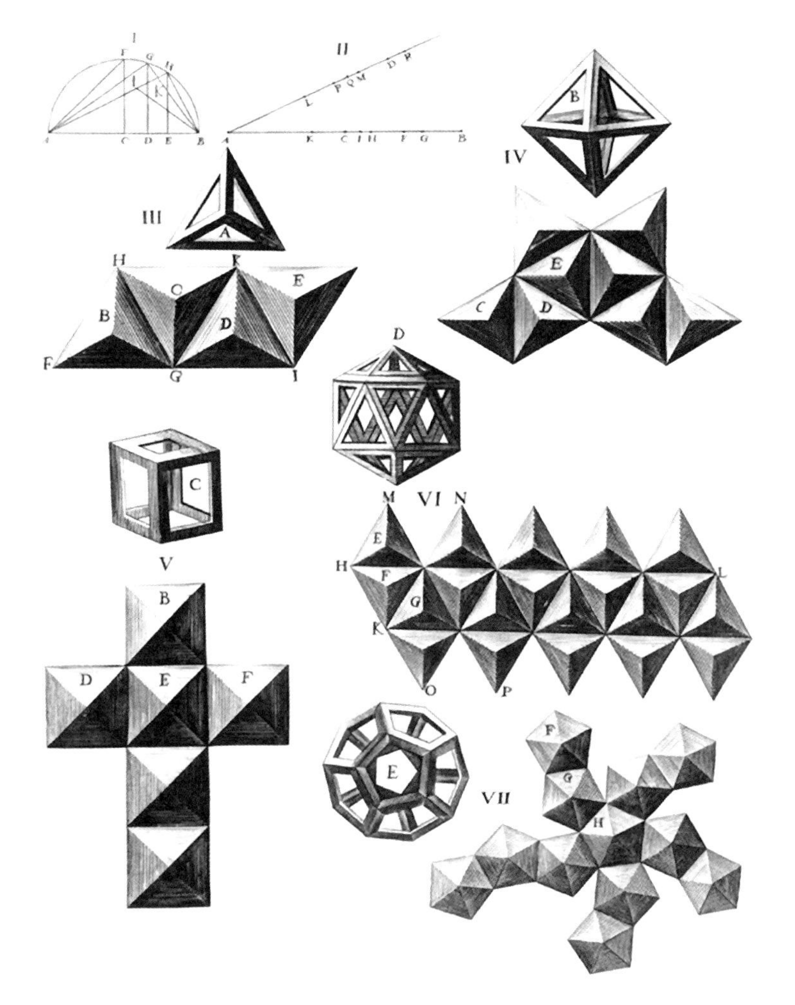

A page from Mario Bettini's Aerarium Philosophiae Mathematicae, *1648, showing nets of polyhedra. Bettini was an influential Jesuit philosopher, mathematician and astronomer.*

Perspective and the Baroque: the discontinuation of fantastical geometry

The enthusiasm for geometric themes and variations more or less began and ended with the various sixteenth century artist–craftsmen–theorists discussed above. By the beginning of the seventeenth century the fashion for geometric invention was waning. Books on perspective continued to appear in Europe for a very long time to come, and the regular and irregular solids still occasionally featured among the stock illustrations for their theses, but these figures were never again the focus of creative attention. Interest in the 'cosmological' aspects of regular figures also declined. The association with Platonic–Pythagorean concepts had never been entirely forgotten, but were now giving way to a more modern, practical mathematics. From now on there was little, if any, sense of artistic playfulness in connection with regular geometrical figures.

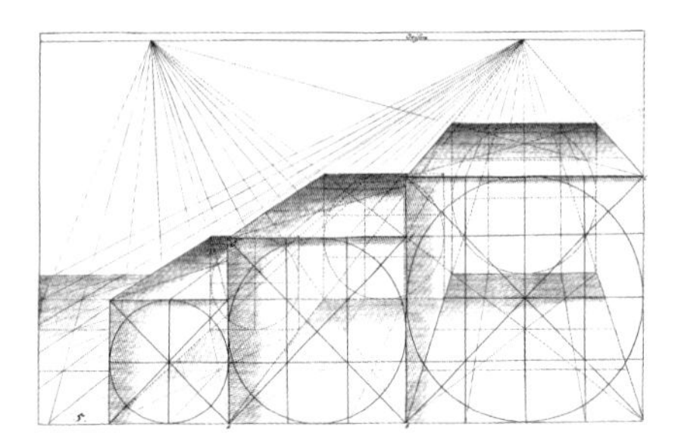

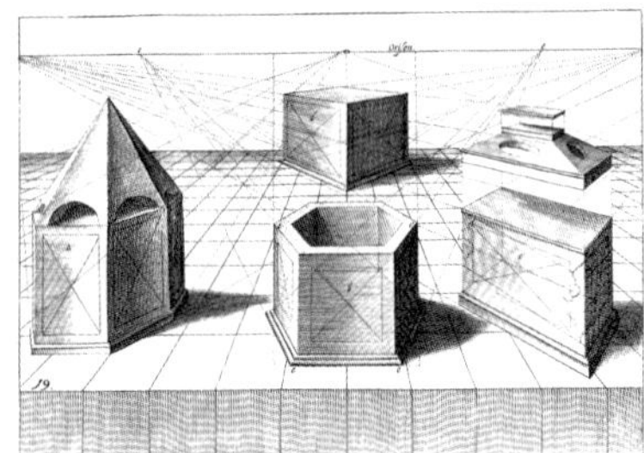

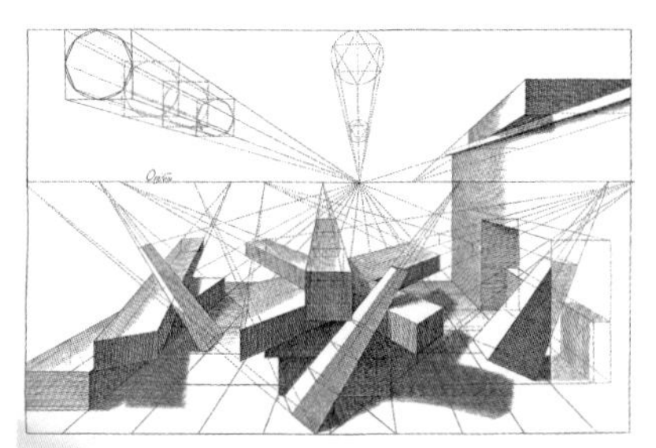

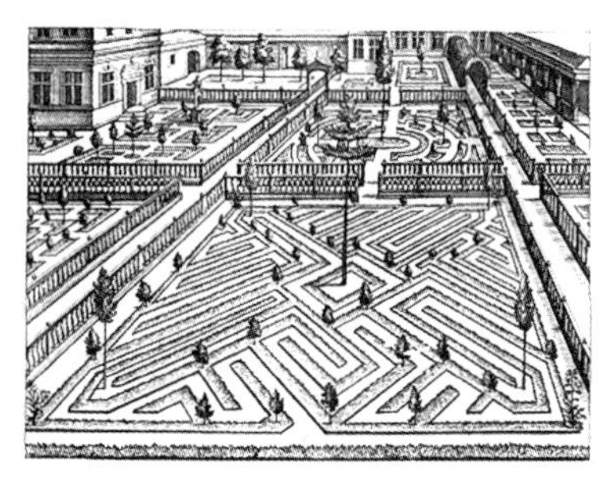

For Vredeman de Vries perspective was primarily a means of presenting his Baroque visions: geometric invention is now subordinated to these schemes.

This period saw the emergence of the Baroque style, and perspective treatises tended now to be produced by architects involved in this movement, and by mathematicians (particularly by French and Italian Jesuits), who incorporated perspective into the new developments taking place in that discipline

The transition to a grander, more expressive architectural style is epitomised by the drawings of Hans Vredeman de Vries (1527–1607), a Dutch architect and engineer. De Vries was responsible for a few modest buildings, and worked on the fortification of Antwerp, but is best known as a theorist. He published a book on garden design and one on *Perspective* (1604), both of which were extremely influential, anticipating the expansive architectural vistas of the Baroque. De Vries does include some geometrical figures in his perspective treatise, but these are very much a prelude to his fantastic architectural visions, both interior and exterior, which were to form the perfect statement for the new seventeenth century European sense of wealth and power. The only geometric imaginativeness to be found here lies in his garden layouts, especially in the garden mazes, of which he seemed particularly fond.

Jacques Androuet du Cerceau (1549–84), who came from a distinguished family of architects, was another notable theorist of this period. He produced a volume *Leçons de Perspective Positive*, but here too the primary function of perspective was to provide a dramatic presentation of grand architectural schemes. In this he too was highly successful, to the extent that he is now regarded as 'the inventor of French architecture'. There is, however, very little use of geometrical figures in his treatise.

As indicated, the other important direction for perspective studies was mathematical. Jean-François Niçeron (1613–46), a French Franciscan monk and mathematician, produced a treatise in 1638 called *La Perpective Curieuse*. This book applies a mathematical approach to such topics as anamorphosis (the artful distortion of images) and *trompe l'oeil*, as well as to perspective. He uses regular figures here in a rather conventional treatment of perspective theory, but does include a fine series of stellated bodies.

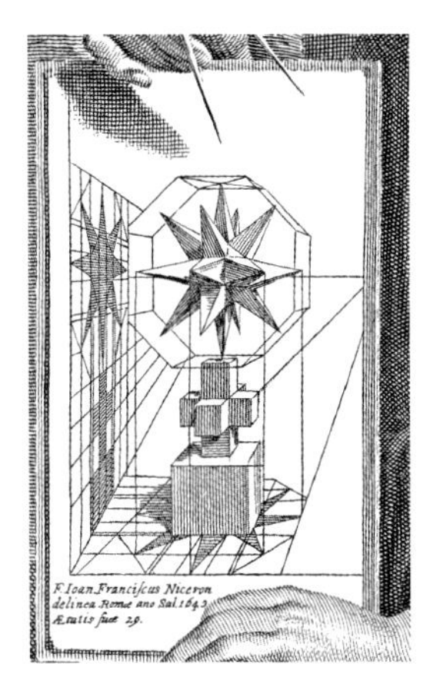

Detail of a portrait of the author Jean-Francois Niceron; from his La Perspective Curieuse, 1638;

Soon after this publication, his compatriot the Jesuit Father Pierre le Dubreuil (1602–70), brought out a huge three-volume tome dealing with perspective, adopting some of Niceron's ideas, and those of various other theorists of the new discipline of projective geometry, which involved him in a bitter controversy and charges of plagiarism. This work was very popular, however, running to no fewer than twenty editions – but his use of geometrical figures is meagre, limited to a couple of pages of rather plain hollow prisms.

In 1693 one of the more prominent figures of the Baroque period, the Jesuit painter Andrea Pozzo (1642–1709), who was particularly famous for his vast *tromp-l'oeil* ceilings, produced a two-volume treatise called *Perspectiva Pictorum et Architectorum*. This work almost marks the end of the association between geometry, in the Euclidean sense, and perspective, since it is entirely concerned with architectural perspective and stage sets, and does not include any geometrical figures at all.

The use of geometric figure and diagrams did of course persist; they are found in various later, eighteenth-century perspective treatises and are employed to demonstrate perspective principles to this day. But the almost magical linkage between idealistic geometry, the representation of three-dimensions in two, and the puissant cosmological notions of the classical past were, ironically, completely over by the age of the enlightenment.

Notes and references

1. The *mazzocchio* was a headdress formed around a wooden or wickerwork frame. Based on medieval originals, it became very popular in Florence in the mid-fifteenth century. Because of its complicated toroidal structure, it became a stock subject of perspective theorists, and was the only non-classical geometric form to be used for this purpose (see Addenda 3, page 269).

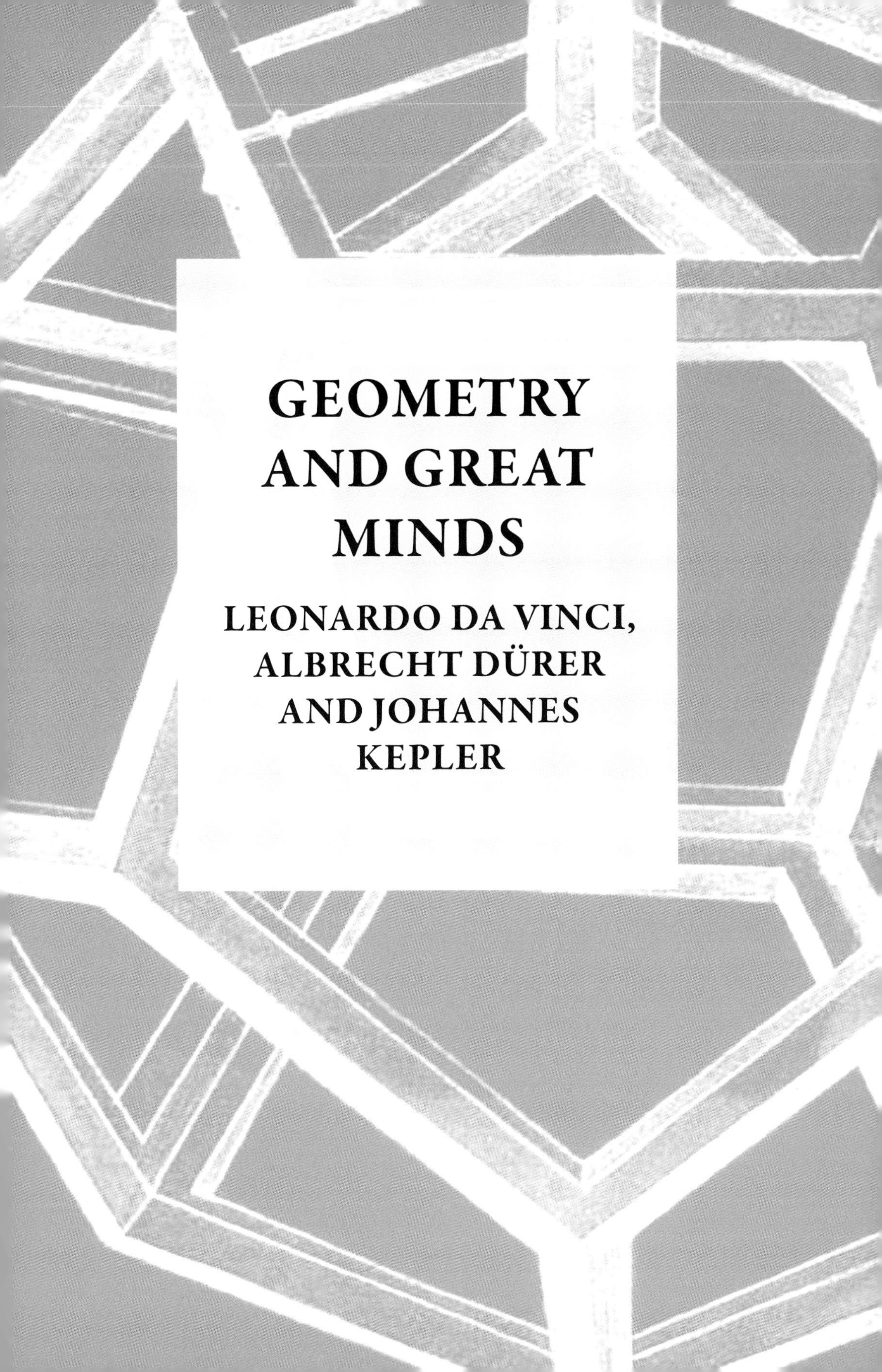

GEOMETRY AND GREAT MINDS

LEONARDO DA VINCI, ALBRECHT DÜRER AND JOHANNES KEPLER

Geometry and great minds: Leonardo, Dürer and Kepler

Leonardo da Vinci (1452–1519)

De Divina Proportione, Venice, 1509

The Renaissance was deeply associated, and inspired by, a revival of Classical Greek and Roman culture and ideas. One of the most productive of the new attitudes that were ushered in at this time was the notion of mathematics as an essential subject, both for the deeper understanding of nature and as a proper basis for art. Leonardo was at the forefront of this movement; his notebooks indicate a continuing interest in many aspects of geometry and perspective, and it is thought extremely likely that he made models of the polyhedra for the drawings in Pacioli's *De Divina Proportione* (which are included here). These notebooks also reveal Leonardo's enduring fascination with the geometric aspects of proportion and volume, and contain sketches of several geometric solids not included in Pacioli, including the entire series of Archimedean solids.

Albrecht Dürer (1471–1528)

Underweysung der Messung, Nuremberg, 1525

Dürer was the most celebrated artist of the northern Renaissance and, in common with Leonardo da Vinci, was thoroughly involved with the Renaissance enthusiasm for science and mathematics, to which he increasingly turned in his later years. In 1525, at the age of 54, he produced a major work on geometry, *Four Books on Measurement* (*Underweysung der Messung mit dem Zirckel und Richtscheyt*), which examined every aspect of geometrical construction that might be applicable to art and the crafts, including the regular polygons and polyhedra. In the last part of this book Dürer also describes and illustrates various devices for drawing in perspective (*proportionslehre*). This interest in geometry and the sciences was already evident more than a decade earlier, in his famous engraving 'Melancholia'.

Johannes Kepler (1571–1630)

Mysterium Cosmographicum, Tubingen, 1596; 1621
Harmonices Mundi, Frankfurt, 1619

Both of the important sixteenth-century astronomers, Tycho Brahe and Johannes Kepler, are known to have possessed copies of Jamnitzer's *Perspectiva Corporum Regularium*, and both were very taken with the cosmological notions that it expressed. Kepler, in particular, was inspired by these ideas in the formation of his own speculations on the structure of the universe. He made a systematic study of the Platonic and Archimedean solids, and attempted to relate their volumetric ratios to distances of the planets from the sun. His discovery that each of the Platonic solids could be inscribed and circumscribed within spheres led to the famous model of 'nested' polyhedra as a representation of the ratios of planetary orbits. Although he later rejected this scheme, the astronomical work for which he became famous, his three laws of planetary motion, was essentially a further development of these ideas.

Tetrahedron, octahedron, icosahedron and dodecahedron:
Leonardo's drawings for Pacioli's De Divina Proportione, *Venice, 1509.*

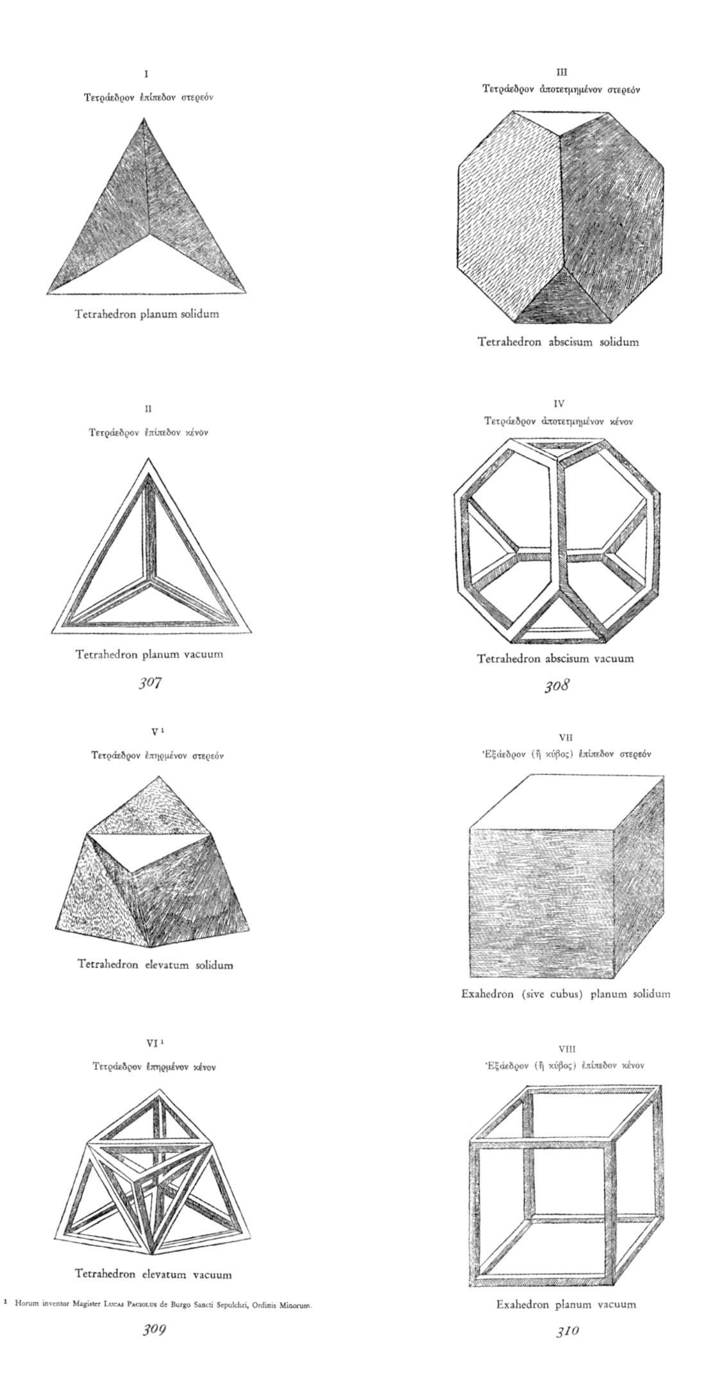

Tetrahedron, truncated tetrahedron, stellated tetrahedron and cube: Leonardo's drawings for Pacioli's De Divina Proportione, *Venice, 1509.*

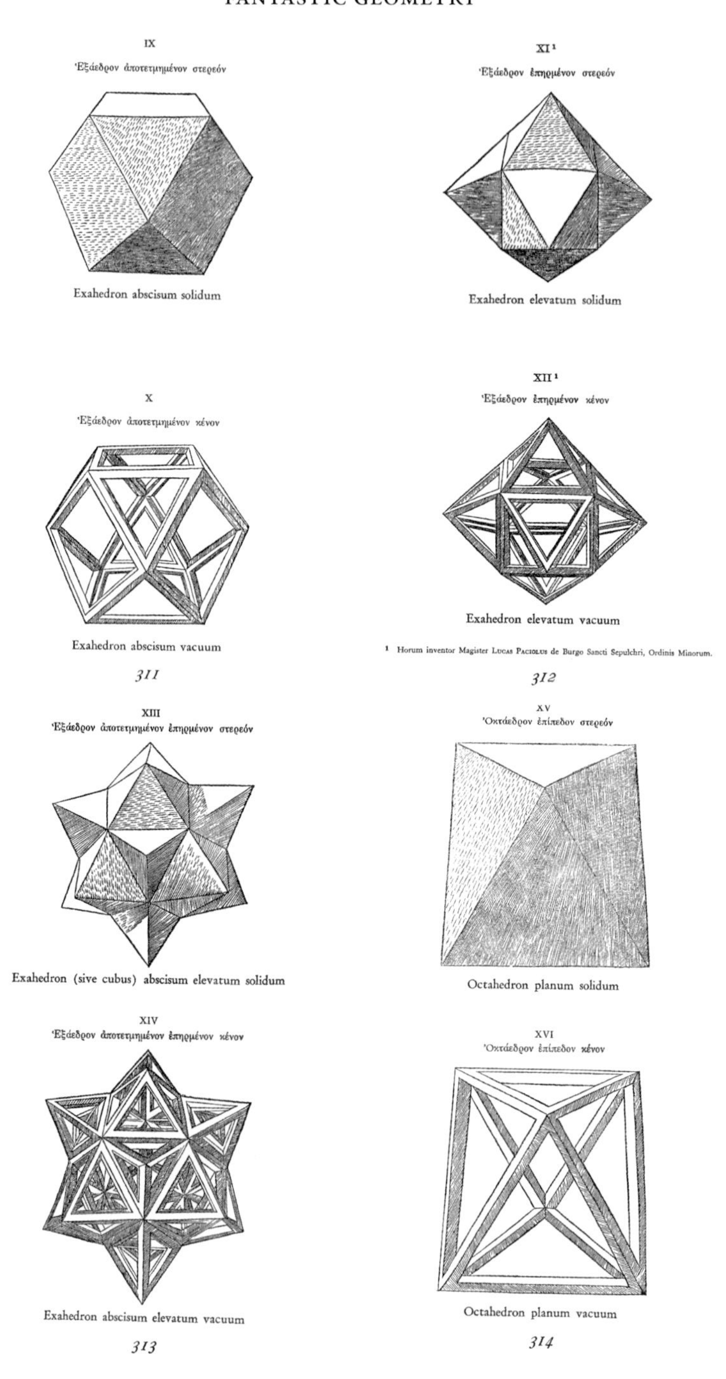

Cuboctahedron, stellated cube, stellated cuboctahedron and octahedron: Leonardo's drawings for Pacioli's De Divina Proportione, *Venice, 1509.*

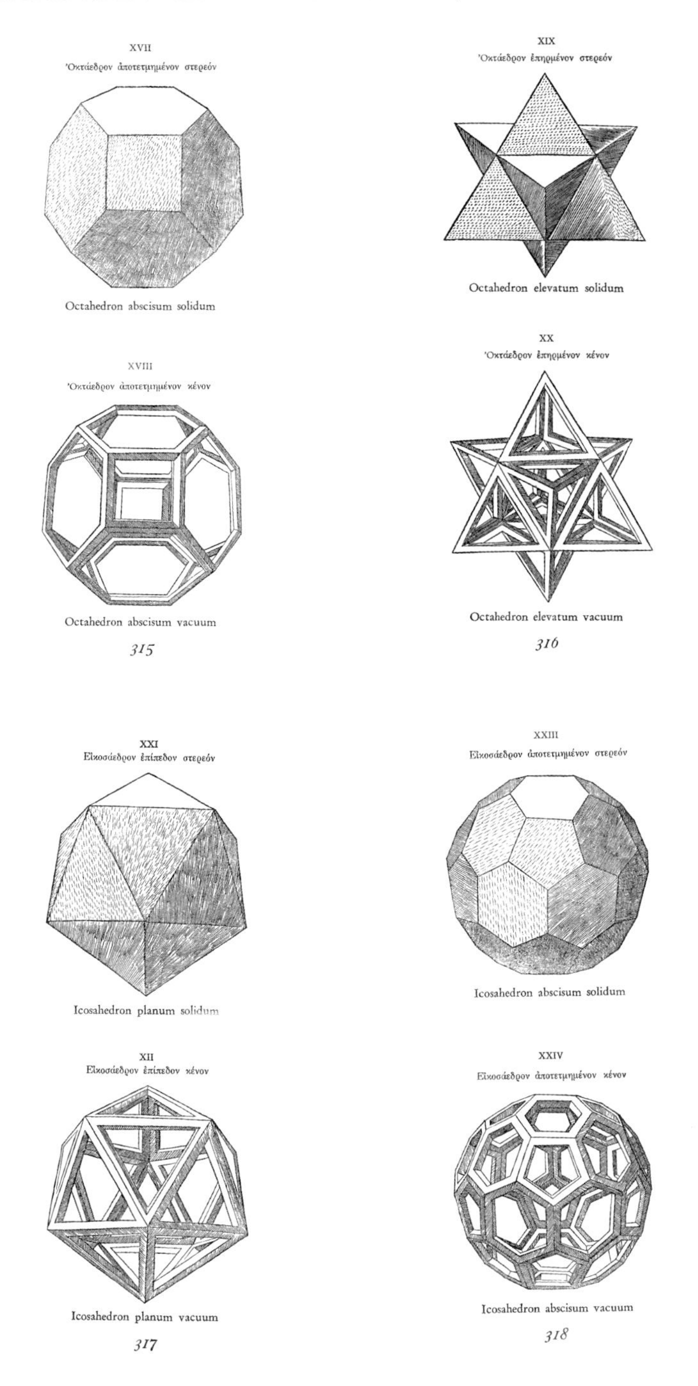

Truncated octahedron, stella octangula, icosahedron and truncated icosahedron: Leonardo's drawings for Pacioli's De Divina Proportione, *Venice, 1509.*

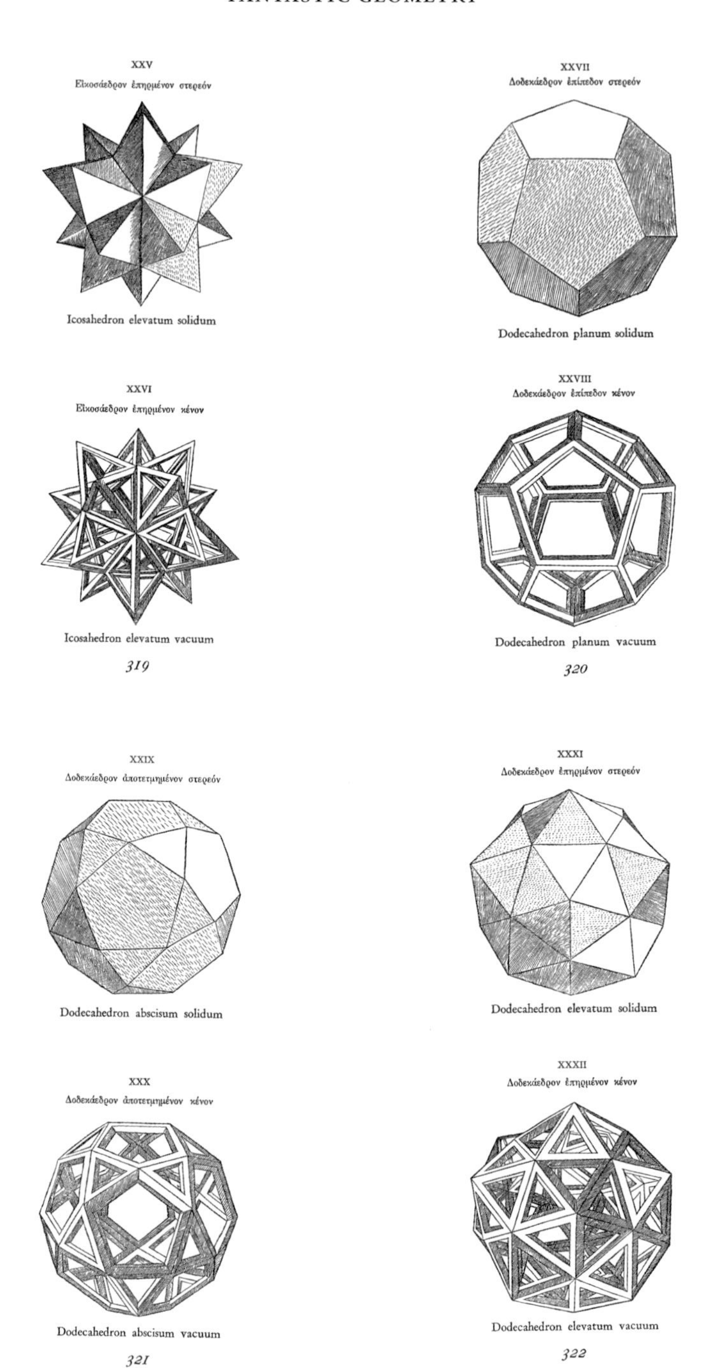

Stellated icosahedron, dodecahedron, icosidodecahedron and stellated dodecahedron, Leonardo's drawings for Pacioli's De Divina Proportione, *Venice, 1509.*

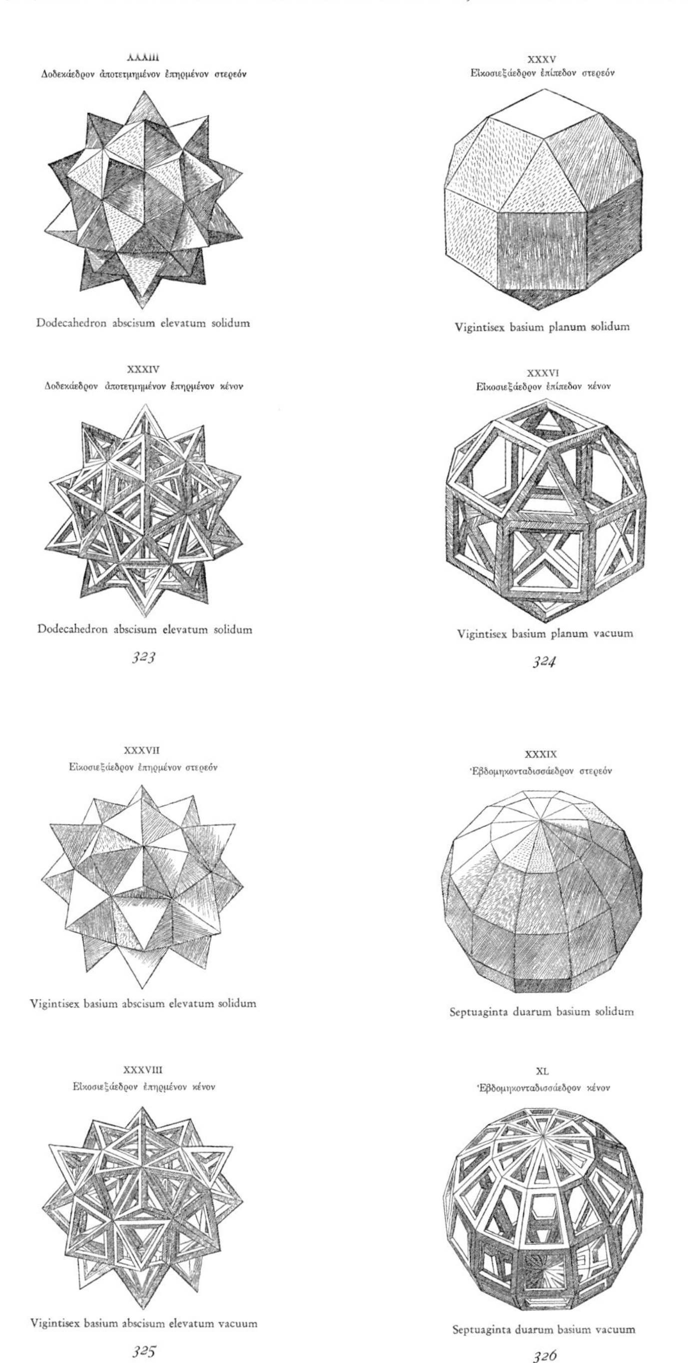

Stellated icosidodecahedron, stellated small rhombicuboctahedron, small rhombicuboctahedron and Campanus sphere; Leonardo's drawings for Pacioli's De Divina Proportione, *Venice, 1509.*

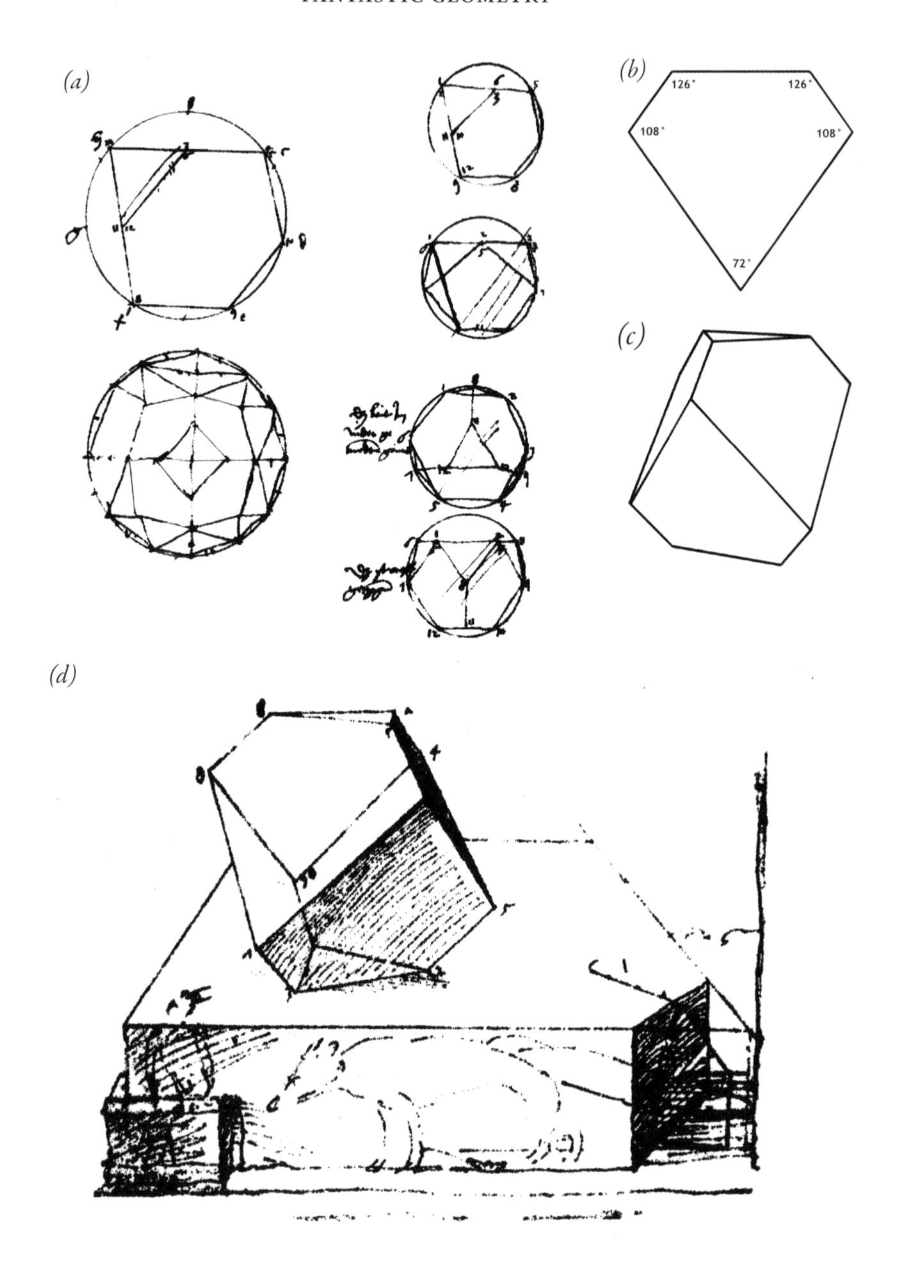

(a) Sketches from a drawing book of Dürer's showing preliminary ideas for the puzzling irregular polyhedra featured in his engraving 'Melencolia'. (b) The face of this figure, which has been seen as a truncated rhombohedron or a partially truncated cube, but is neither. (c) Peter Schreiber (1999) has noted that it consists of a distorted cube with rhombic faces of 72°, which is then truncated to present bounding triangular faces. (d) An earlier sketch, again from a drawing book, with the playful addition of a fox chasing a duck.

'Melencolia', 1514. This enigmatic and much-debated print, quite apart from its aesthetic intentions, clearly reflects Dürer's interests in science and mathematics. It features a number of architectural instruments and craftsmen's tools, together with an array of allegorical items including a compass, empty scales, an hourglass and a magic square. The nature of the solid figure (see opposite), with its faint trace of a skull (possibly of the artist's mother) has generated a great deal of speculation.

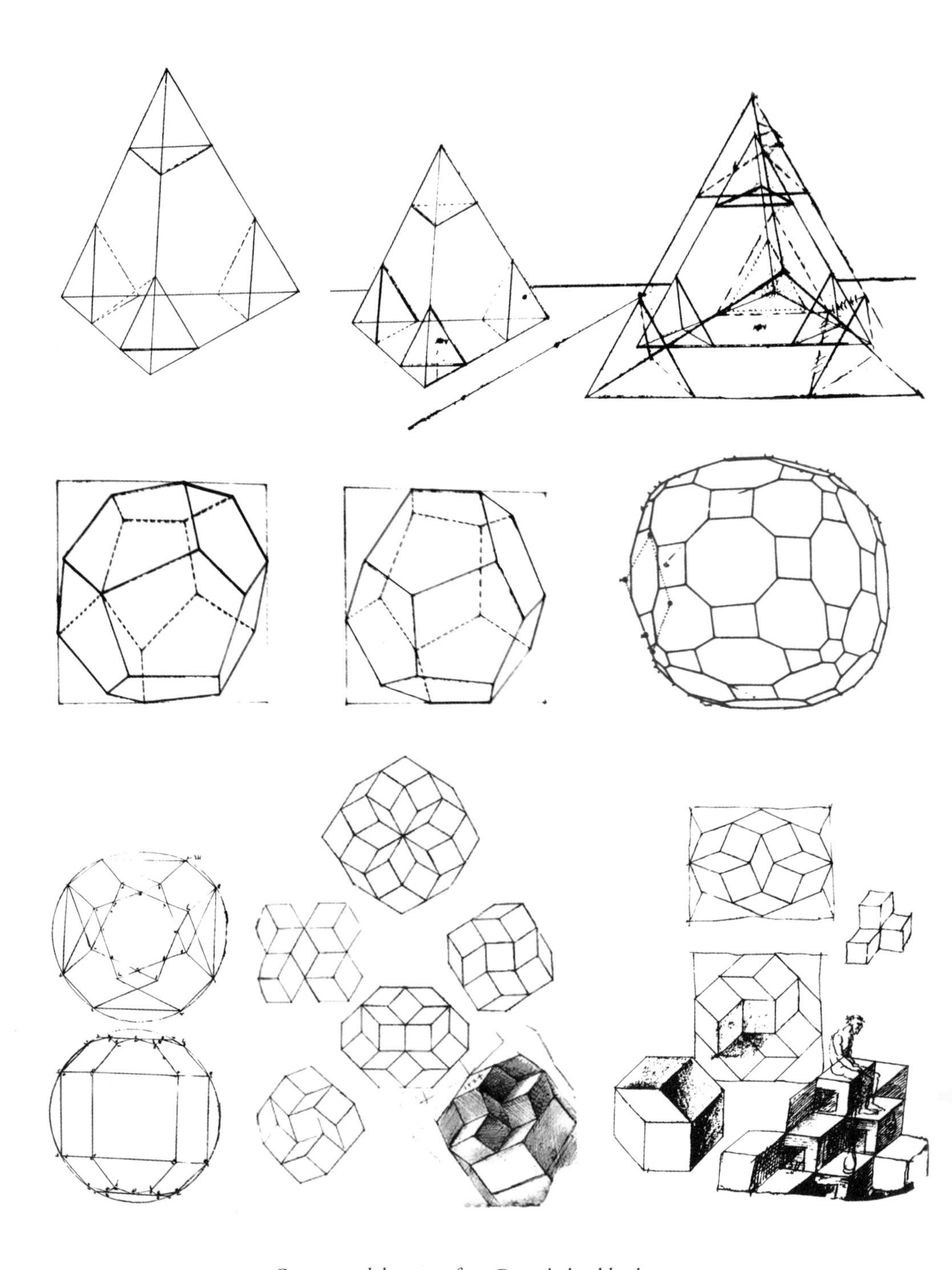

Geometrical drawings from Dürer's sketchbooks.

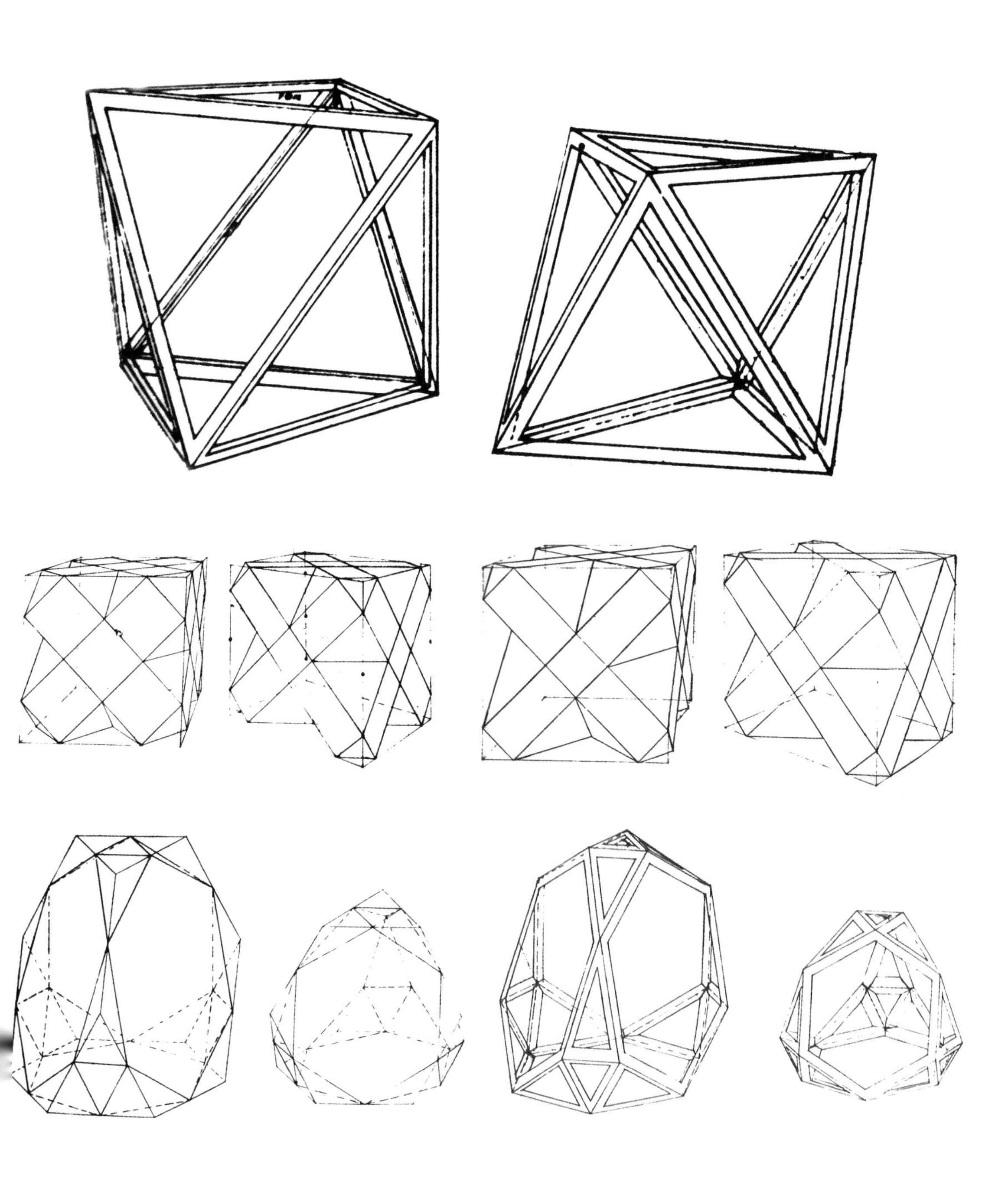

Geometrical drawings from Dürer's sketchbooks.

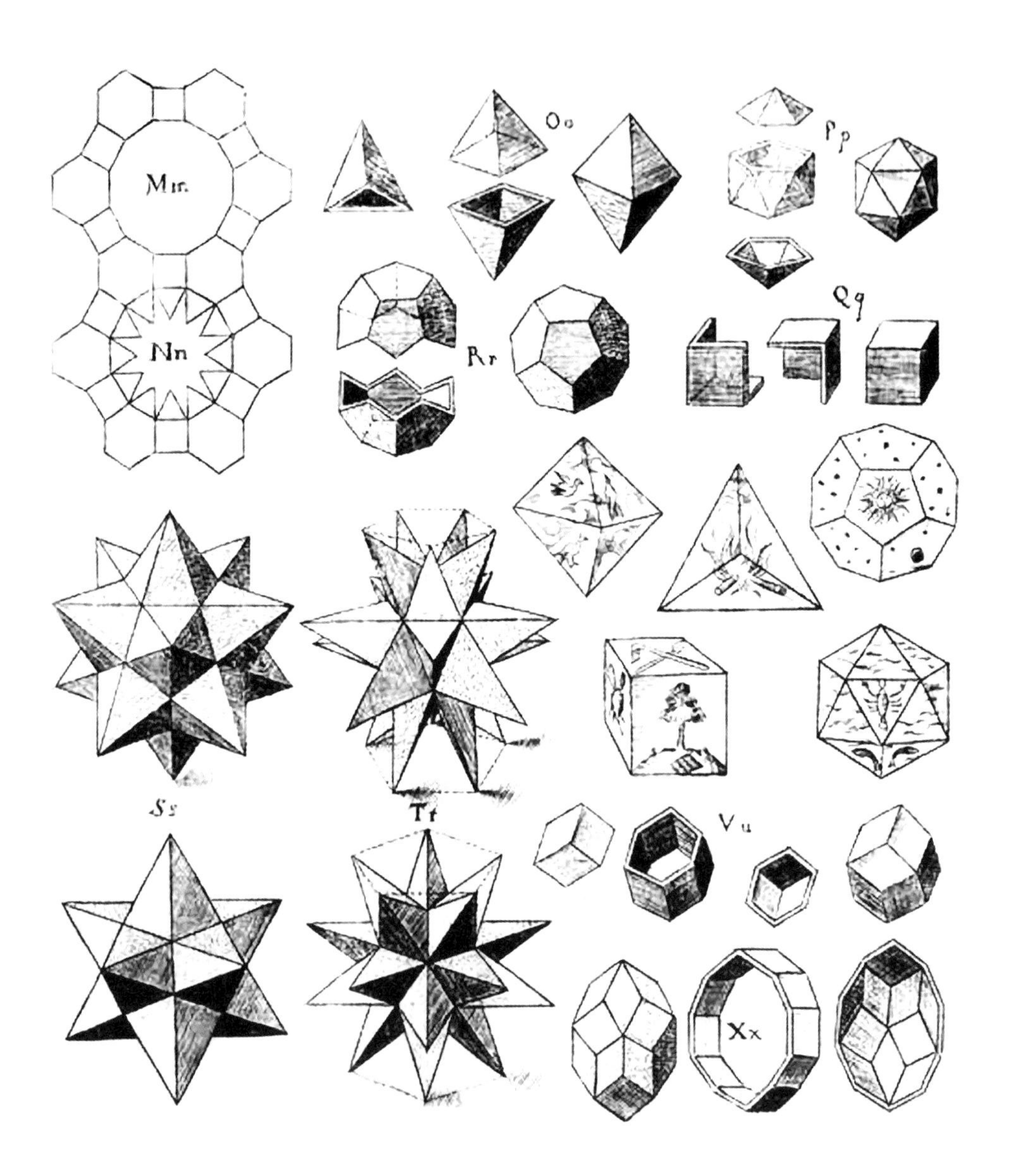

Kepler's investigations into plane and polyhedral geometry (above), showing the Platonic identification of the five regular solids with the four basic elements plus the cosmos; he also describes the small stellated polyhedron, from the Harmonices Mundi*, 1619. Kepler firmly believed that the secret of universal order could be found in geometry, that 'Geometry was co-eternal with the divine mind'; the illustrations on the page opposite show regular 2- and 3-dimensional arrangements from the* Harmonices Mundi.

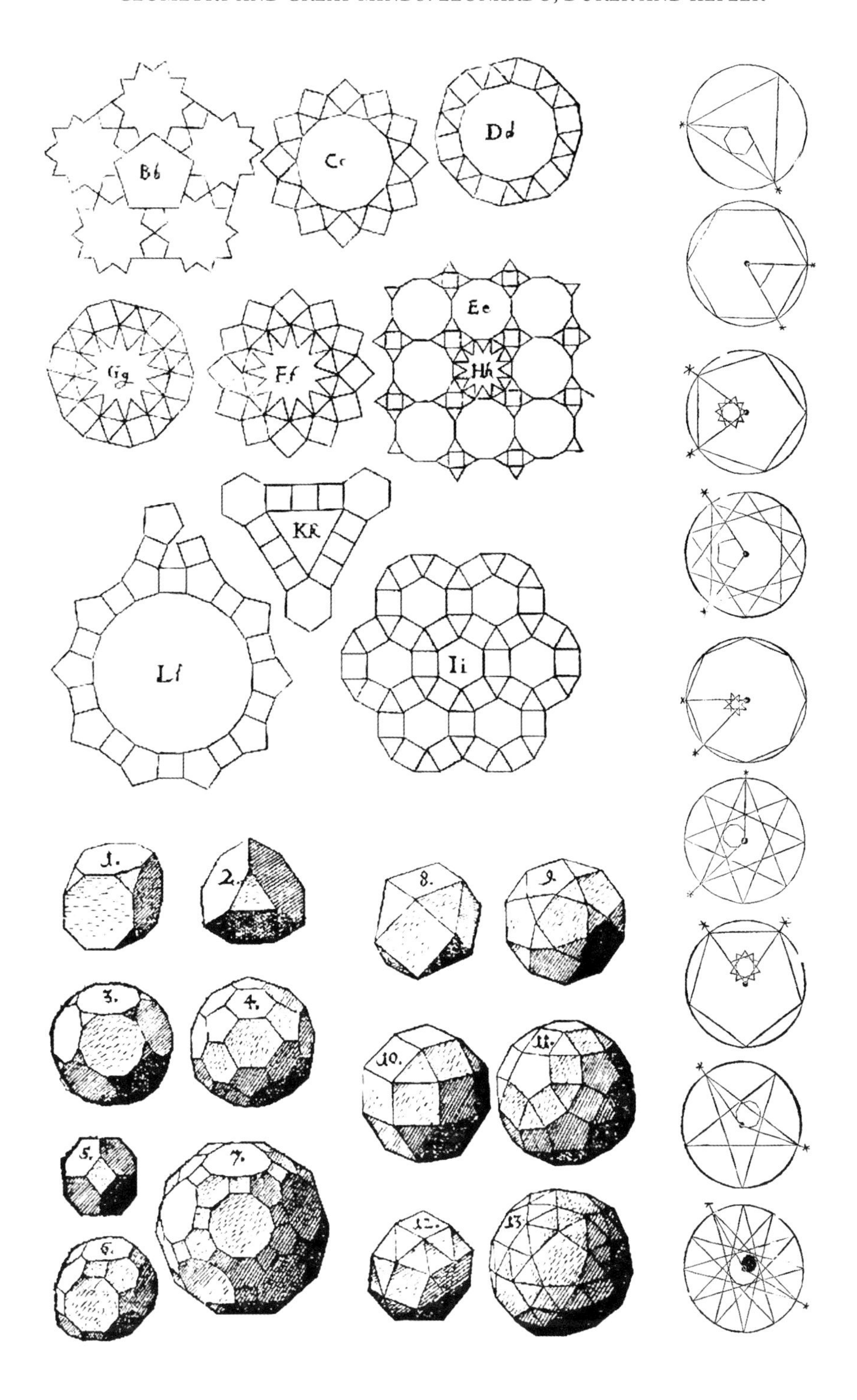
Bb
Cc
Dd
Gg
Ff
Ee
Hh
Kk
Ll
Ii

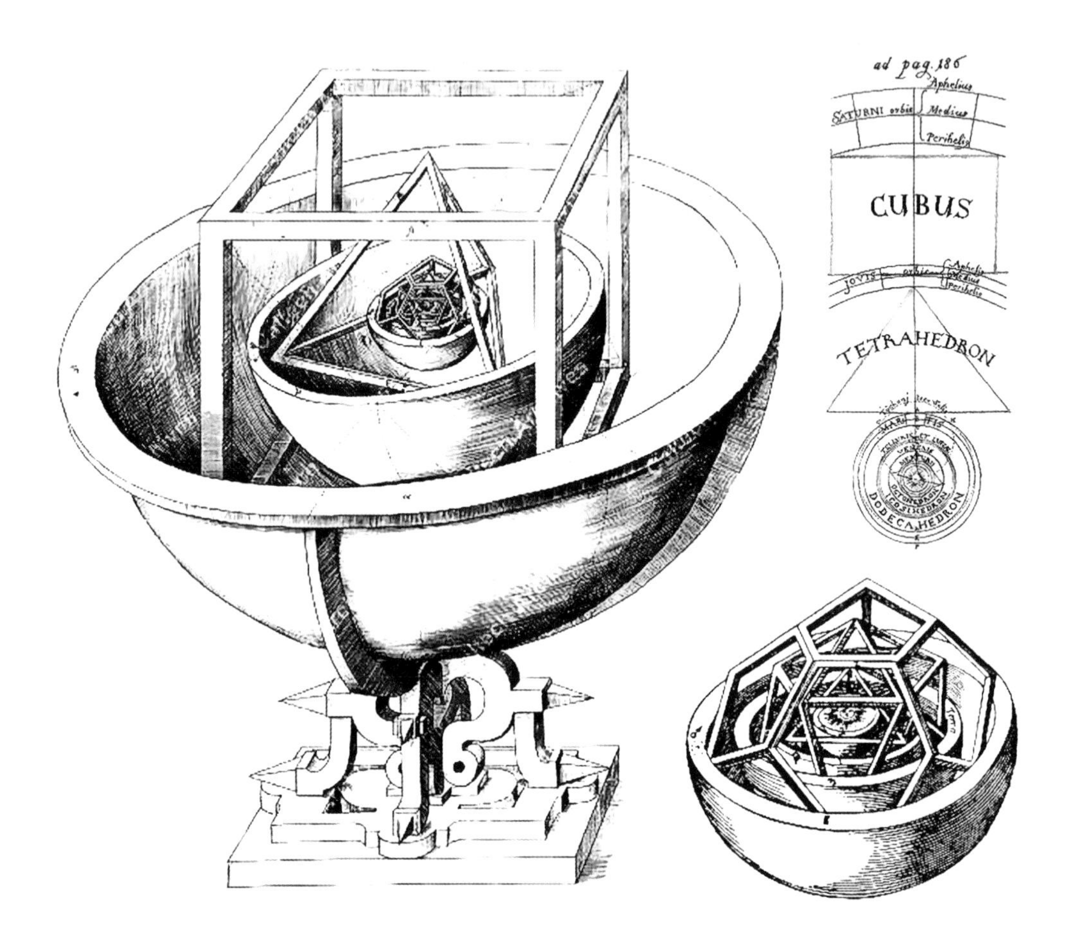

Kepler's attempt to account for the relationships between the planetary orbits; from his Mysterium Cosmographicum, *1596. Here he states his intention to show that 'the most great and good Creator, in this creation of the moving universe and the arrangements of the heavens, looked to these five regular solids, which have been so celebrated from the time of Pythagoras and Plato down to our own, and that he fitted to the nature of those solids the number of the heavens, their proportions and the law of their motion'. This scheme involved an octahedron between the orbits of Mercury and Venus, an icosahedron between Venus and Earth, a dodecahedron between Earth and Mars, a tetrahedron between Mars and Jupiter, and a cube between Jupiter and Saturn. Kepler was so convinced that he had discovered the basis of a celestial harmony that he pursued the idea of developing this model into a 'cosmic bowl' that would dispense beverages appropriate to the symmetries of the various polyhedra and the planets that they represented – a scheme which was never realised.*

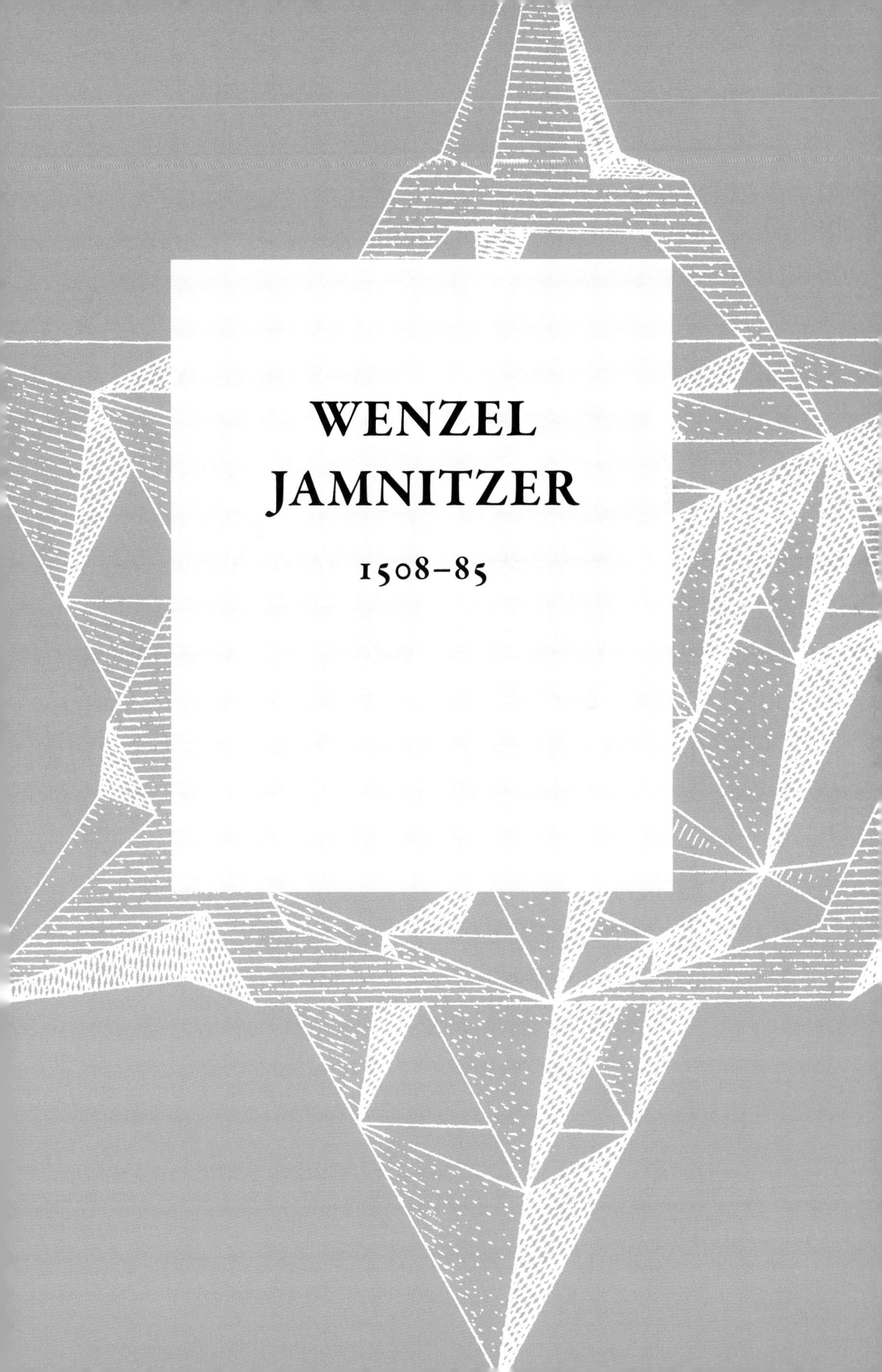

WENZEL JAMNITZER

1508–85

Wenzel Jamnitzer

Perspectiva Corporum Regularium, Nuremberg, 1568

In this extraordinary work of geometric imagination Jamnitzer uses a cosmological scheme of his own, based on the regular Platonic solids, to explore their capacity for infinite variation. As he explains in the subtitle to the *Perspectiva*, this is 'a diligent exposition of how the five regular solids, of which Plato writes in the *Timaeus* and Euclid in his *Elements*, are carefully brought into perspective using a particularly new, thorough and proper method never before employed. And appended to this a fine introduction how out of the same five bodies one can go on endlessly making many other bodies of various kinds and shapes'.

The work has been described as a 'visual fugue composed to the glory of the harmony of the Universe' (Bedini). The underlying principle seems to be derived from the Platonic notion of these solids as 'elements' – earth, air, fire and water – and thereby as the foundation of physical reality. Jamnitzer certainly felt that he had succeeded both in 'inventing a method of perspective' and 'the study of elementary forces'.

It has to be admitted that the scheme that he adopted, at least for the polyhedral variations in the first part of his book, is somewhat idiosyncratic. In the first place, each solid is ascribed a vowel ('a' for the tetrahedron, 'e' for the octahedron, 'i' for the cube, 'o' for the icosahedron, 'u' for the dodecahedron). Every solid/vowel section has 24 illustrations; the solid itself is followed by 23 variations. The number of variations is thought to have been determined by the 24 letters of the Greek alphabet.

The second part is rather less schematic, or perhaps the scheme is less obvious. It begins with ten pairs of transparent, or skeletised, regular solids 'in the Italian manner', followed by six pages of spherical variations. There are then four pairs of pyramidal/conical variants, and the collection is finished off with three plates of rotundas (somewhat reminiscent of *mazzocchio*, that staple of perspective treatises).

In his time Wenzel Jamnitzer was the most famous goldsmith in Europe, and many of the productions of his workshop can still be seen in museums across Europe. But these ornate objets, somewhat overdecorated with semi-precious stones, corals and shells, project an entirely different aesthetic impression from the geometric purity of the *Perspectiva Corporum Regularium*. Jamnitzer clearly had an extremely inventive artistic imagination. However, to modern tastes his reputation is bound to rest on his later productions, which derived from his enduring preoccupation with the cosmological aspects and aesthetic possibilities of Platonic figures.

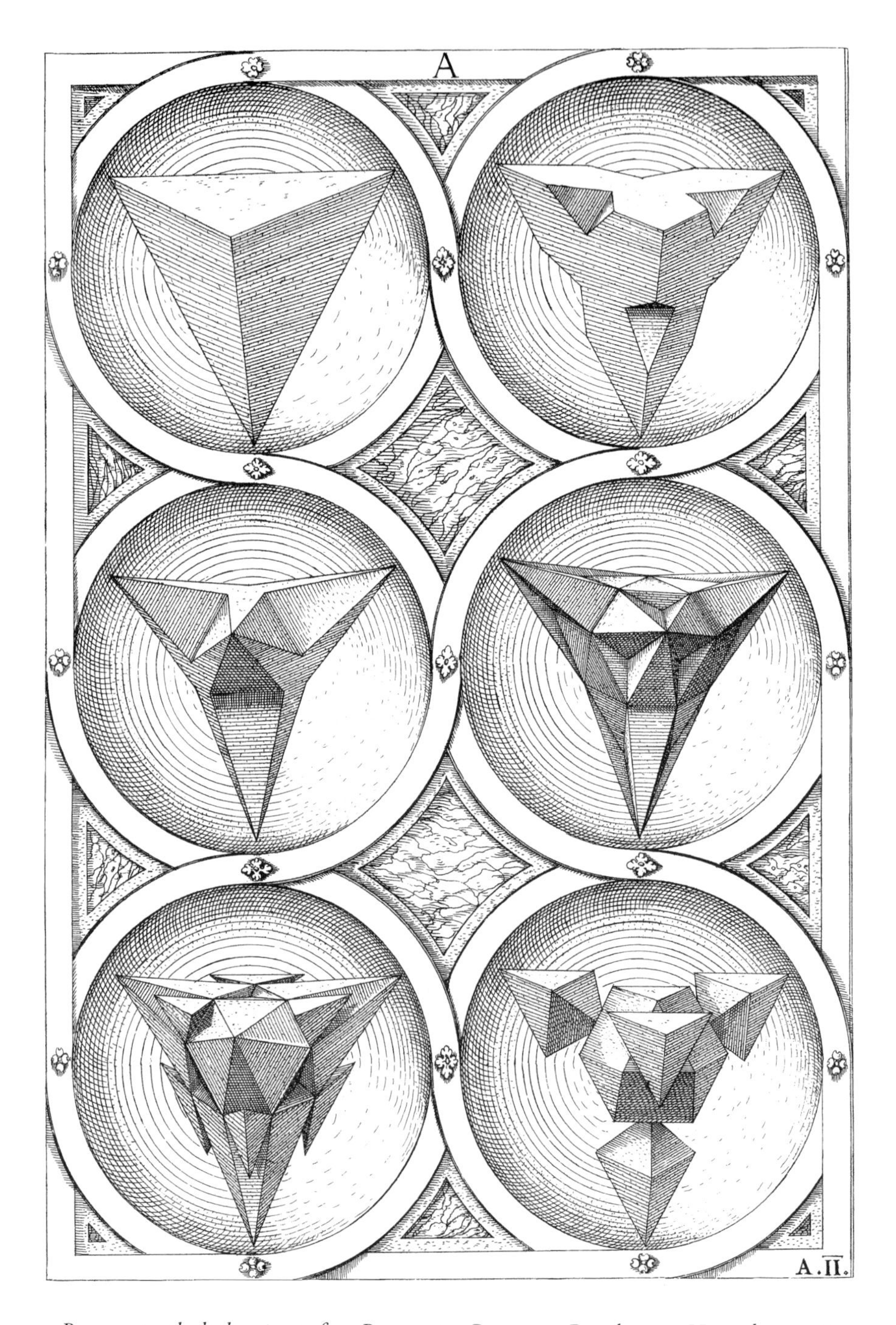

Page A2, tetrahedral variants; from Perspectiva Corporum Regularium, *Nuremberg, 1568.*

Page A3, tetrahedral variants; from Perspectiva Corporum Regularium, *Nuremberg, 1568.*

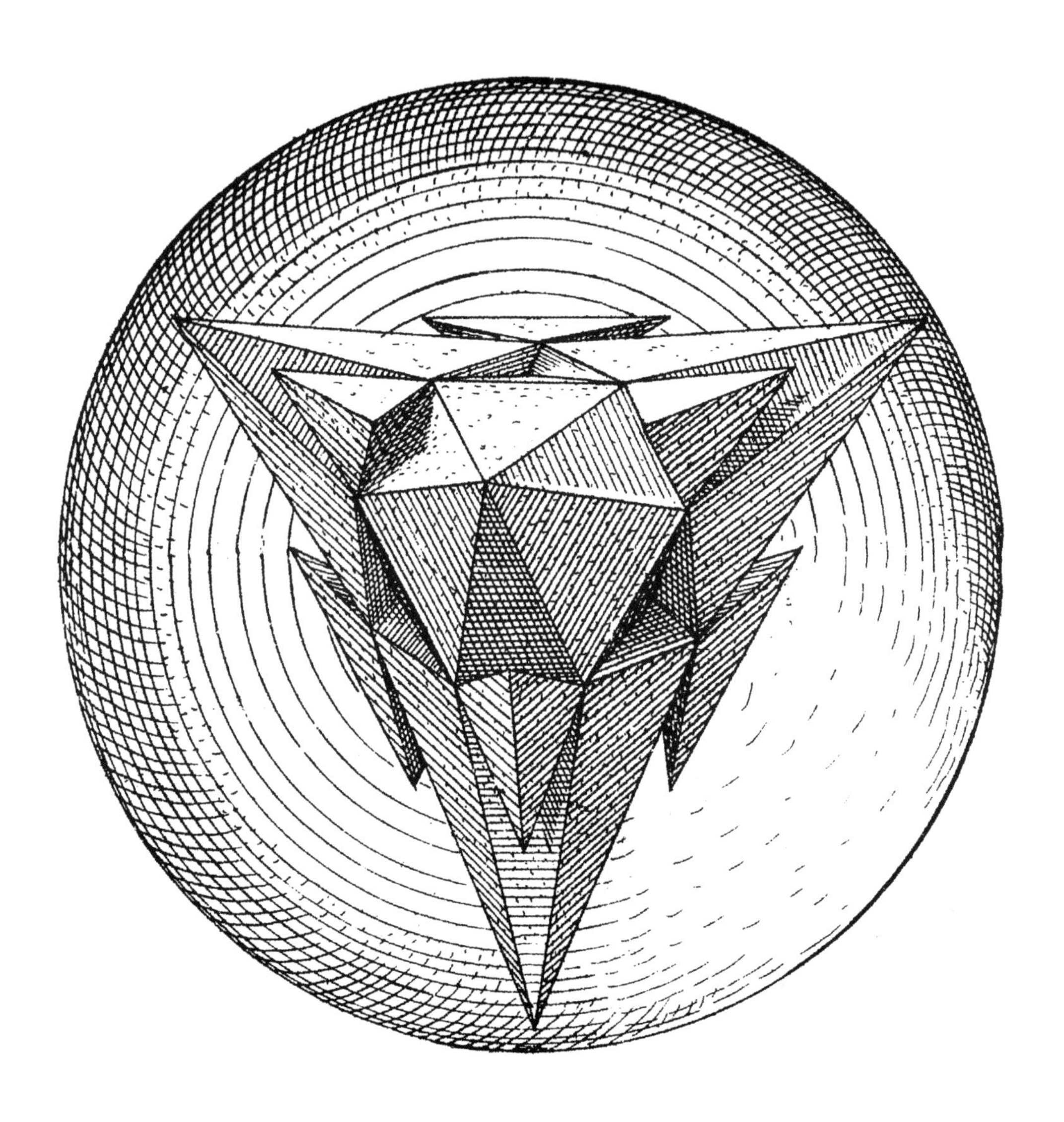

Detail from page A2, Perspectiva Corporum Regularium, *Nuremberg, 1568.*

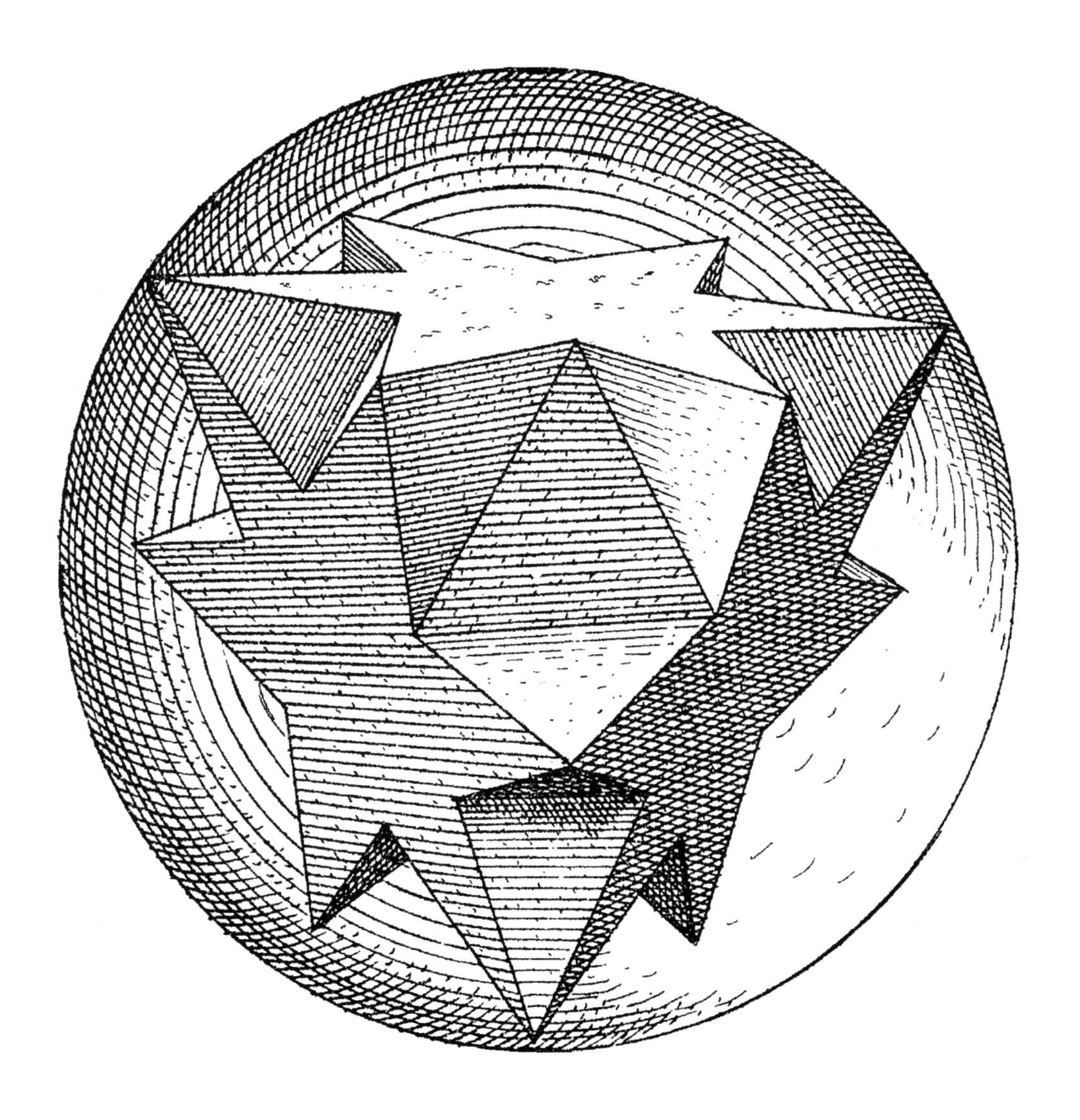

Detail from page A2, Perspectiva Corporum Regularium, *Nuremberg, 1568.*

Page A4, tetrahedral variants; from Perspectiva Corporum Regularium, *Nuremberg, 1568.*

Page A5, tetrahedral variants; from Perspectiva Corporum Regularium*, Nuremberg, 1568.*

Detail from page A4, Perspectiva Corporum Regularium, *Nuremberg, 1568.*

Detail from page A4, Perspectiva Corporum Regularium, *Nuremberg, 1568.*

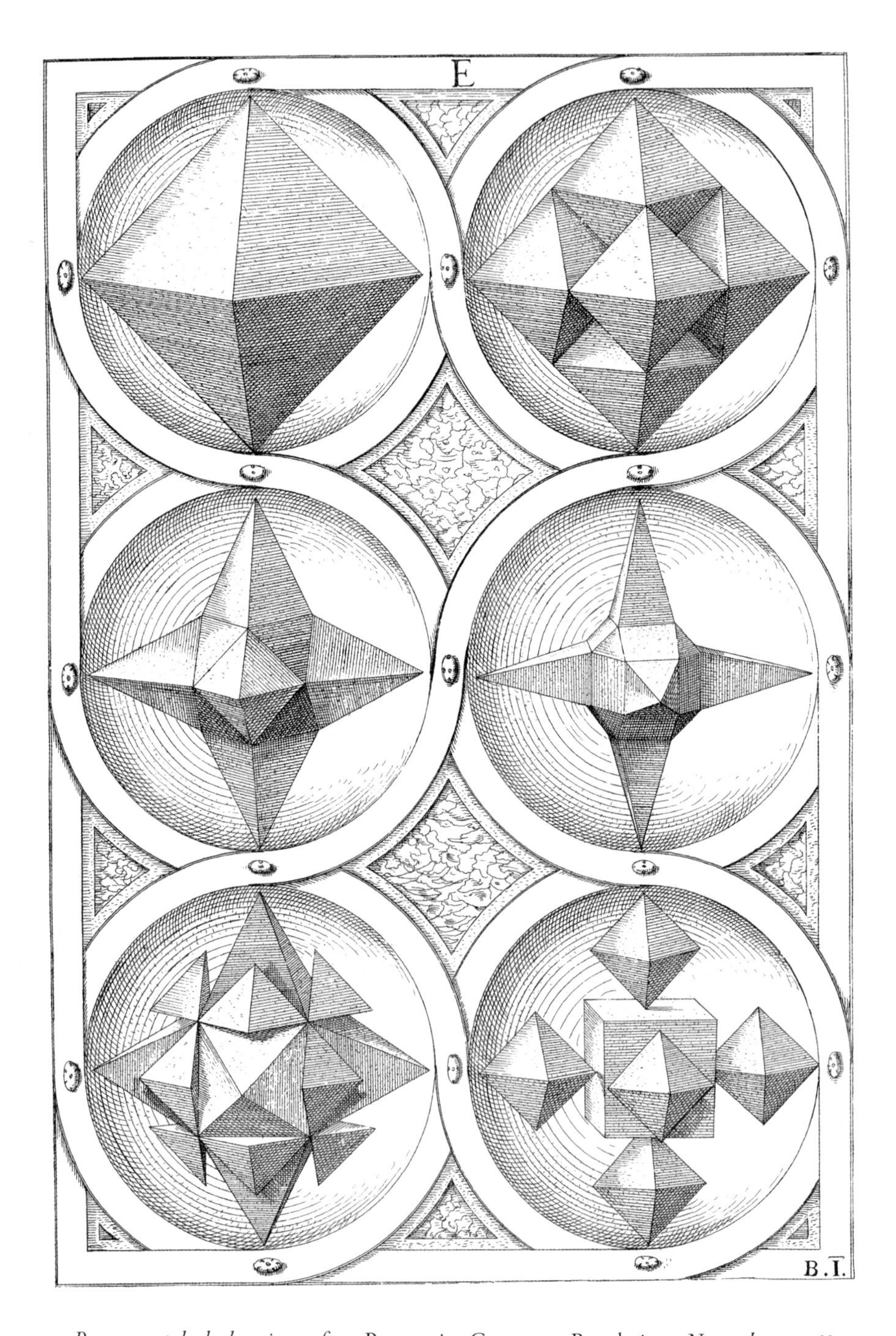

Page B1, octahedral variants; from Perspectiva Corporum Regularium, *Nuremberg, 1568.*

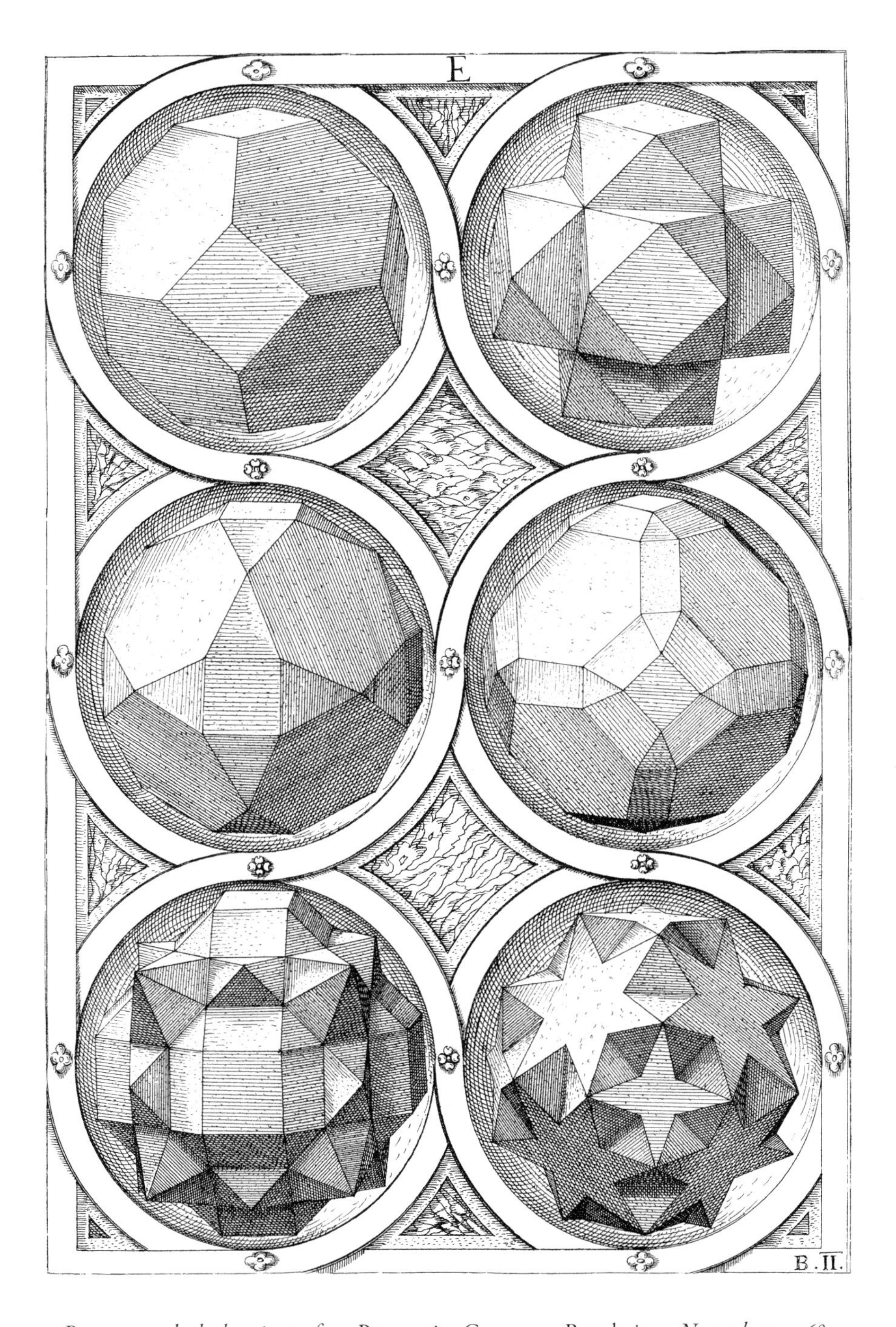

Page B2, octahedral variants; from Perspectiva Corporum Regularium, *Nuremberg, 1568.*

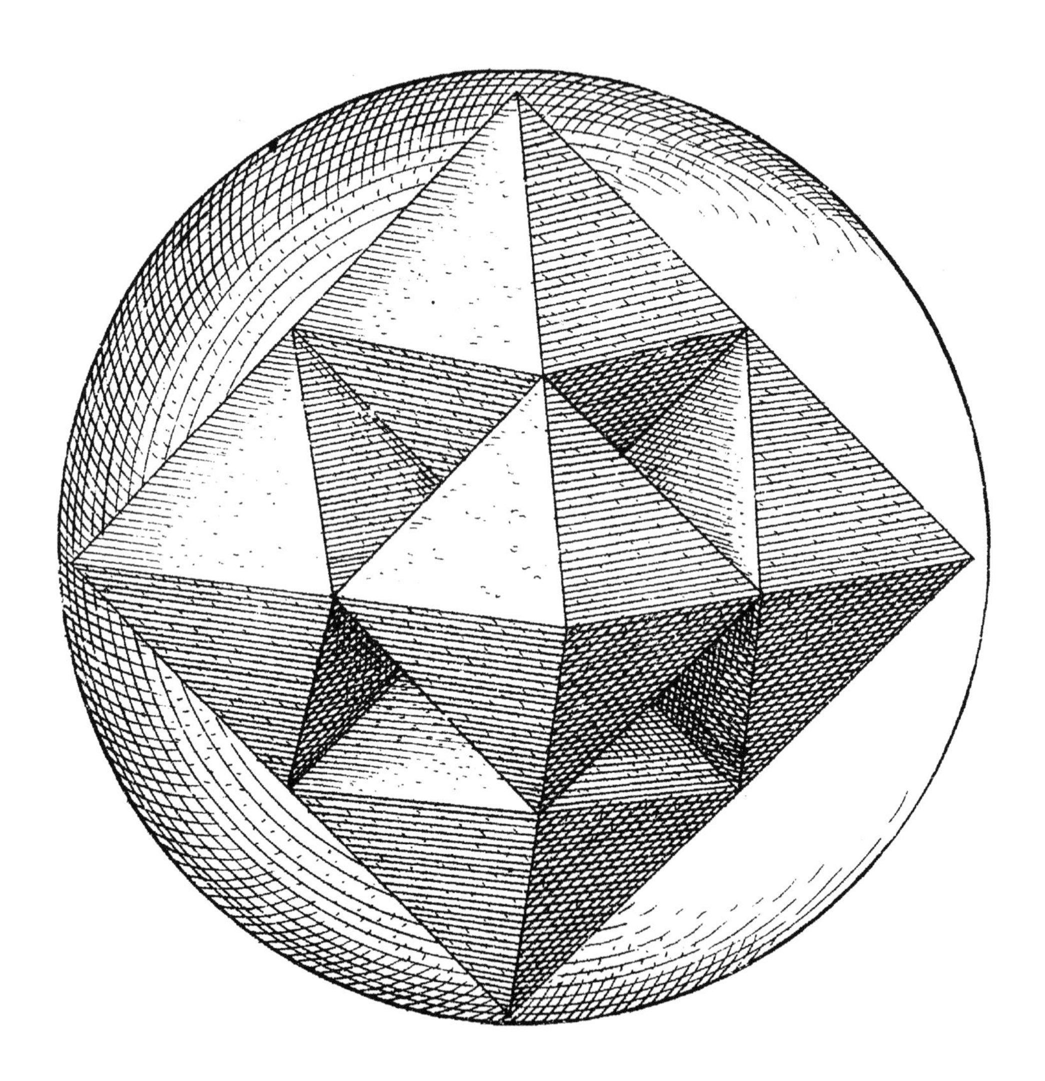

Detail from page B1, Perspectiva Corporum Regularium, *Nuremberg, 1568.*

Detail from page B2, Perspectiva Corporum Regularium, *Nuremberg, 1568.*

Page B3, *octahedral variants; from* Perspectiva Corporum Regularium, *Nuremberg, 1568.*

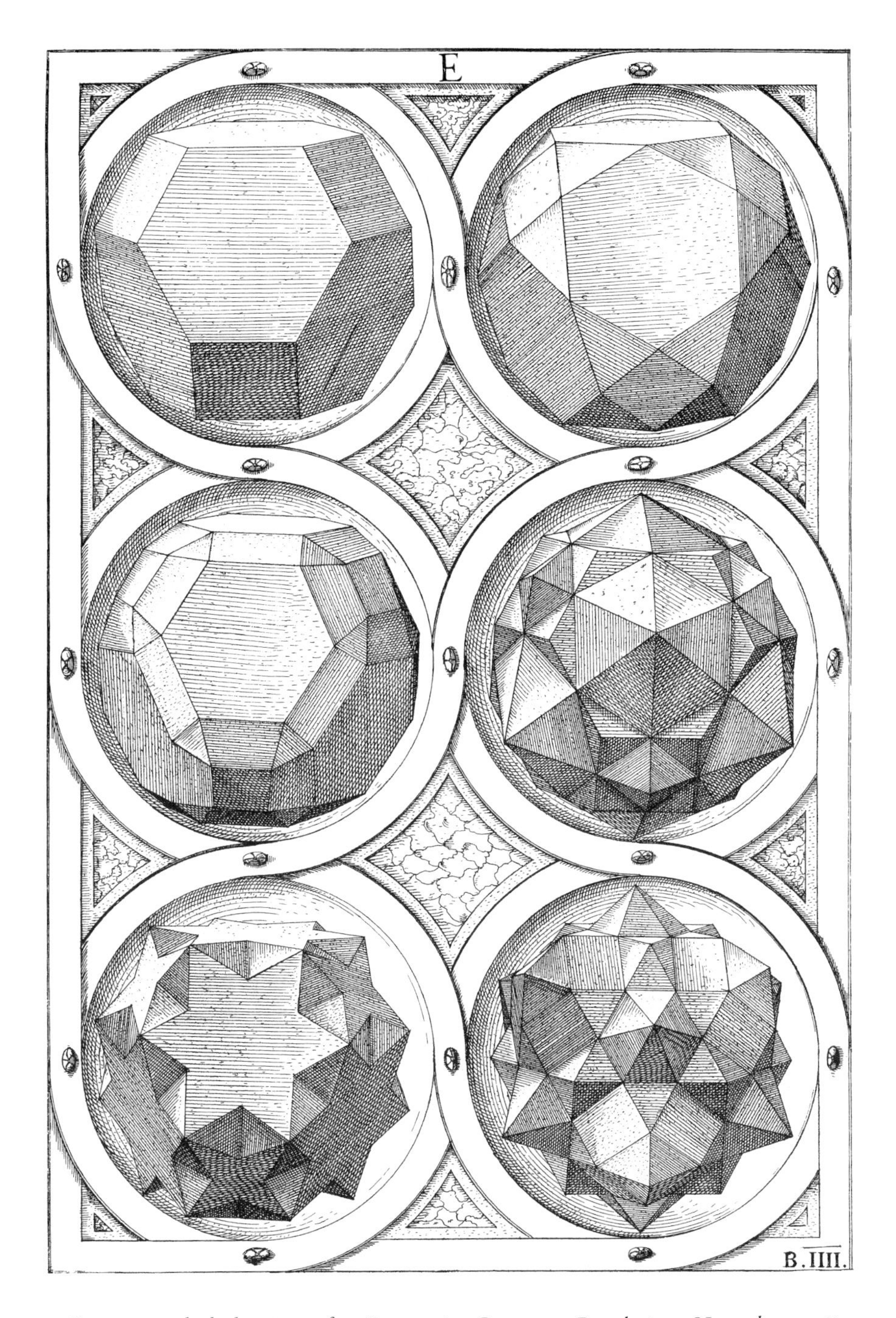

Page B4, octahedral variants; from Perspectiva Corporum Regularium, *Nuremberg, 1568.*

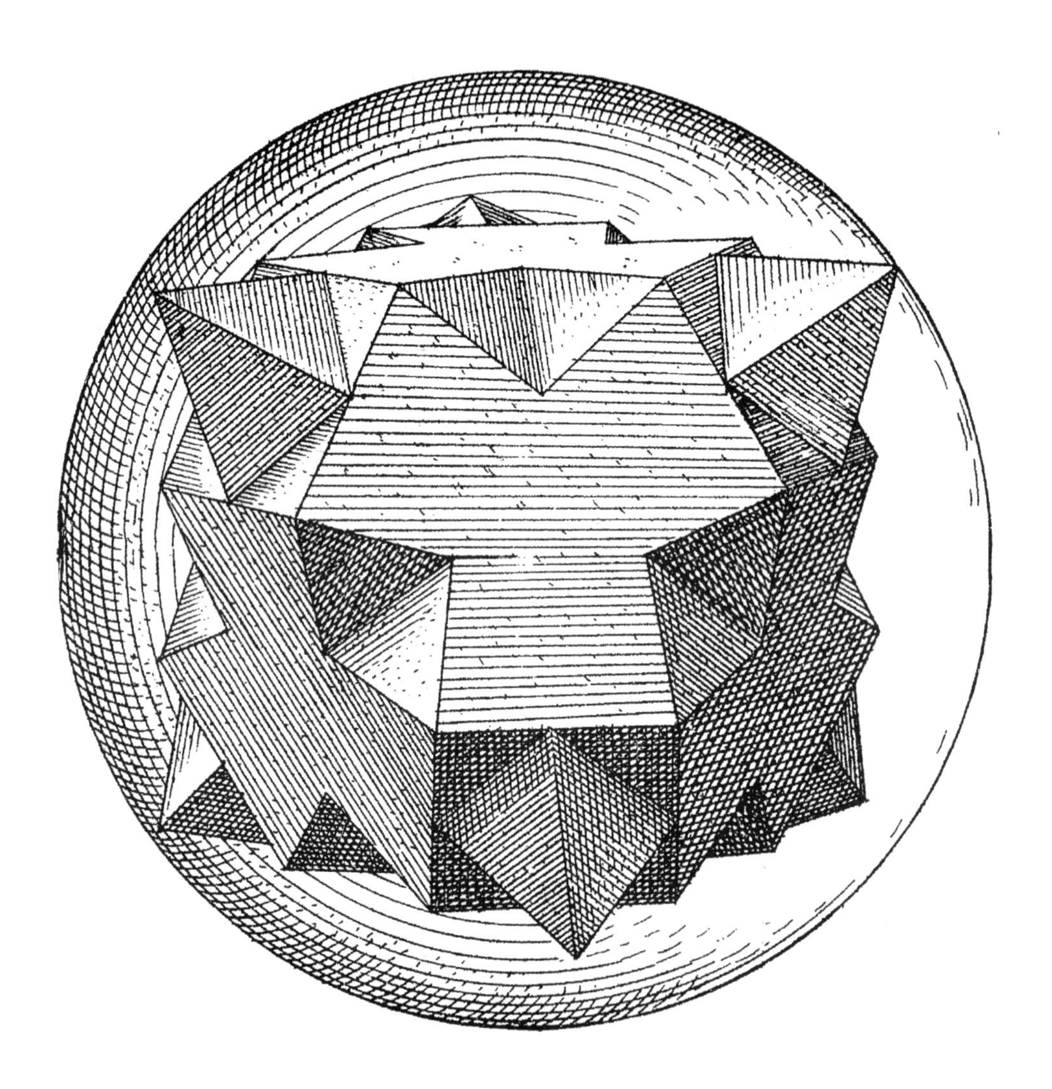

Detail from page B3, Perspectiva Corporum Regularium, *Nuremberg, 1568.*

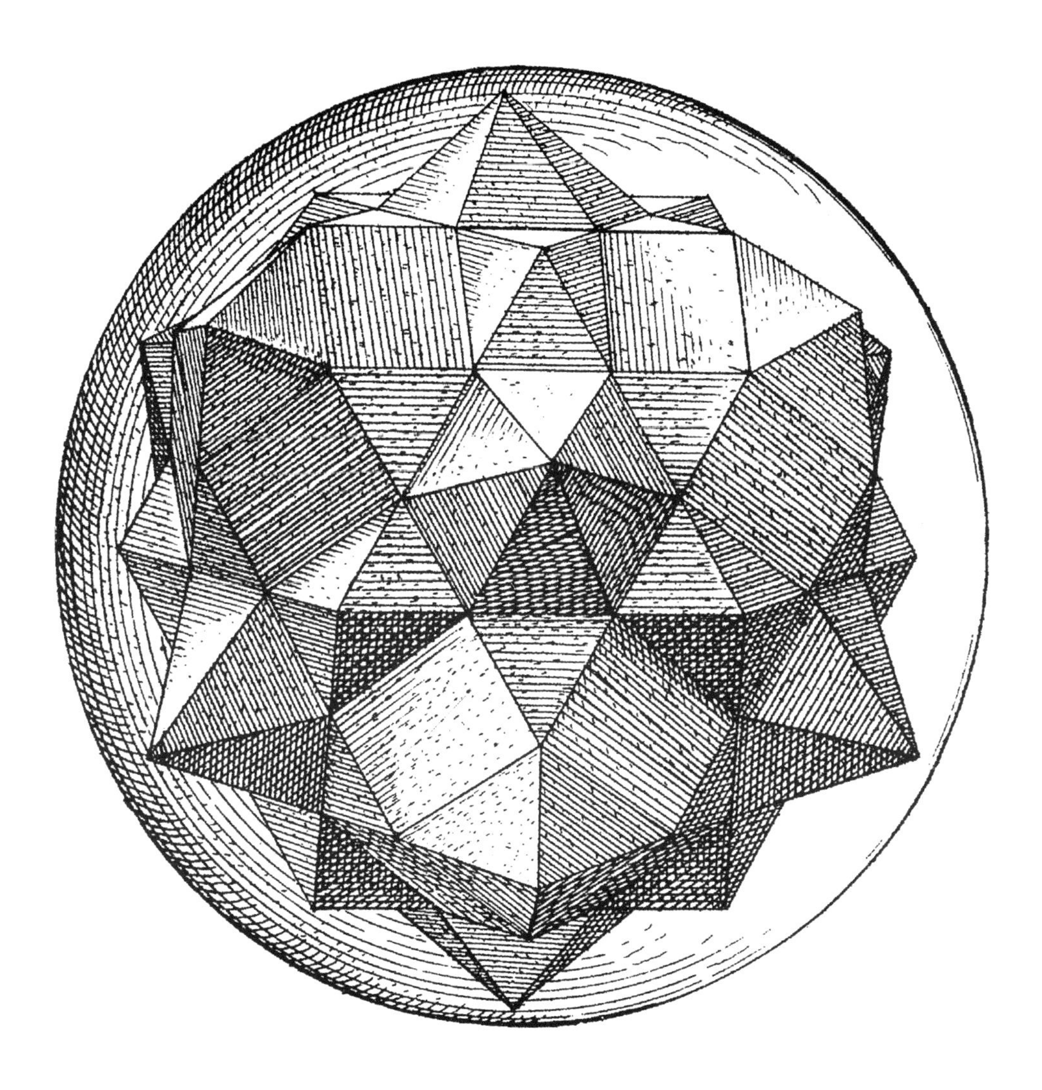

Detail from page B4, Perspectiva Corporum Regularium, *Nuremberg, 1568.*

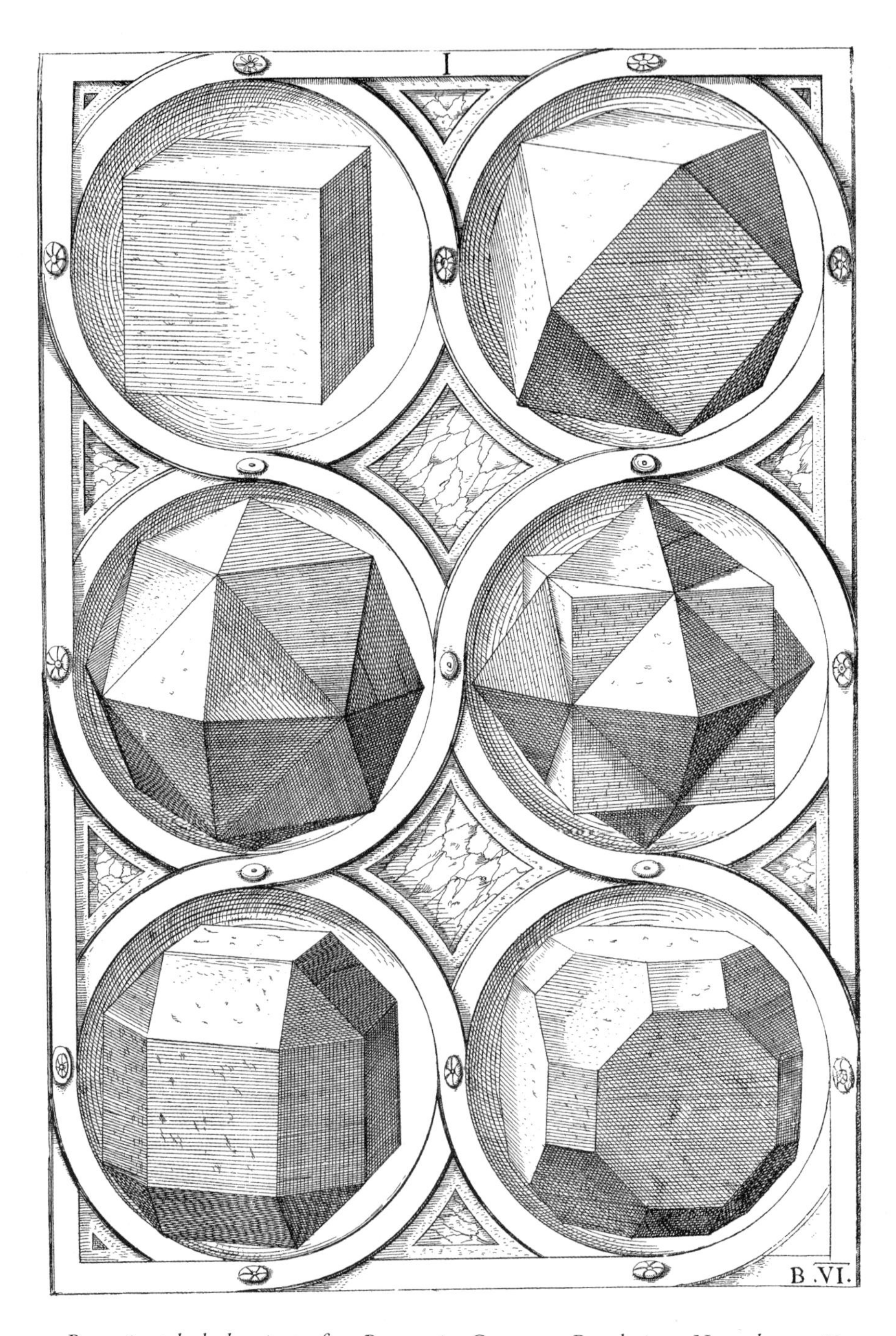

Page B6, octahedral variants; from Perspectiva Corporum Regularium*, Nuremberg, 1568.*

Page CI, cubic variants; from Perspectiva Corporum Regularium, *Nuremberg, 1568.*

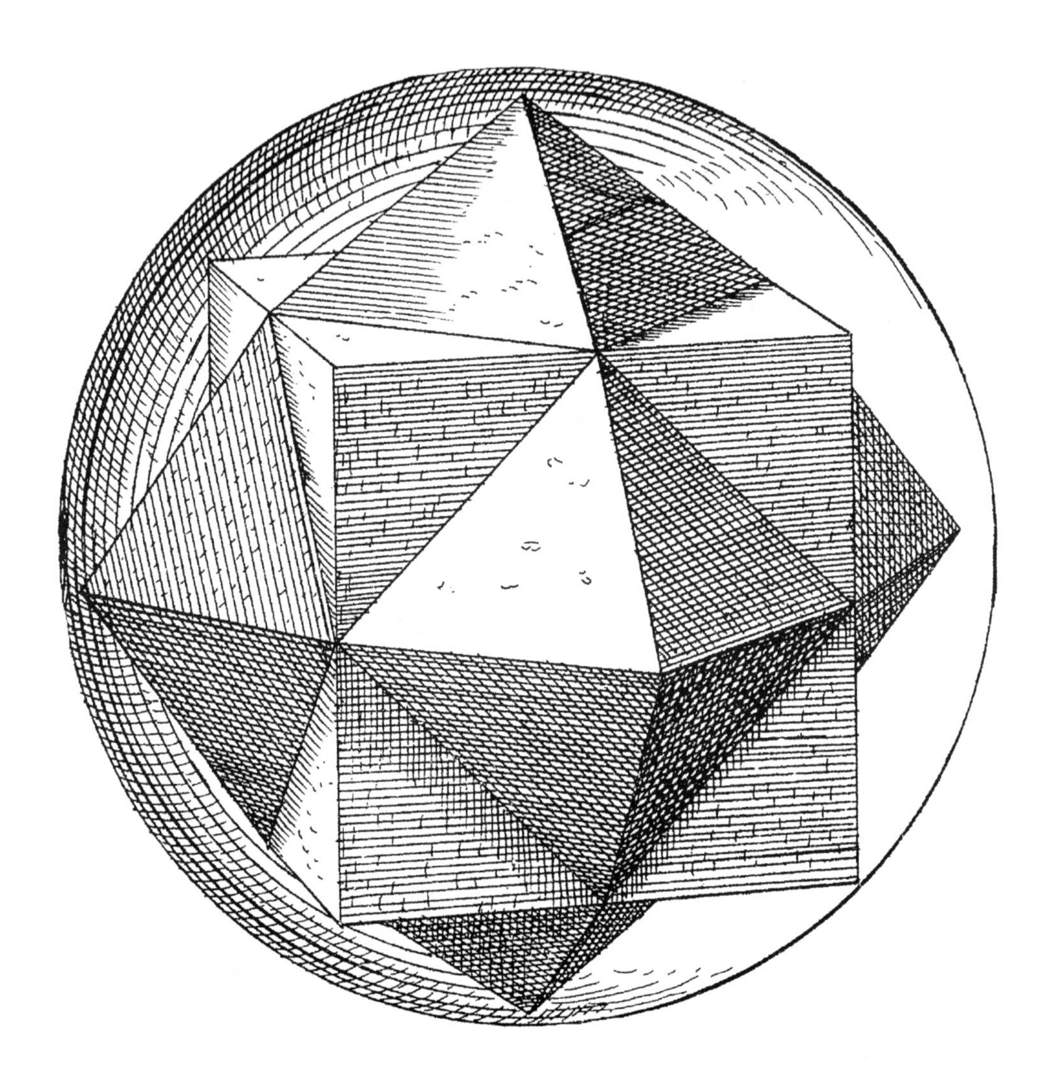

Detail from page B6, Perspectiva Corporum Regularium, *Nuremberg, 1568.*

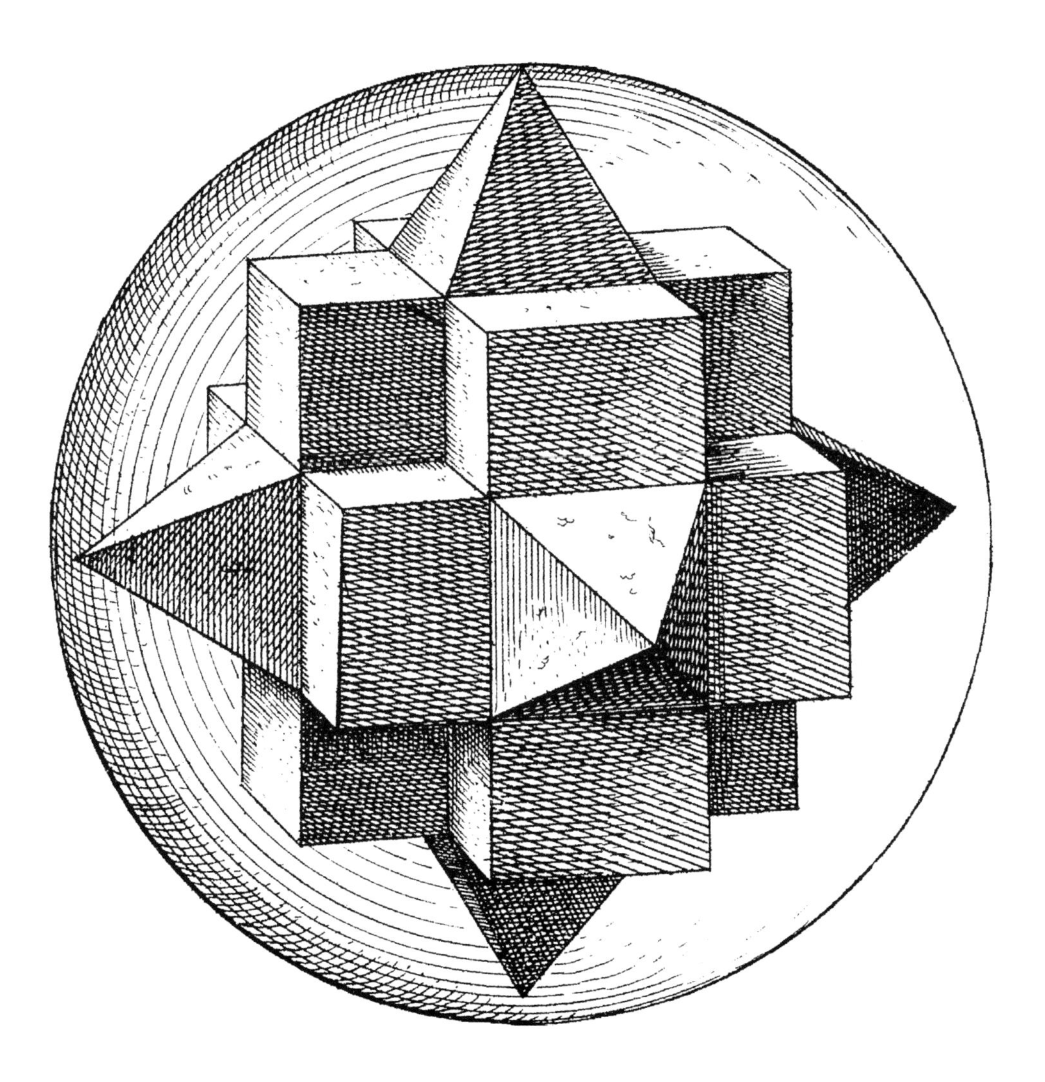

Detail from page C1, Perspectiva Corporum Regularium, *Nuremberg, 1568.*

Page C2, cubic variants; from Perspectiva Corporum Regularium, *Nuremberg, 1568.*

Page c3, cubic variants; from Perspectiva Corporum Regularium, *Nuremberg, 1568.*

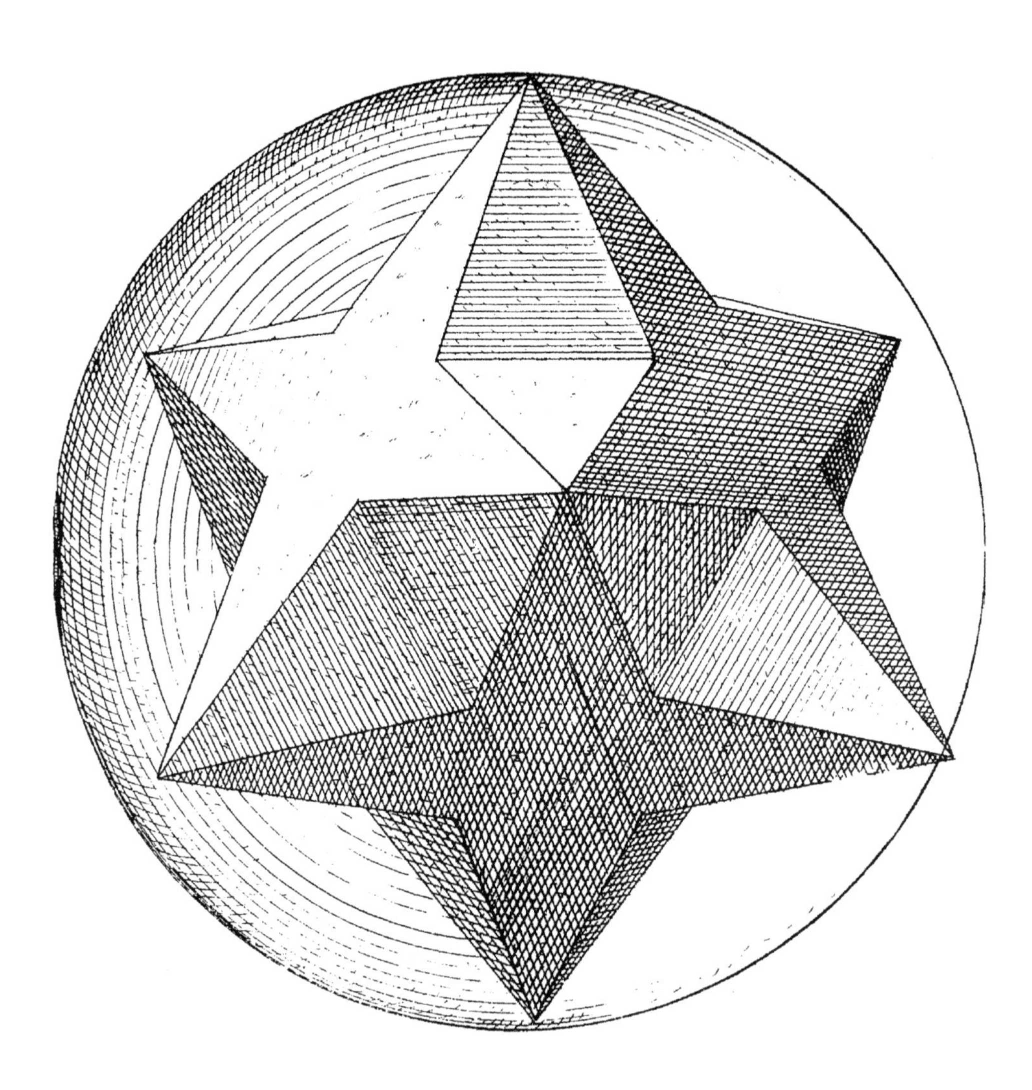

Detail from page c2, Perspectiva Corporum Regularium, *Nuremberg, 1568.*

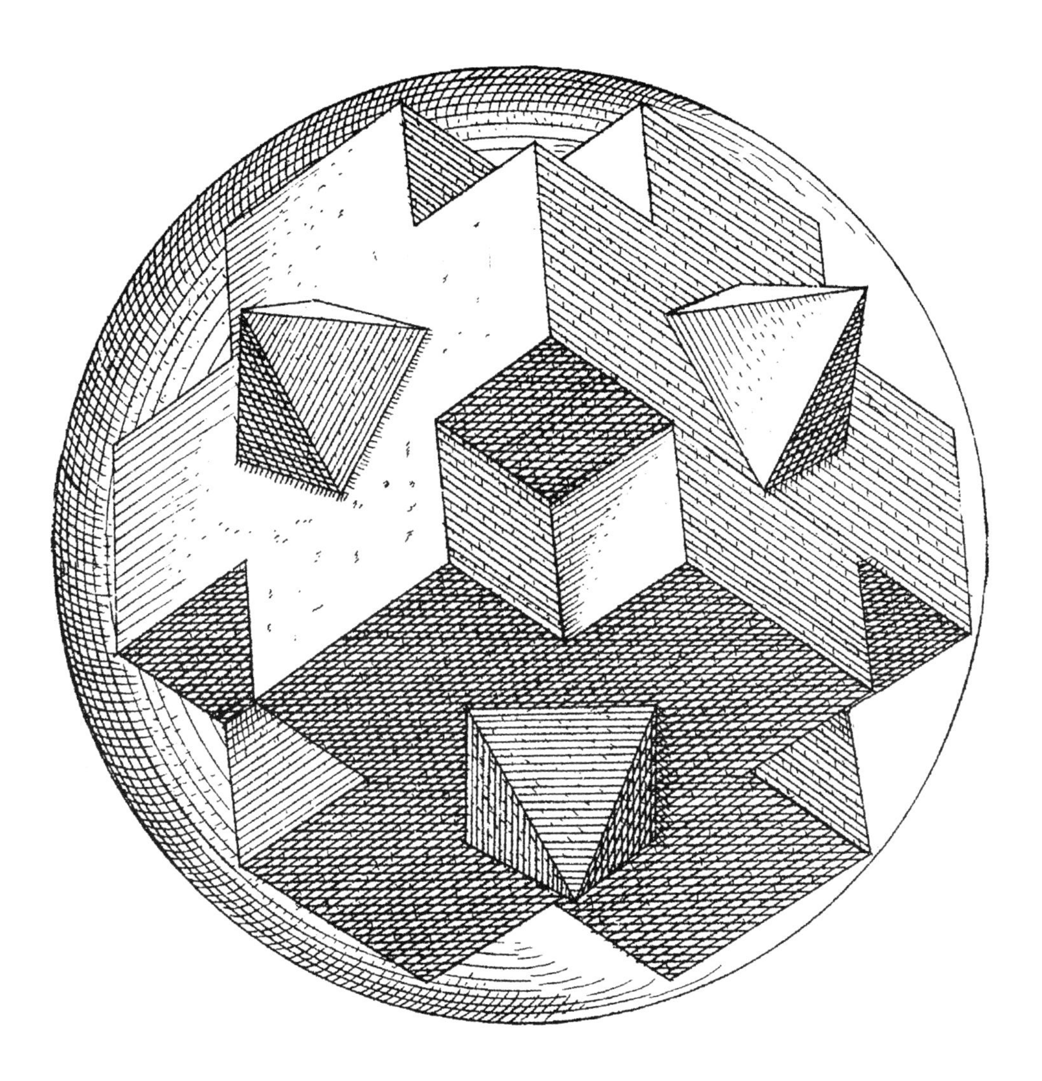

Detail from page c3, Perspectiva Corporum Regularium*, Nuremberg, 1568.*

Page C5, icosahedral variants; from Perspectiva Corporum Regularium, *Nuremberg, 1568.*

Page C6, icosahedral variants; from Perspectiva Corporum Regularium, *Nuremberg, 1568.*

Detail from page c5, Perspectiva Corporum Regularium, *Nuremberg, 1568.*

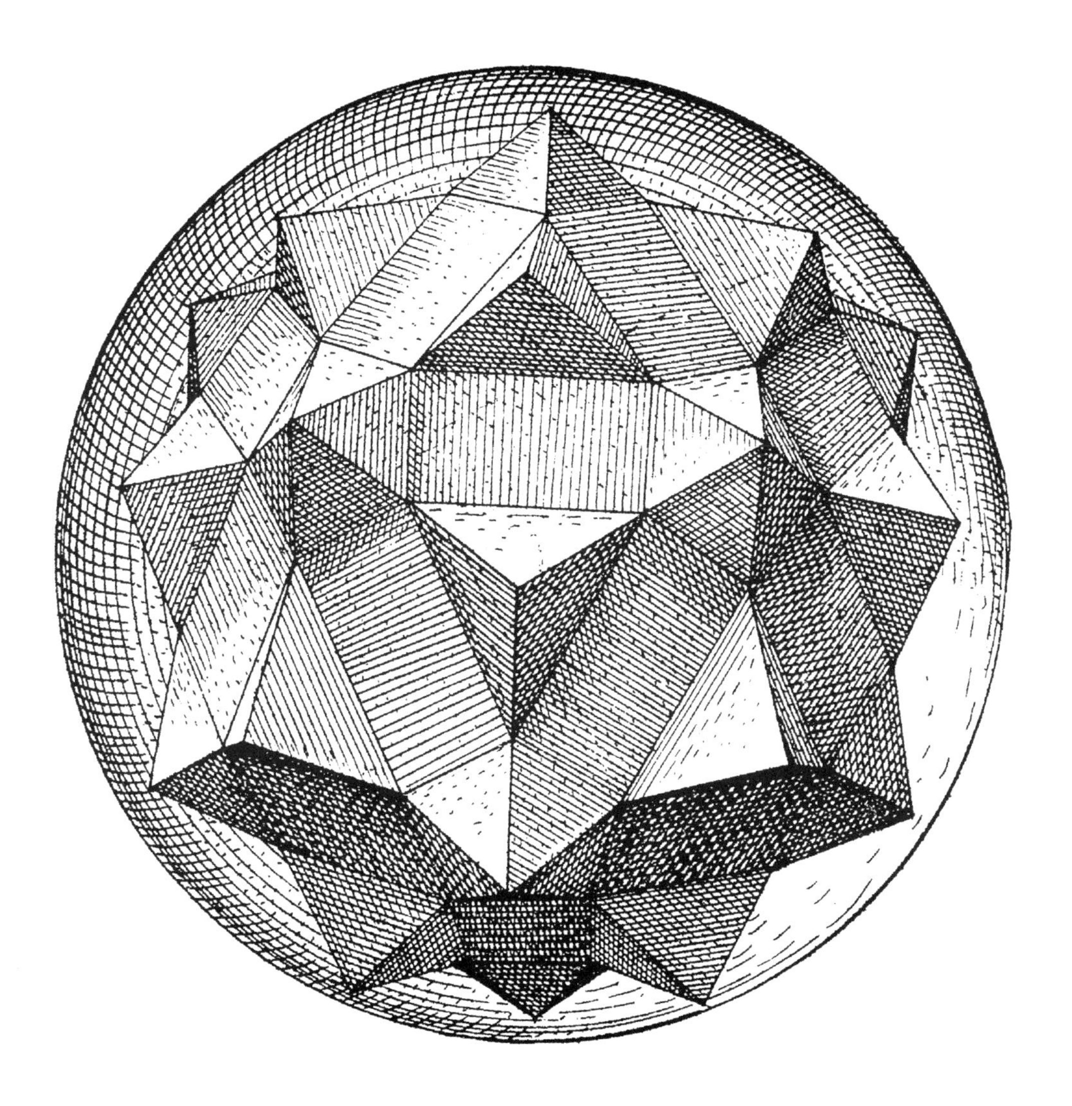

Detail from page C6, Perspectiva Corporum Regularium, *Nuremberg, 1568.*

Page DI, *icosahedral variants; from* Perspectiva Corporum Regularium, *Nuremberg, 1568.*

Page D2, *icosahedral variants; from* Perspectiva Corporum Regularium, *Nuremberg, 1568.*

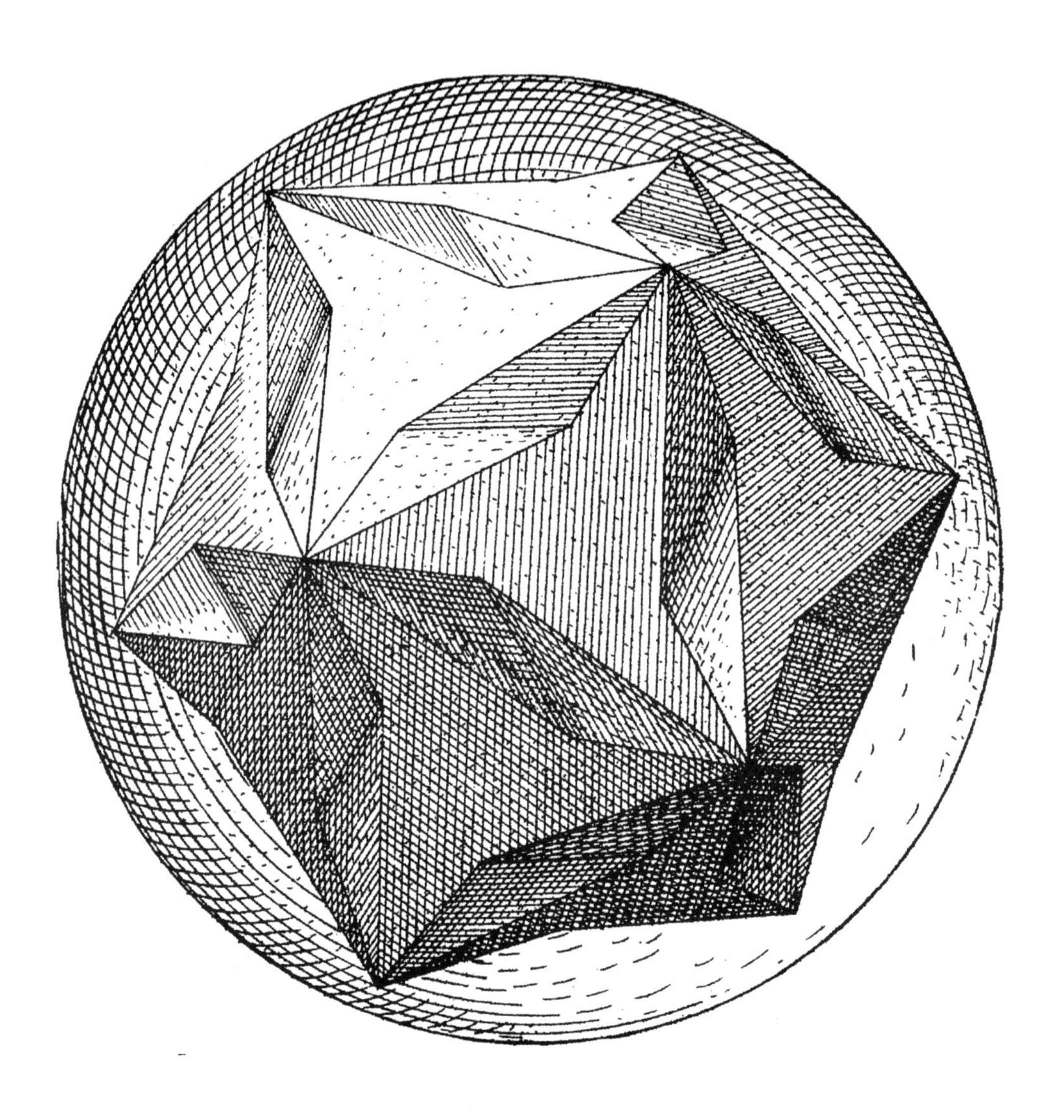

Detail from page D1, Perspectiva Corporum Regularium, *Nuremberg, 1568.*

Detail from page D1, Perspectiva Corporum Regularium, *Nuremberg, 1568.*

Detail from page D2, Perspectiva Corporum Regularium, *Nuremberg, 1568.*

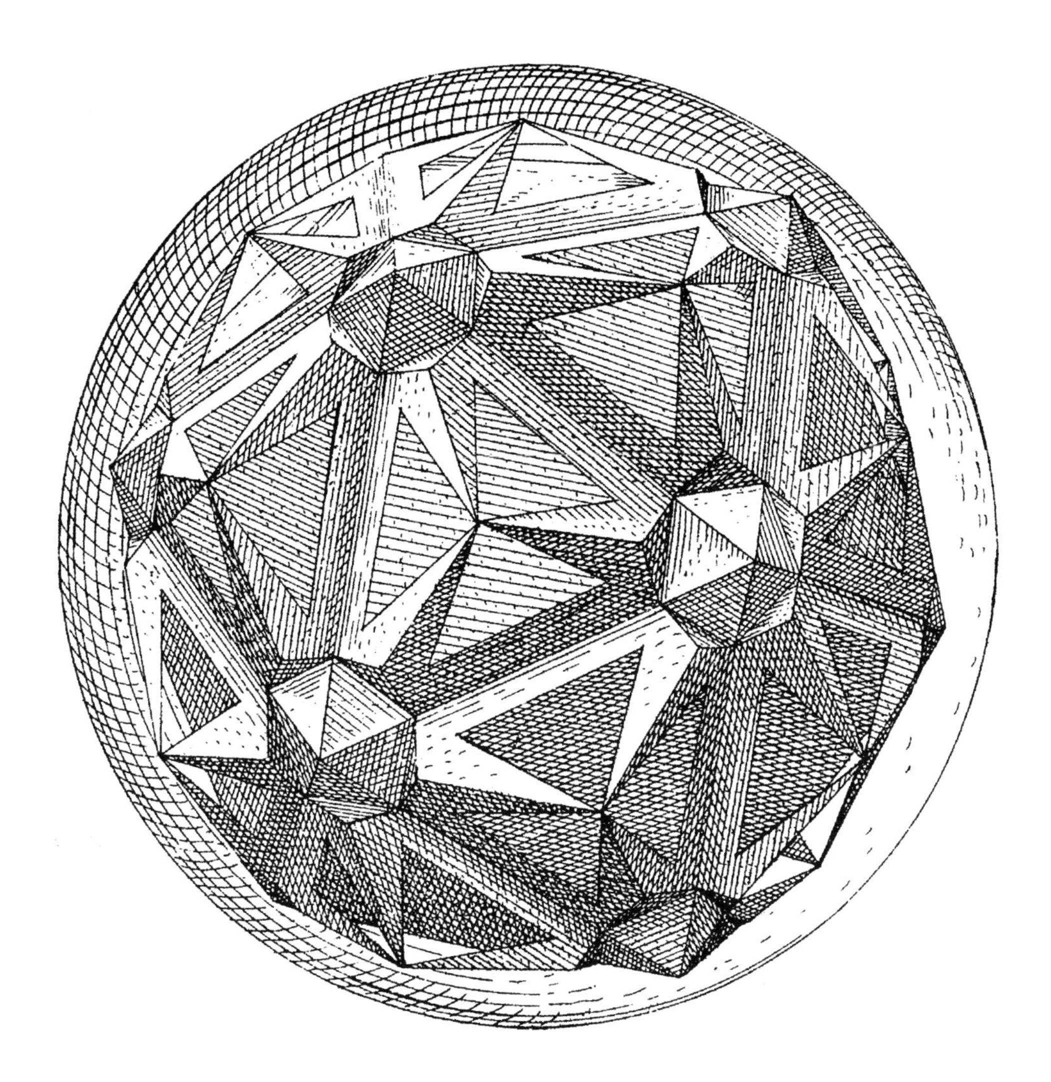

Detail from page D2, Perspectiva Corporum Regularium*, Nuremberg, 1568.*

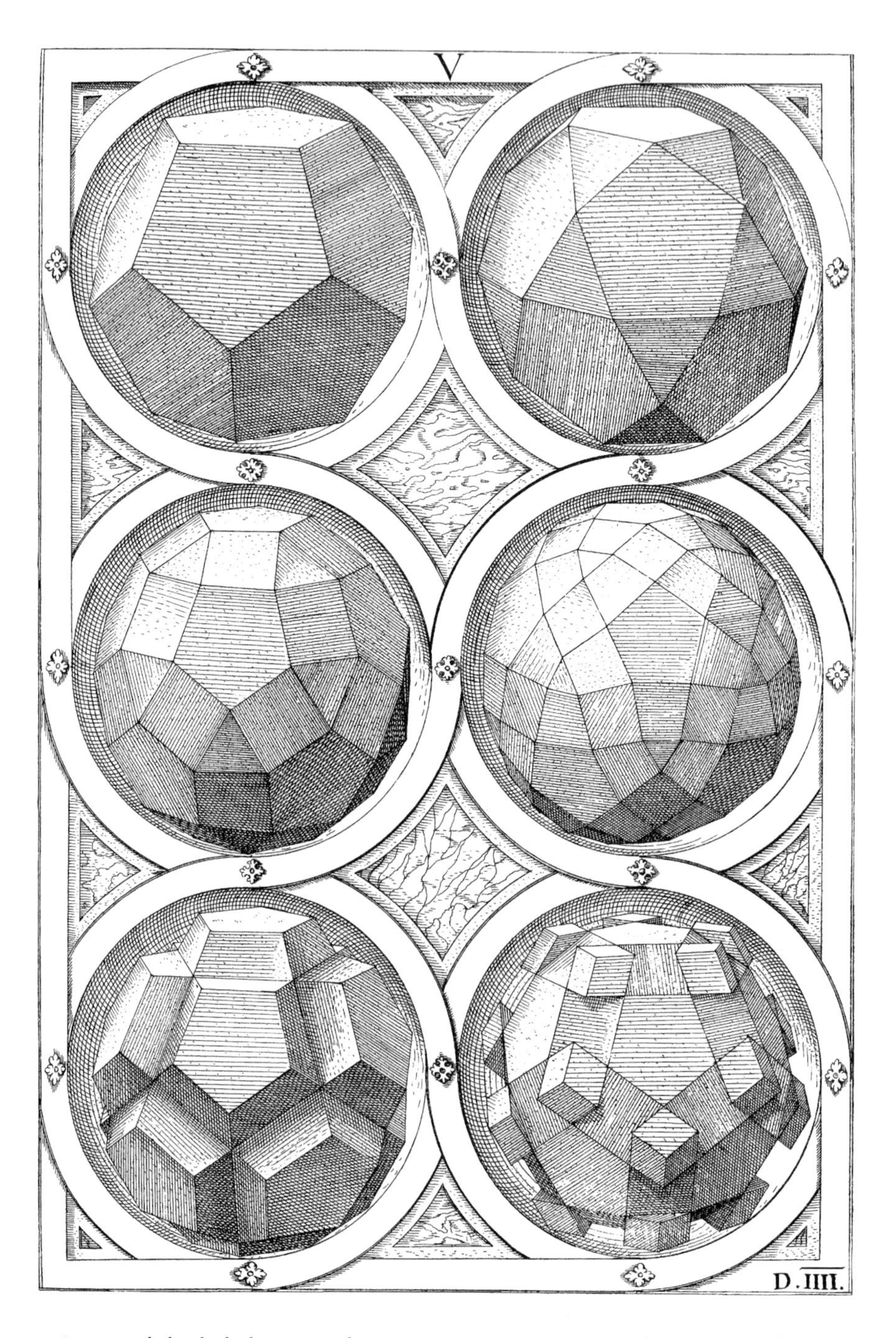

Page D4, *dodecahedral variants; from* Perspectiva Corporum Regularium, *Nuremberg, 1568.*

Page DV, *dodecahedral variants; from* Perspectiva Corporum Regularium, *Nuremberg, 1568.*

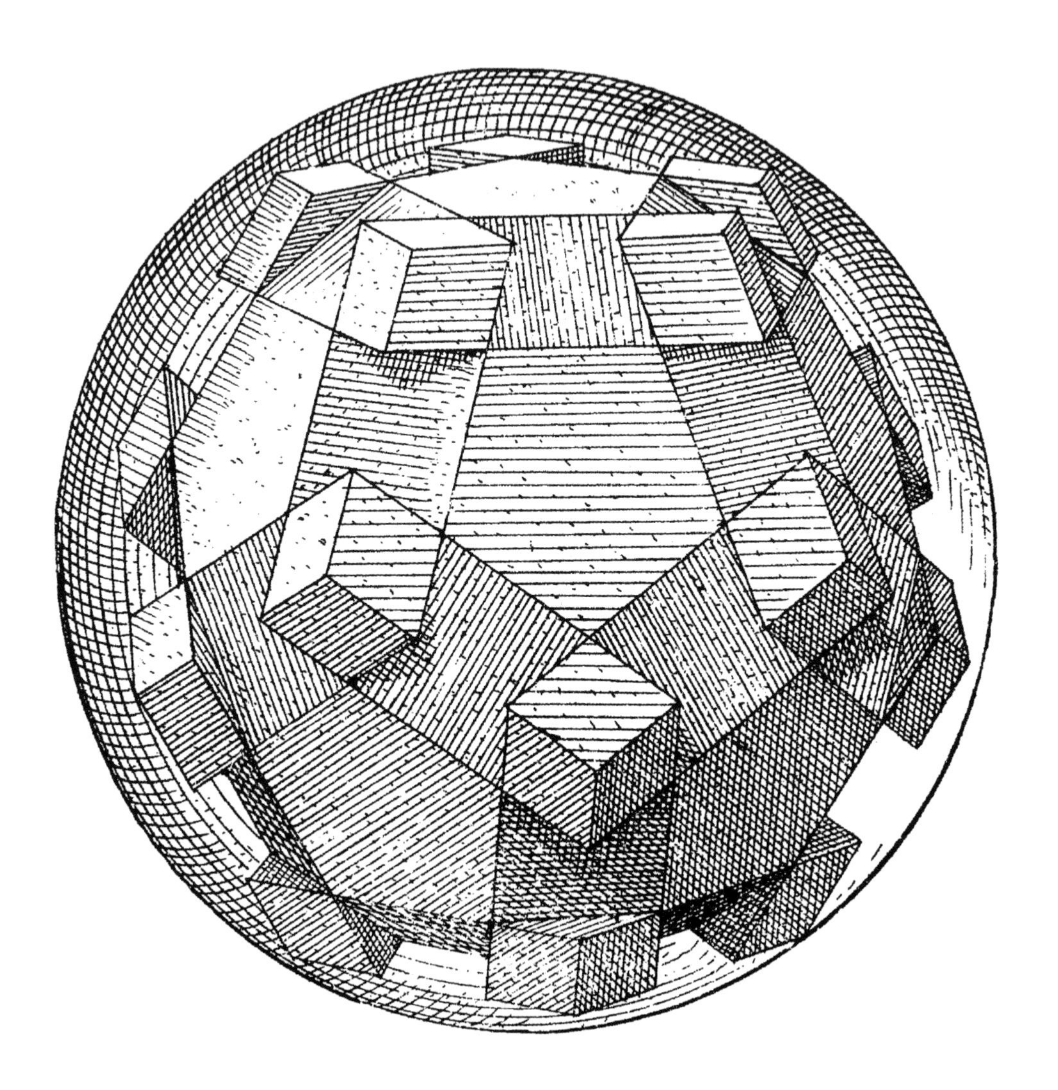

Detail from page D4, Perspectiva Corporum Regularium, *Nuremberg, 1568.*

Detail from page D5, Perspectiva Corporum Regularium*, Nuremberg, 1568.*

Page D6, dodecahedral variants; from Perspectiva Corporum Regularium, *Nuremberg, 1568.*

Page E1, dodecahedral variants; from Perspectiva Corporum Regularium, *Nuremberg, 1568.*

Detail from page D6, Perspectiva Corporum Regularium, *Nuremberg, 1568.*

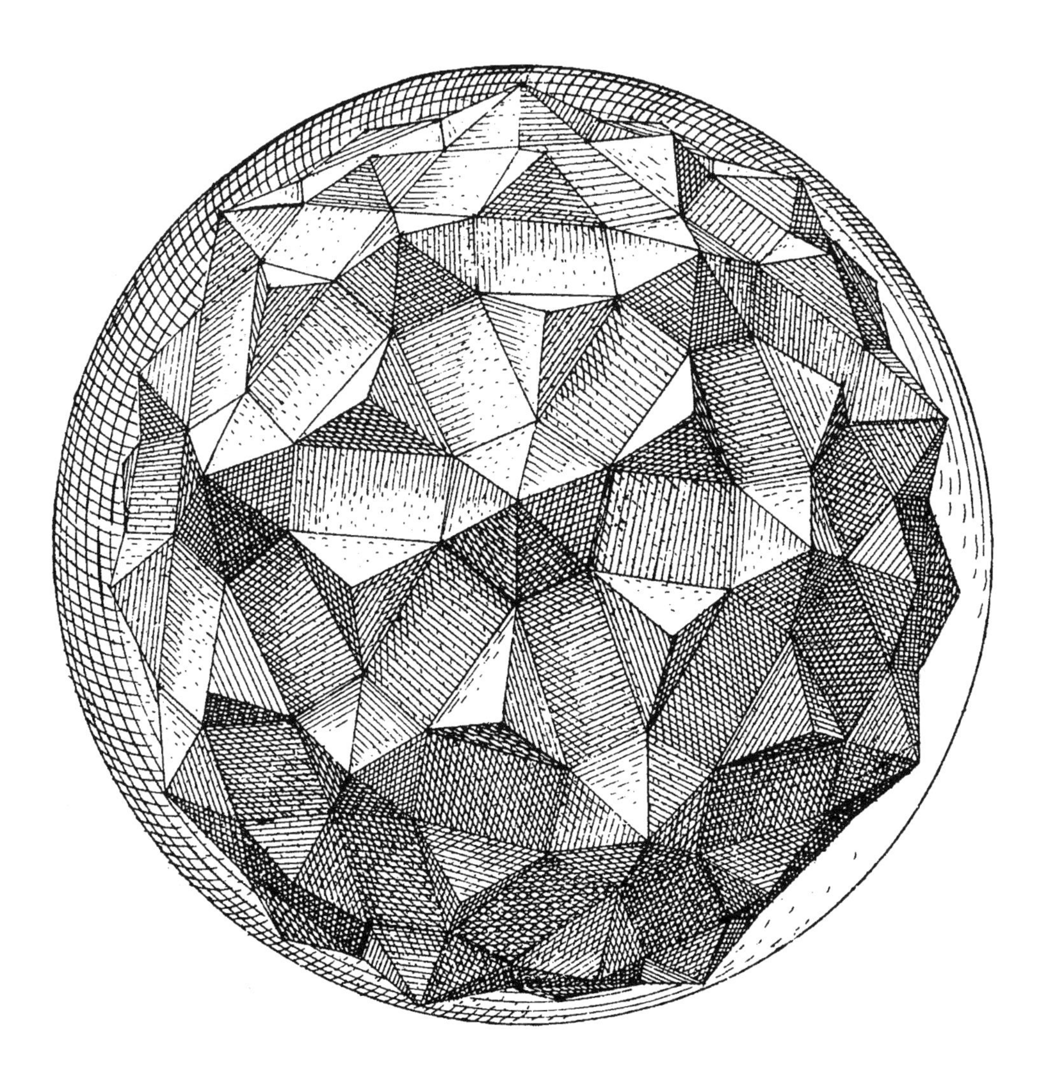

Detail from page E1, Perspectiva Corporum Regularium, *Nuremberg, 1568.*

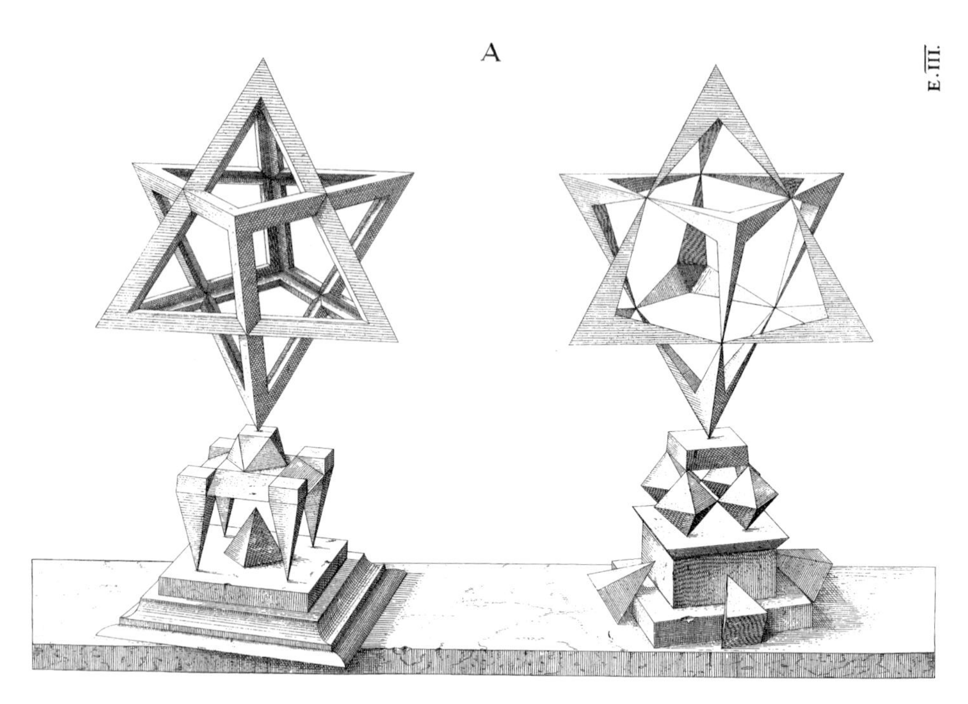

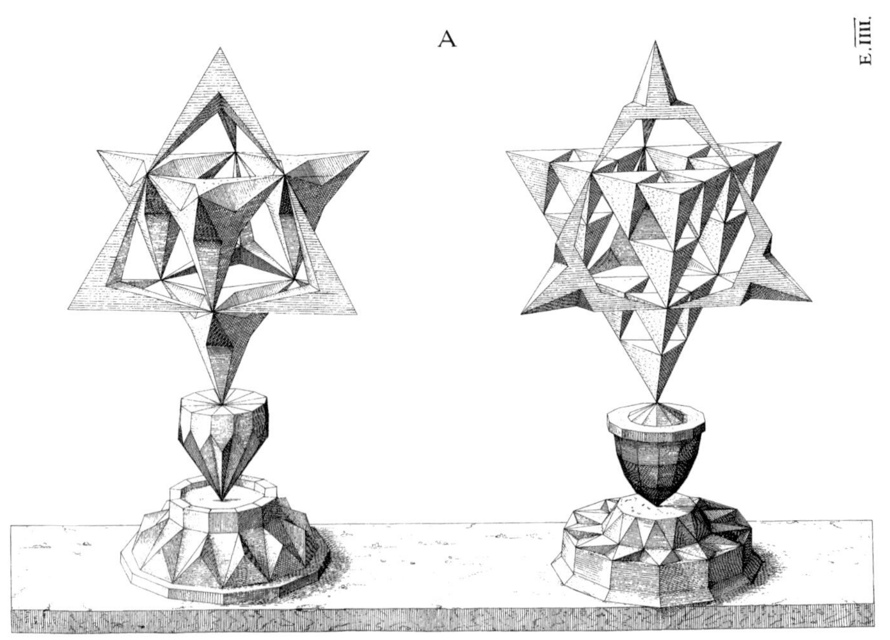

Page E3, *skeletised tetrahedral variants; page* E4, *skeletised tetrahedral variants; from* Perspectiva Corporum Regularium, *Nuremberg, 1568.*

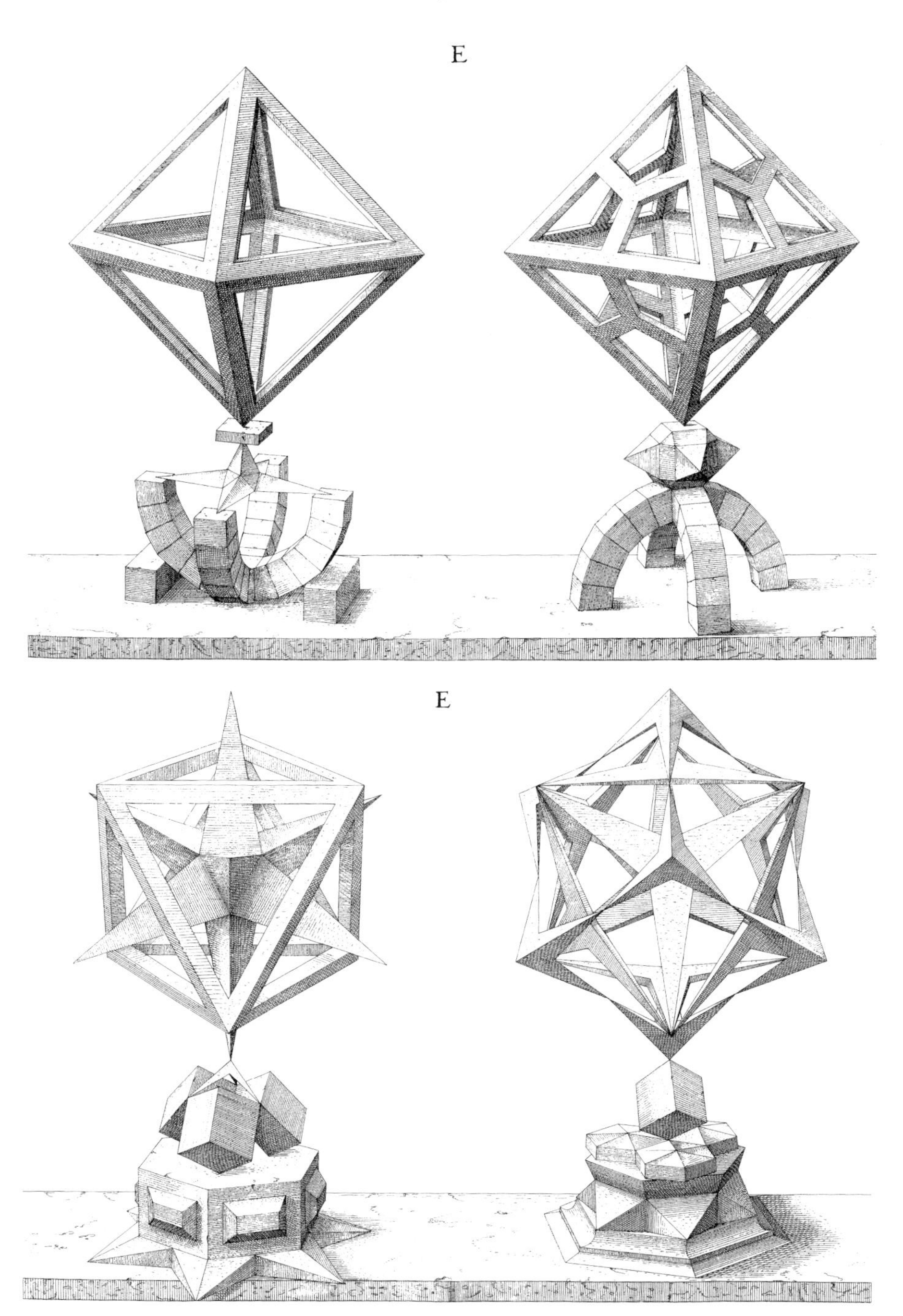

Page E5, skeletised octahedral variants; page E6, skeletised and star tetrahedral variants; from Perspectiva Corporum Regularium, *Nuremberg, 1568.*

Detail from page E3, Perspectiva Corporum Regularium, *Nuremberg, 1568.*

Detail from page E4, Perspectiva Corporum Regularium, *Nuremberg, 1568.*

Detail from page E5, Perspectiva Corporum Regularium, *Nuremberg, 1568.*

Detail from page E6, Perspectiva Corporum Regularium, *Nuremberg, 1568.*

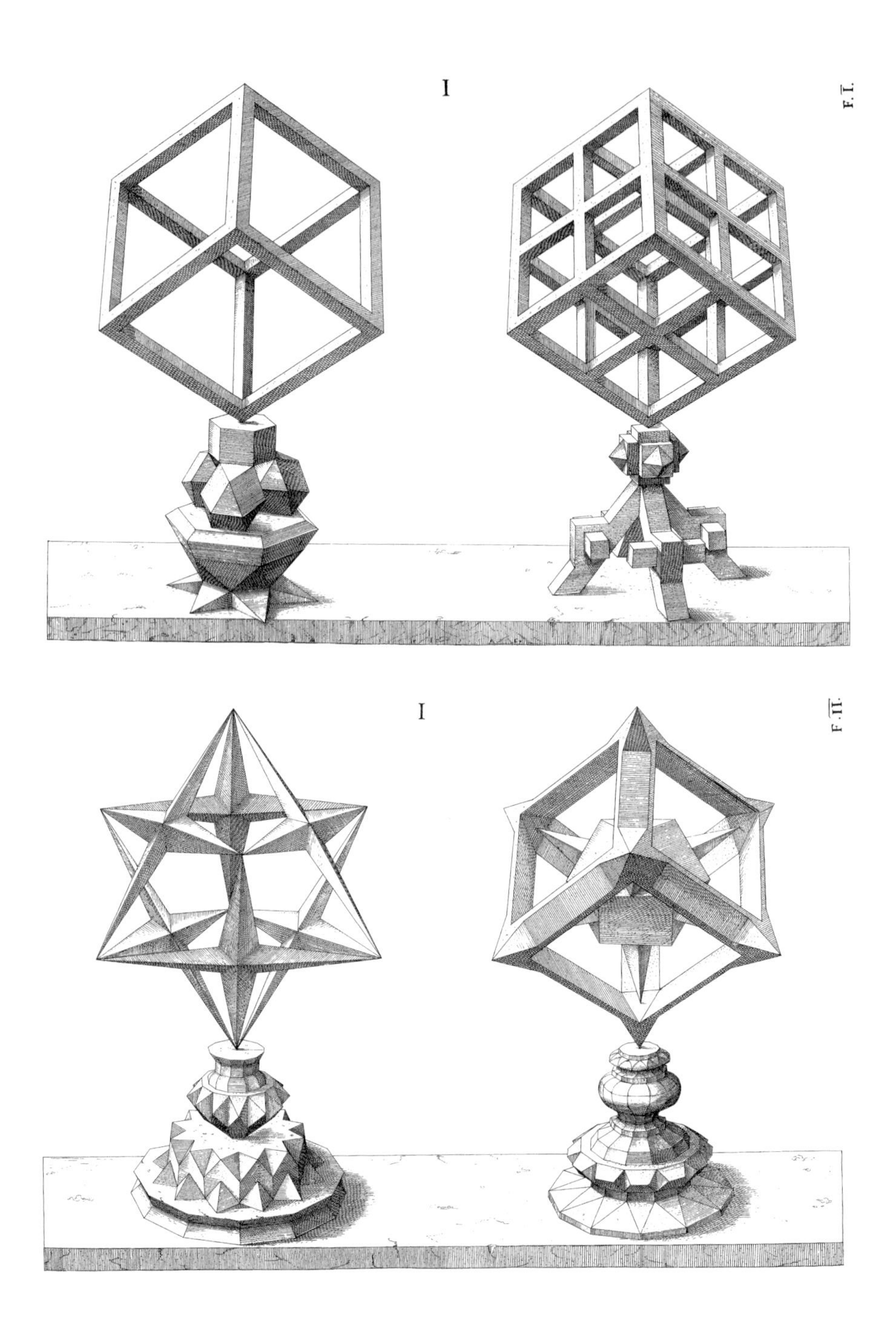

Page F1, skeletised cubic variants; page F2, star skeletised cubic variants; from Perspectiva Corporum Regularium, *Nuremberg, 1568.*

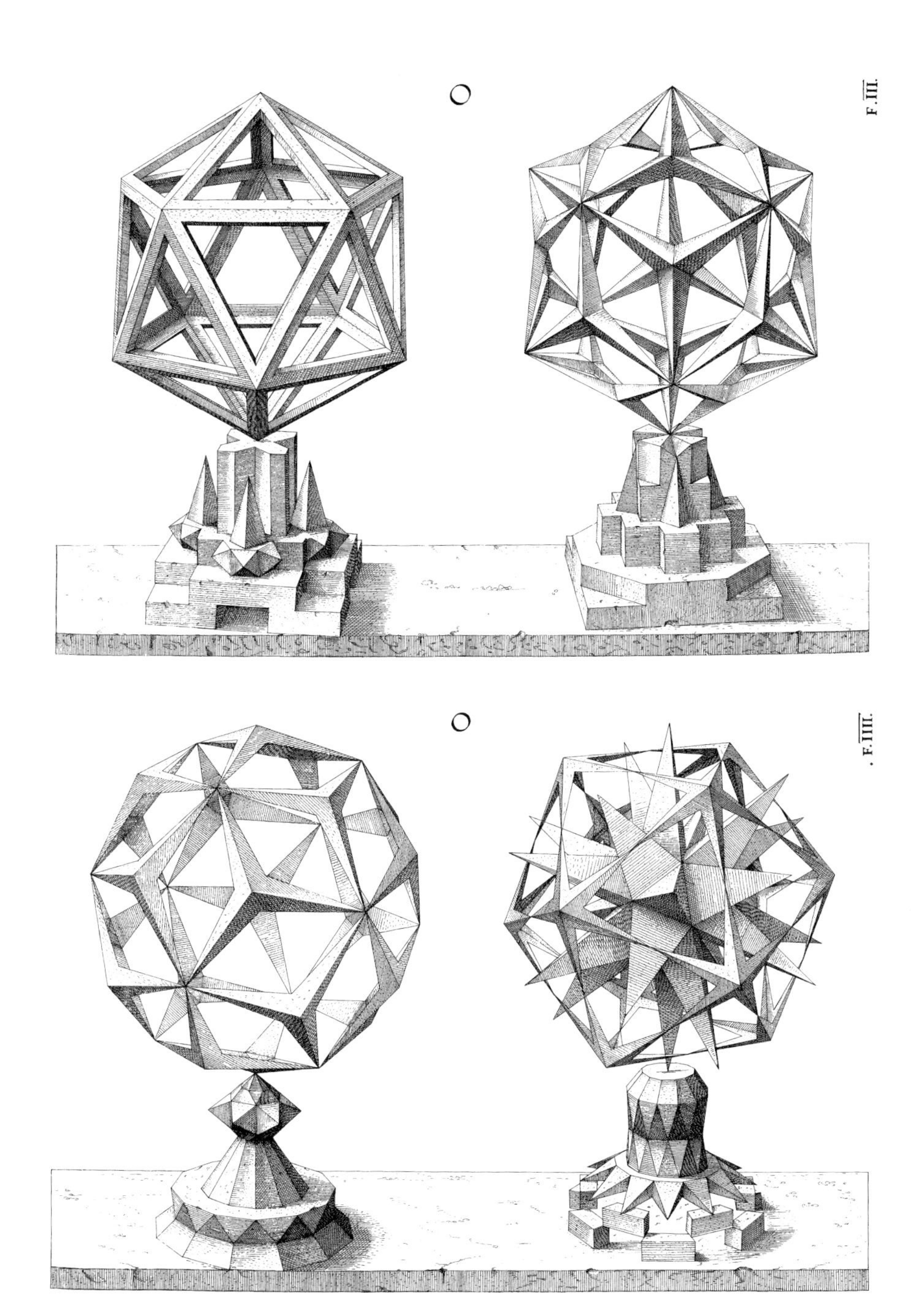

Page F3, skeletised and star icosahedral variants; page F4, star icosahedral variants; from Perspectiva Corporum Regularium, *Nuremberg, 1568.*

Detail from page F2, Perspectiva Corporum Regularium, *Nuremberg, 1568.*

Detail from page F3, Perspectiva Corporum Regularium, *Nuremberg, 1568.*

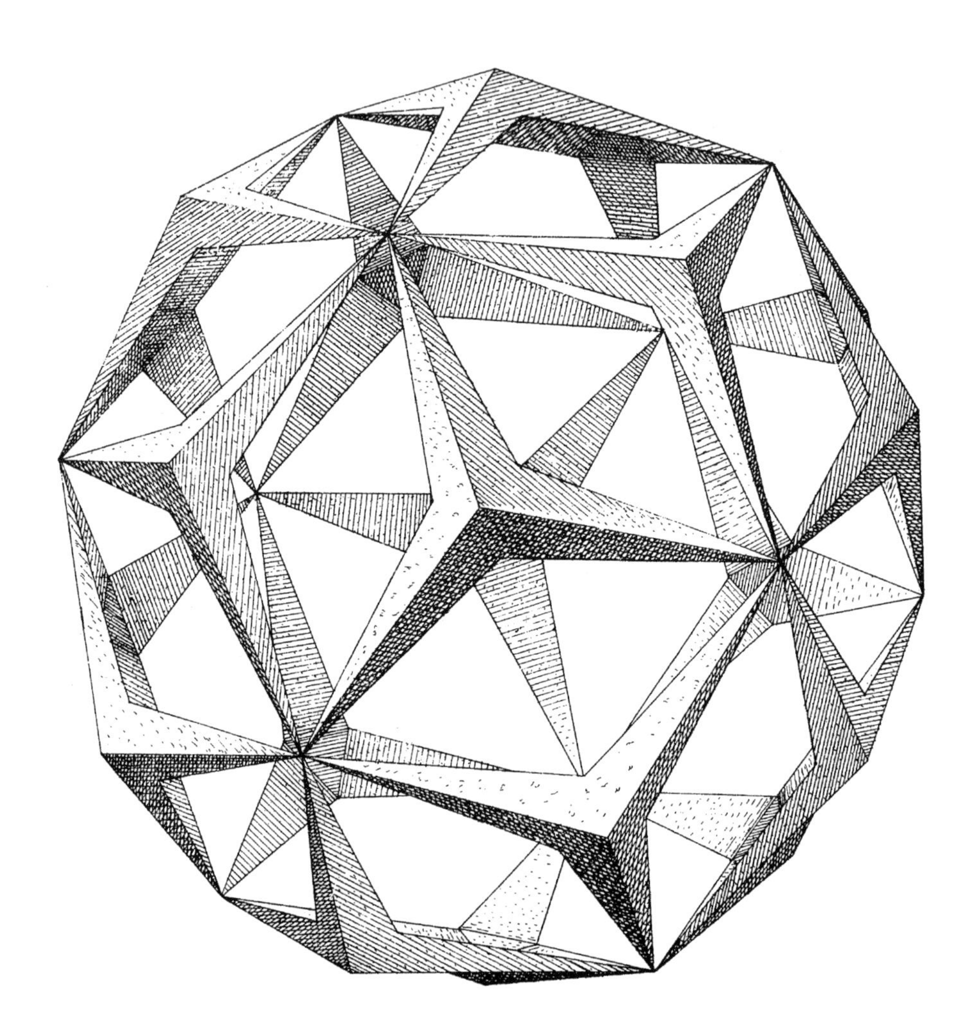

Detail from page F4, Perspectiva Corporum Regularium, *Nuremberg, 1568.*

Detail from page F4, Perspectiva Corporum Regularium, *Nuremberg, 1568.*

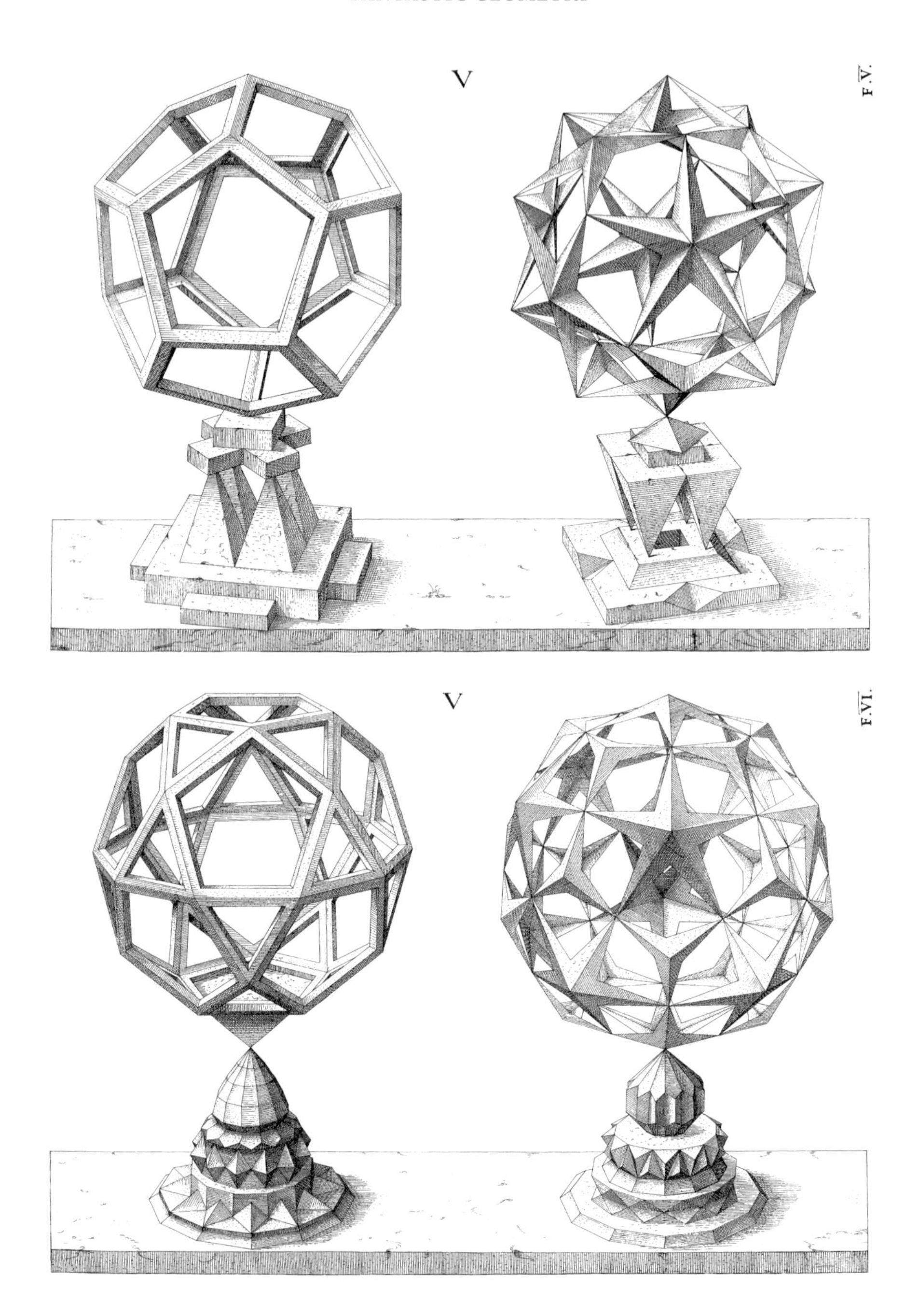

Page F5, skeletised and star dodecahedral variants; page F6, skeletised and star icosidodecahedral variants; from Perspectiva Corporum Regularium, *Nuremberg, 1568.*

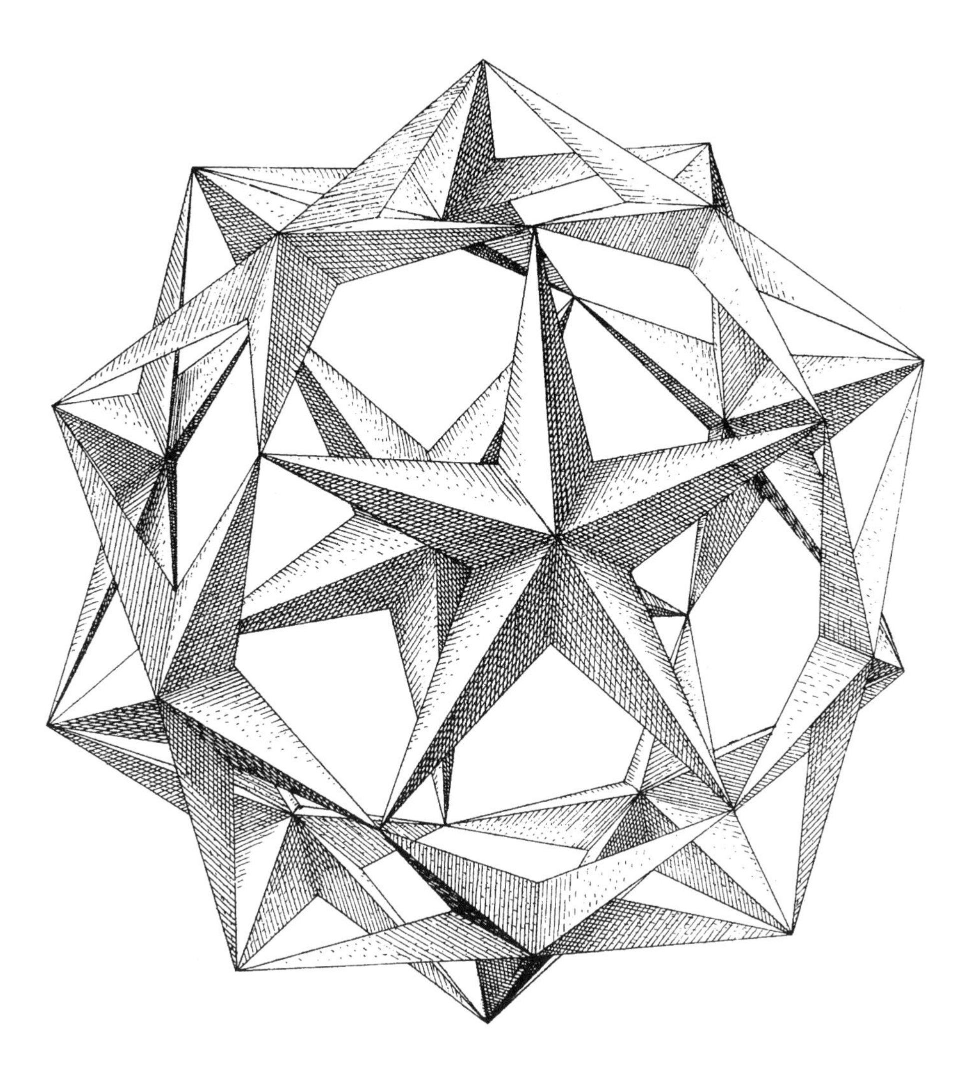

Detail from page F5, Perspectiva Corporum Regularium, *Nuremberg, 1568.*

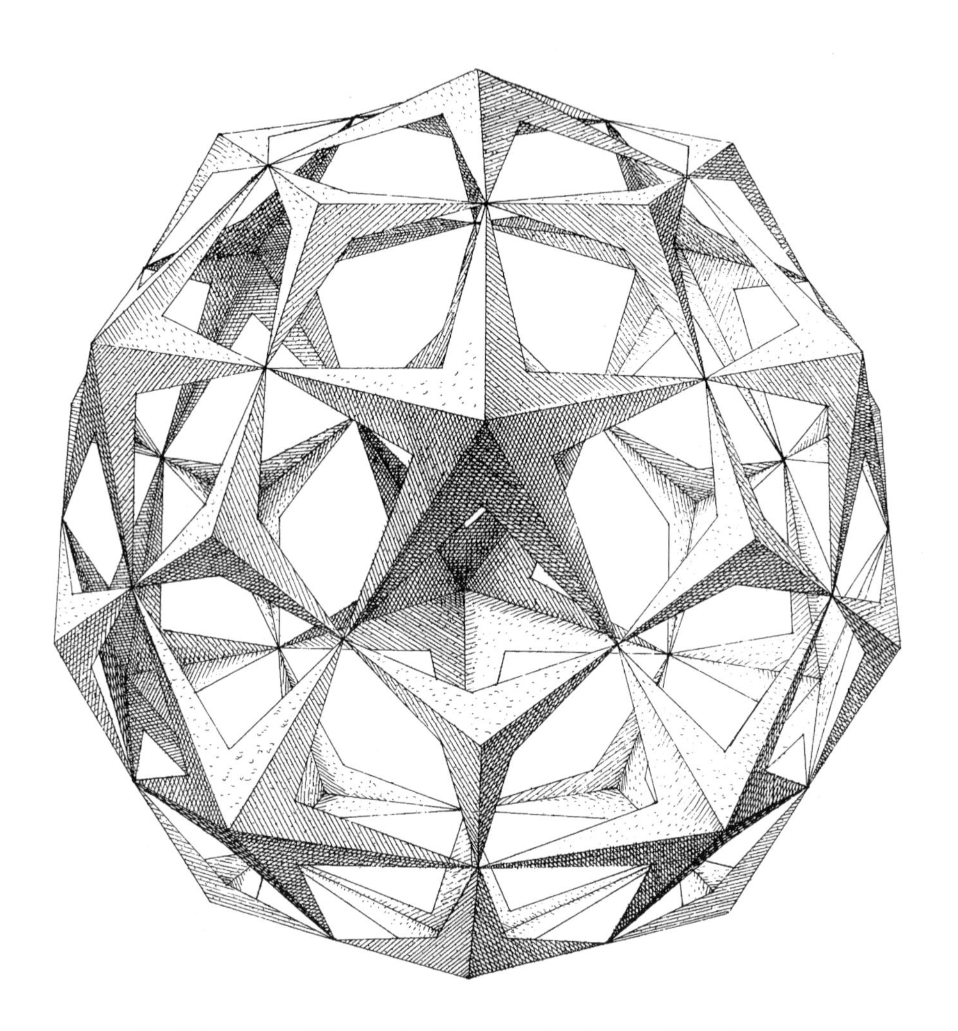

Detail from page F6, Perspectiva Corporum Regularium, *Nuremberg, 1568.*

Page G1, spherical variants; page G2, spherical variants;
from Perspectiva Corporum Regularium, *Nuremberg, 1568.*

Page G3, *spherical variants; page* G4, *spherical variants;*
from Perspectiva Corporum Regularium, *Nuremberg, 1568.*

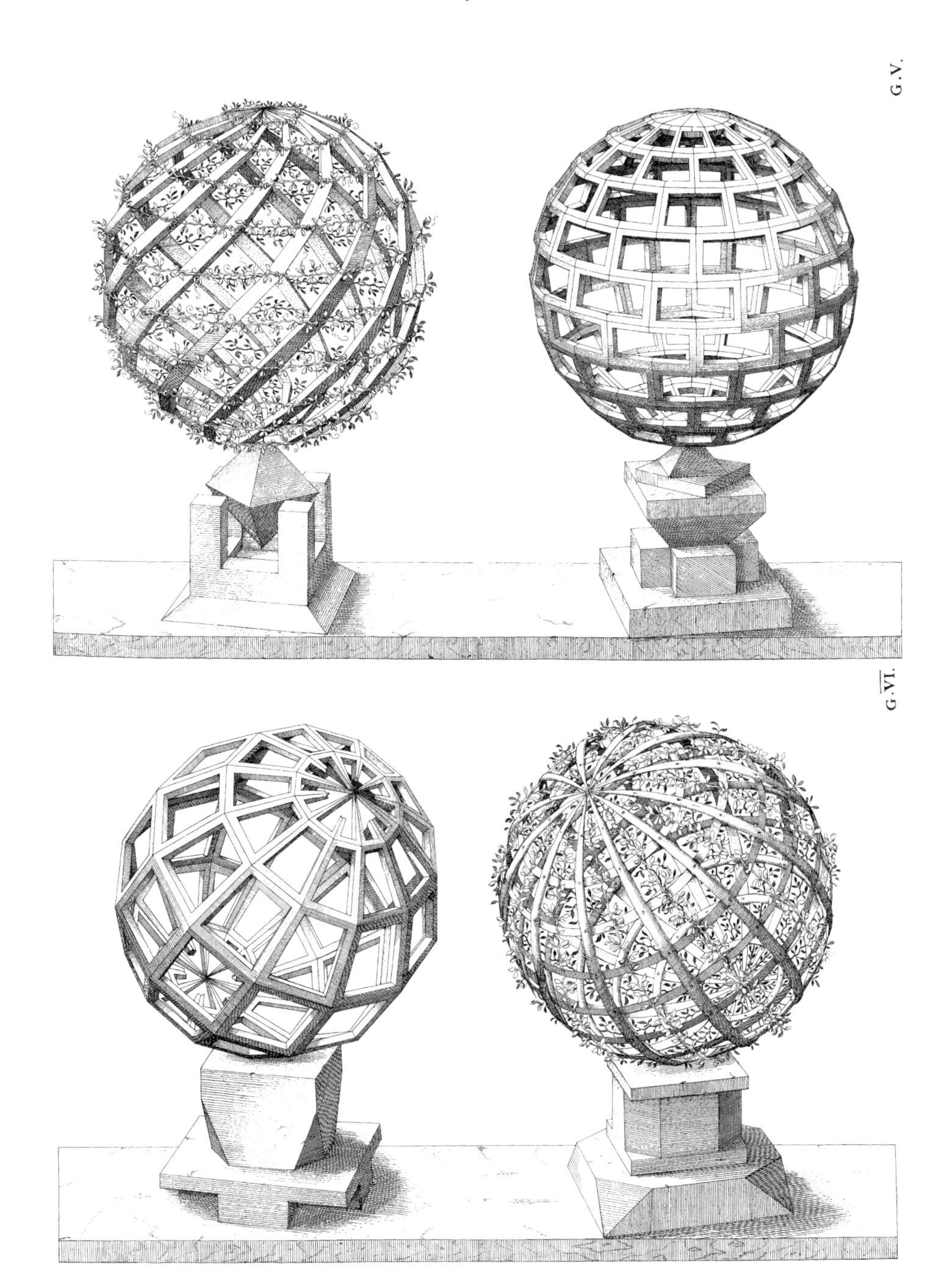

Page G5, spherical variants; page G6, spherical variants;
from Perspectiva Corporum Regularium, *Nuremberg, 1568.*

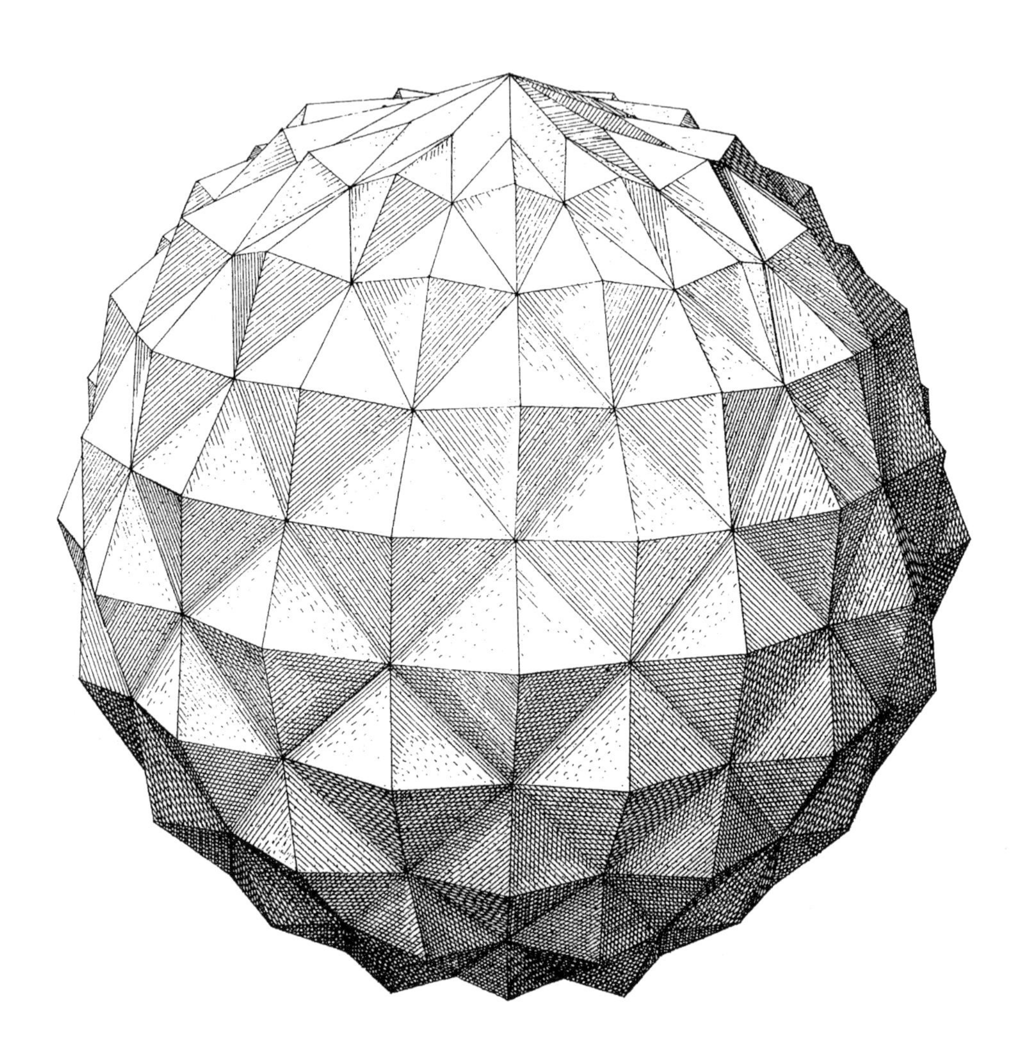

Detail from page G4, Perspectiva Corporum Regularium, *Nuremberg, 1568.*

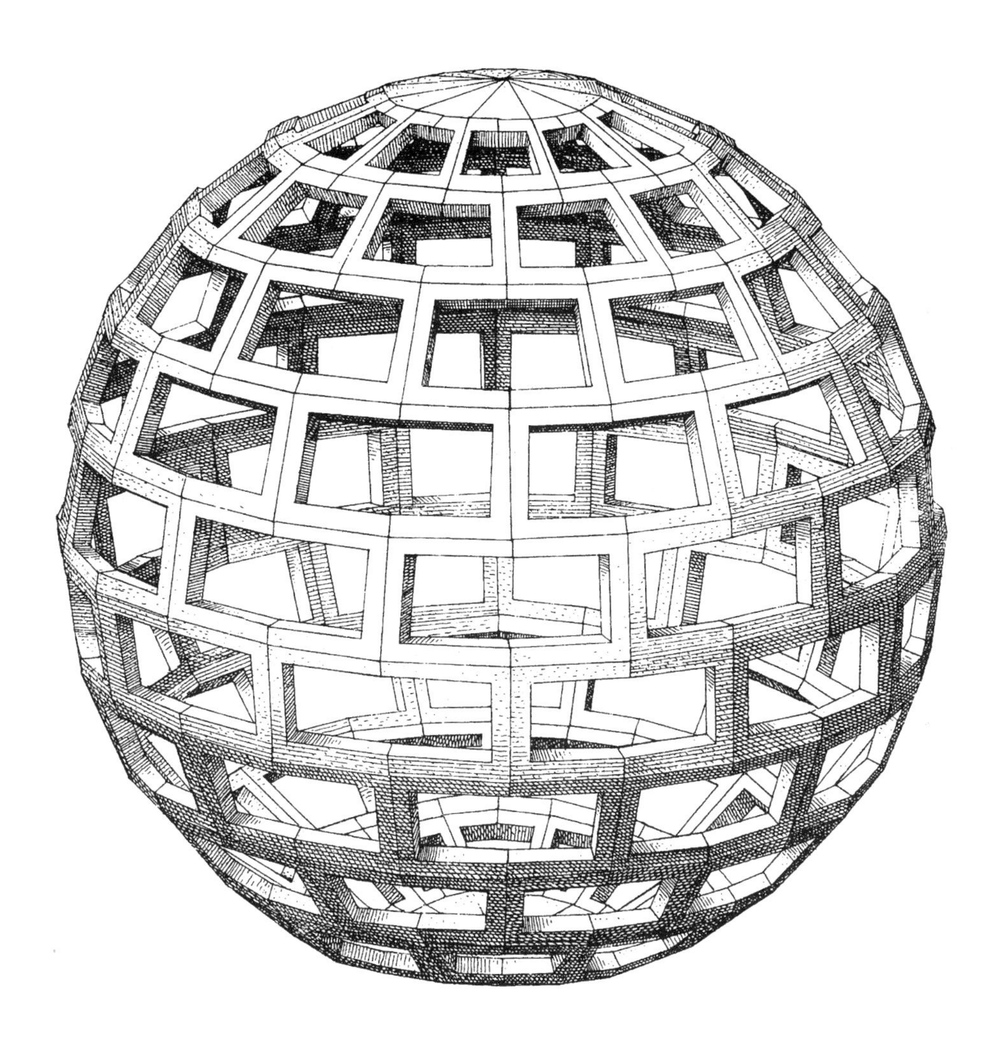

Detail from page G5, Perspectiva Corporum Regularium, *Nuremberg, 1568.*

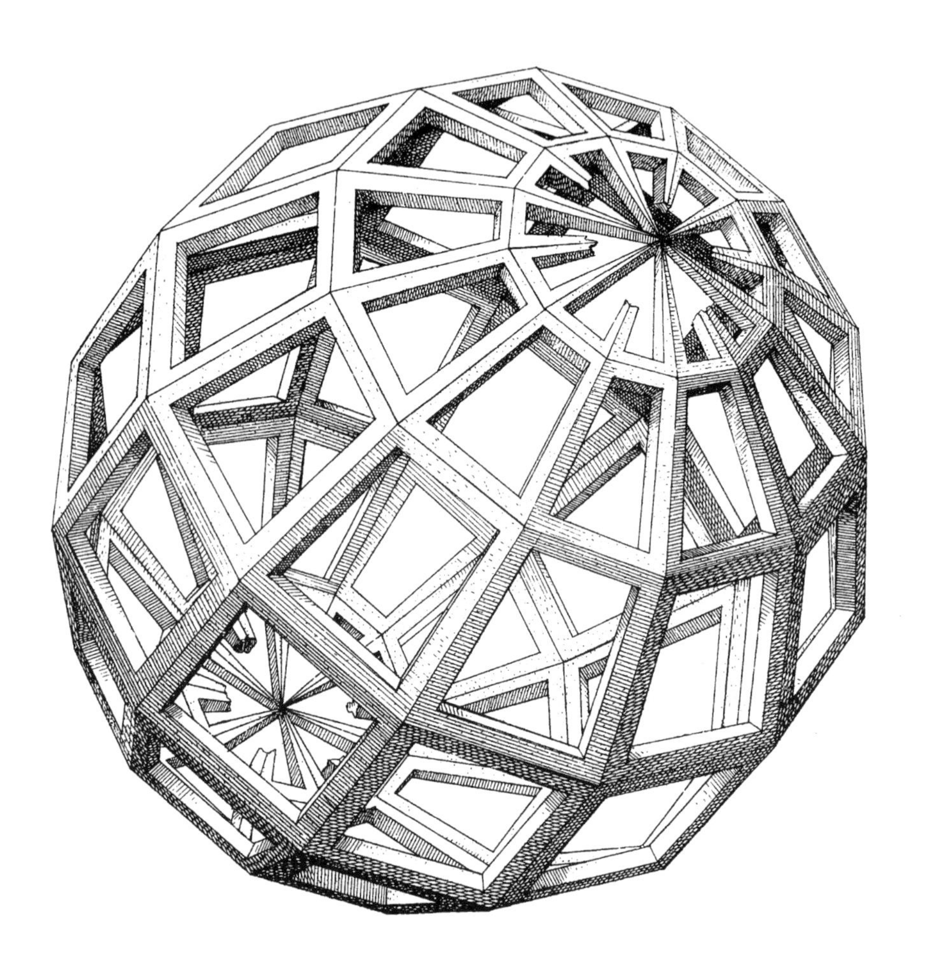

Detail from page G6, Perspectiva Corporum Regularium, *Nuremberg, 1568.*

Detail from page G6, Perspectiva Corporum Regularium*, Nuremberg, 1568.*

Page H1*, conical variants; page* H2*, conical variants;*
from Perspectiva Corporum Regularium*, Nuremberg, 1568.*

Detail from page H1, Perspectiva Corporum Regularium, *Nuremberg, 1568.*

Detail from page H2, Perspectiva Corporum Regularium, *Nuremberg, 1568.*

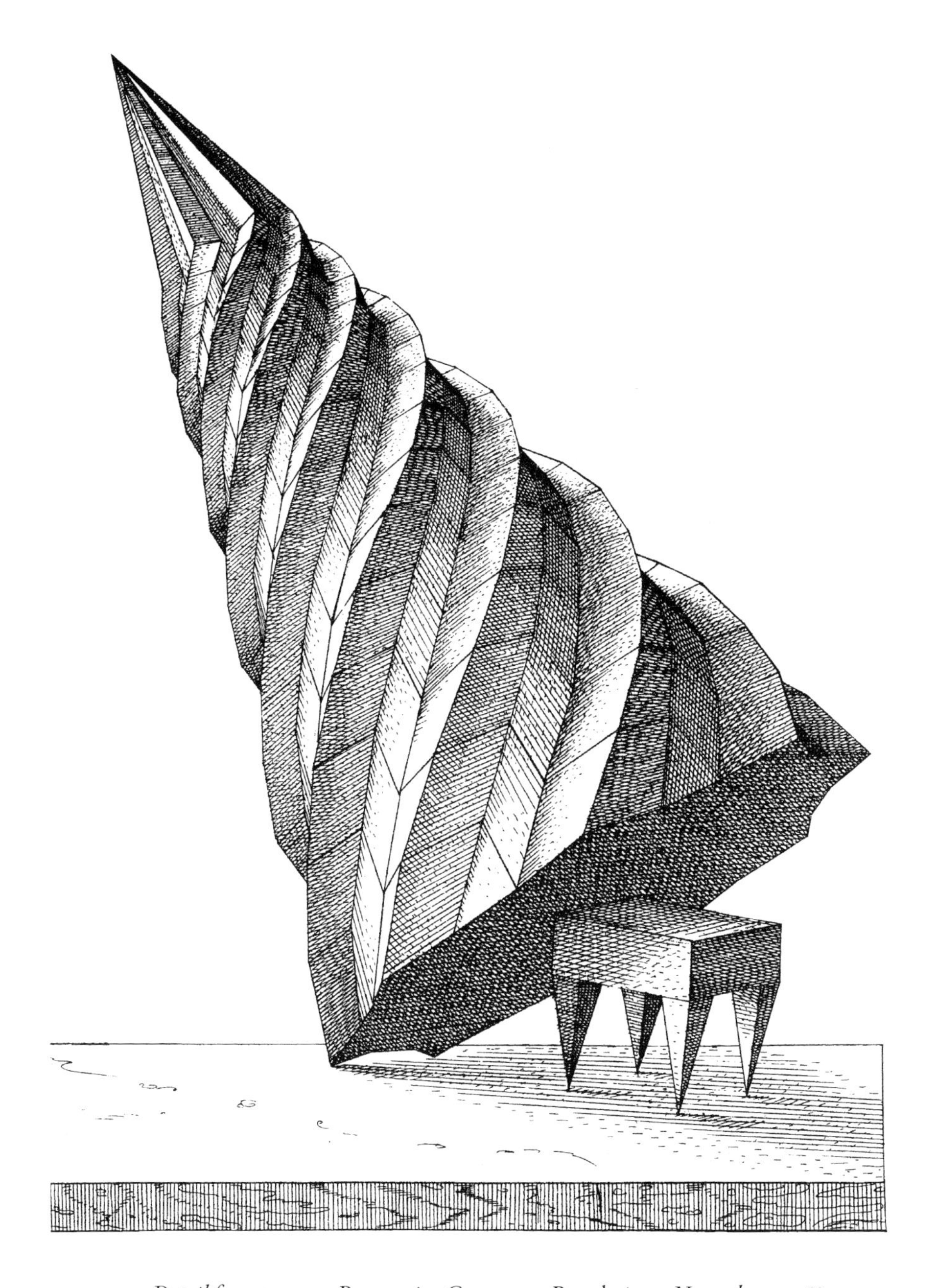

Detail from page H2, Perspectiva Corporum Regularium, *Nuremberg, 1568.*

Page H3, conical variants; page H4, conical variants;
from Perspectiva Corporum Regularium, *Nuremberg, 1568.*

Detail from page H3, Perspectiva Corporum Regularium, *Nuremberg, 1568.*

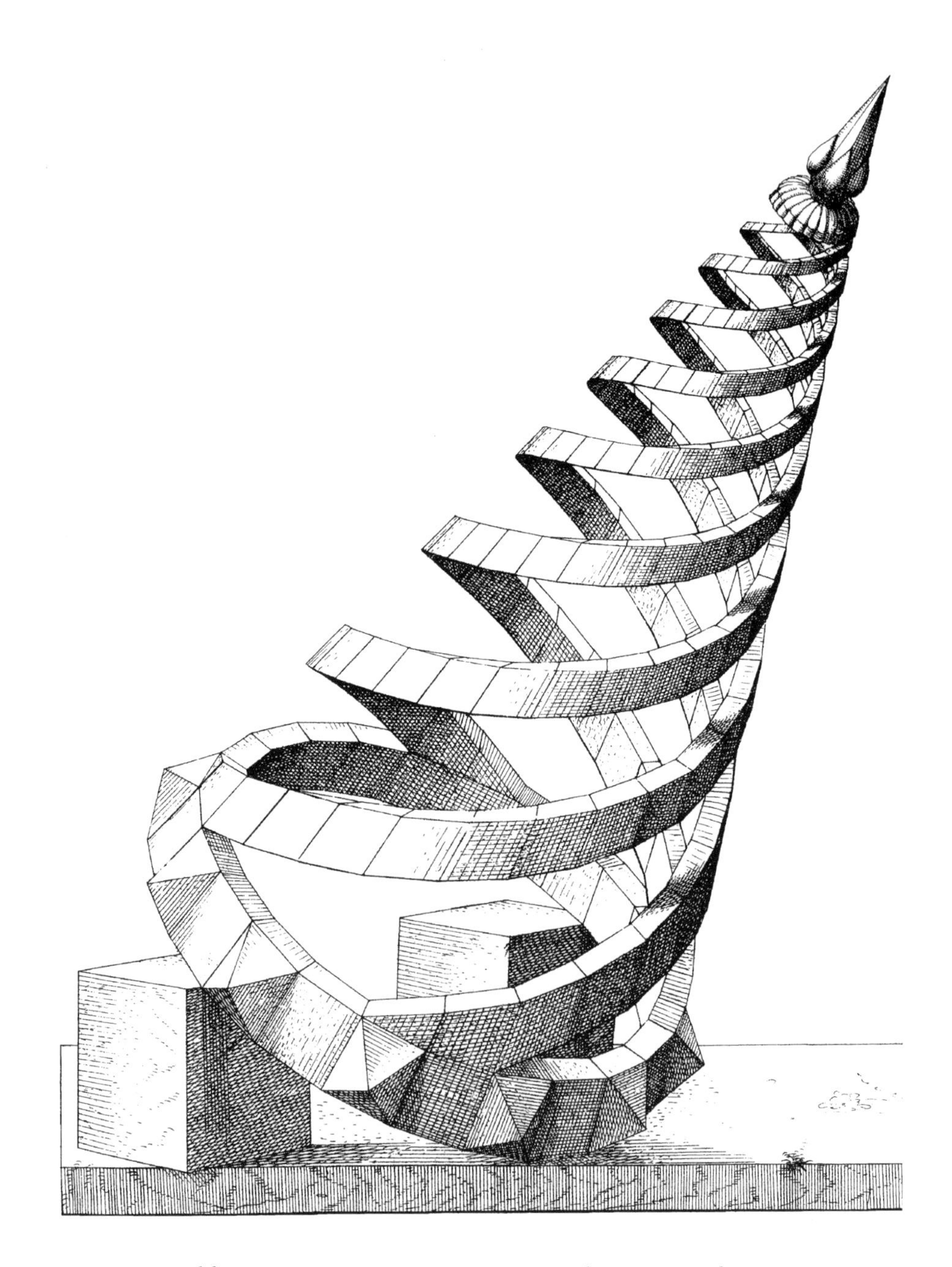

Detail from page H4, Perspectiva Corporum Regularium, *Nuremberg, 1568.*

Detail from page H4, Perspectiva Corporum Regularium, *Nuremberg, 1568.*

Pages 11 and 12, variations on mazzocchio *form;*
from Perspectiva Corporum Regularium, *Nuremberg, 1568.*

Detail from page 11, Perspectiva Corporum Regularium, *Nuremberg, 1568.*

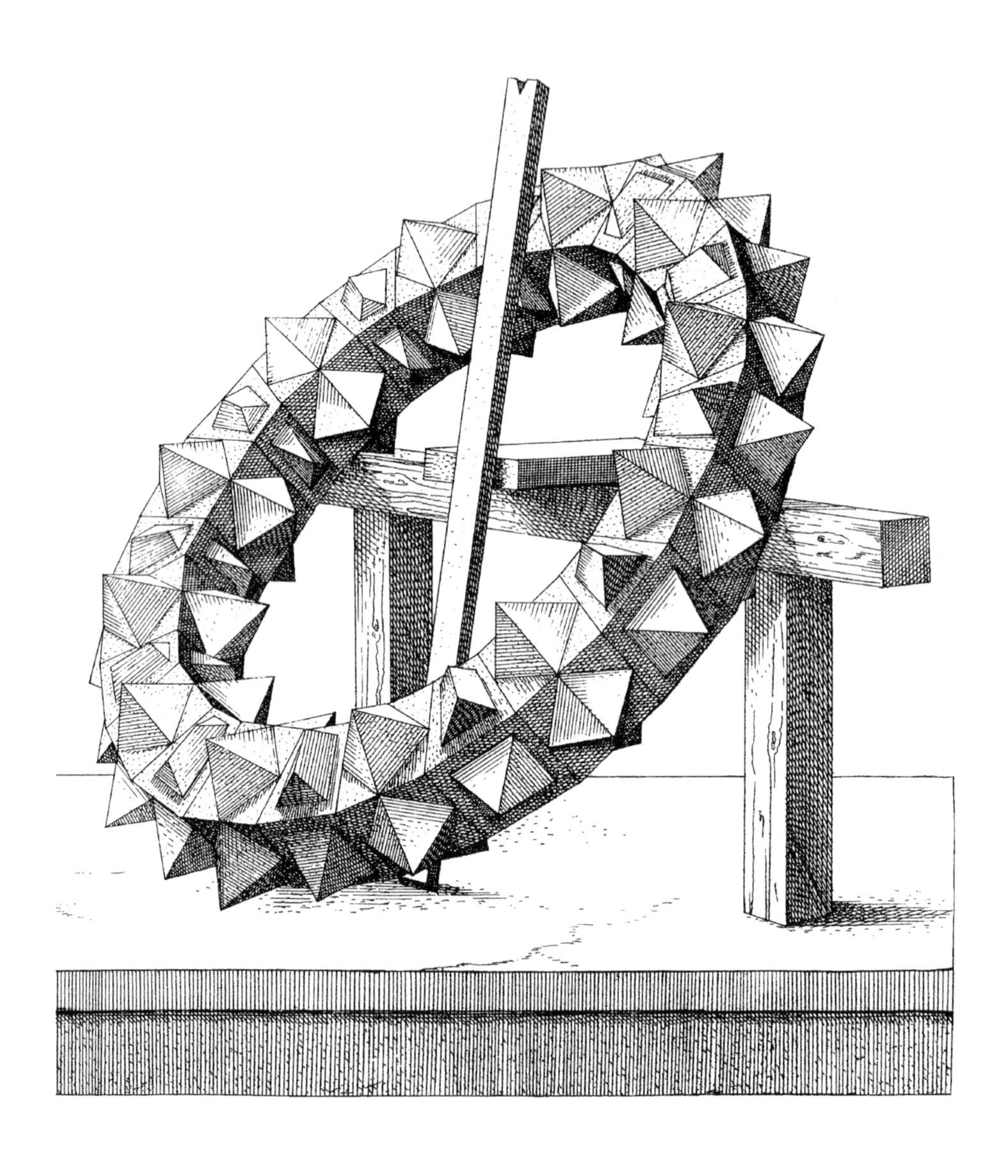

Detail from page 11, Perspectiva Corporum Regularium, *Nuremberg, 1568.*

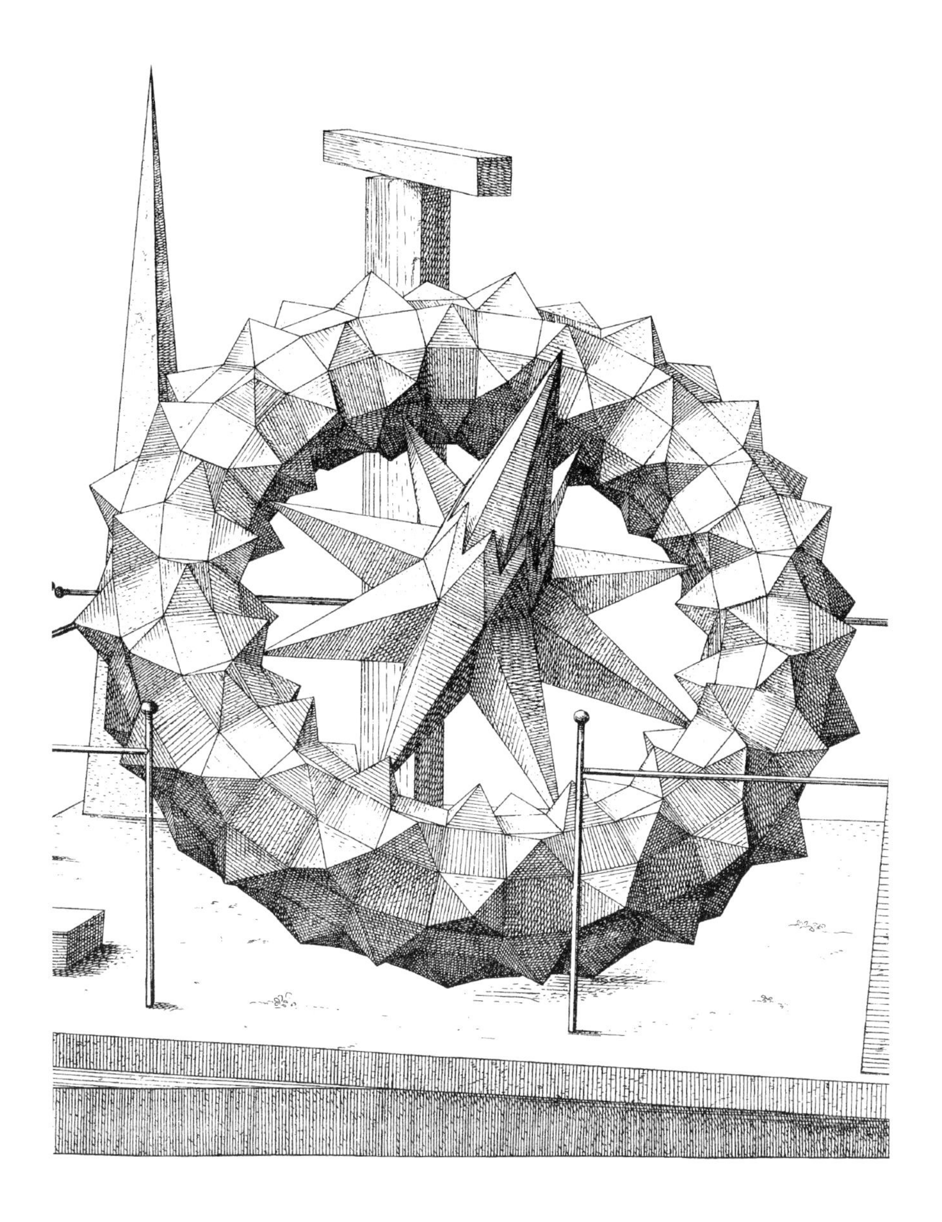

Pages 11 and 12, variations on a mazzocchio *form,*
from Perspectiva Corporum Regularium*, Nuremberg, 1568.*

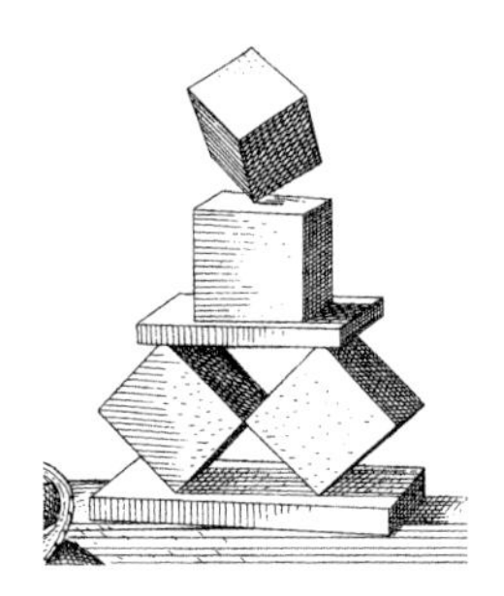
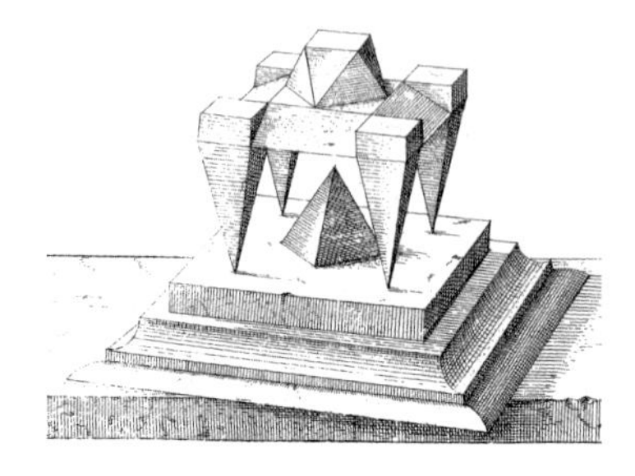
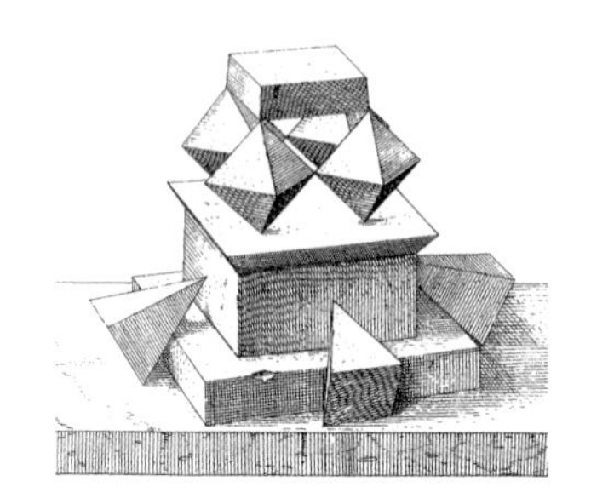
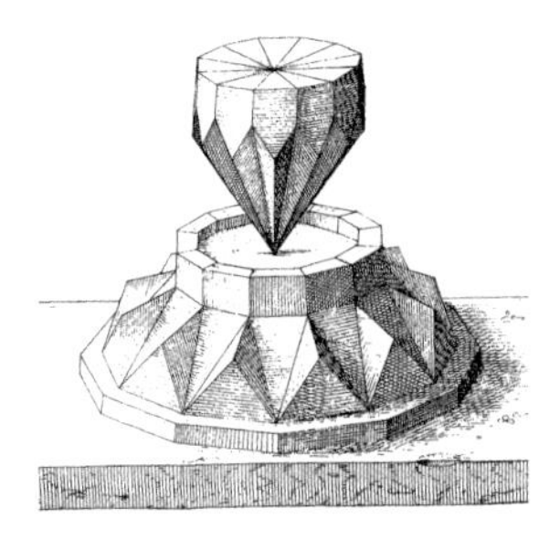
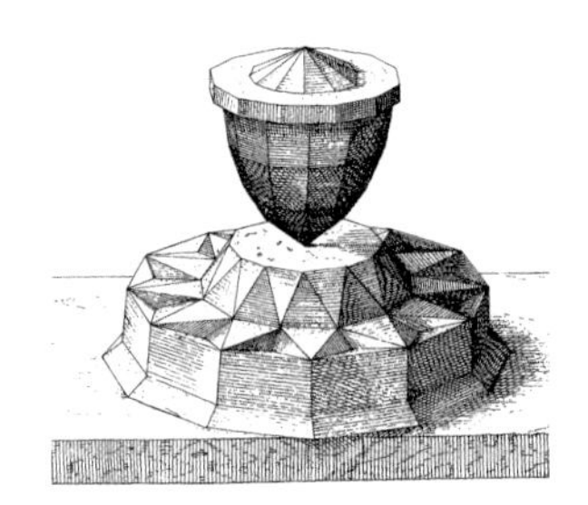
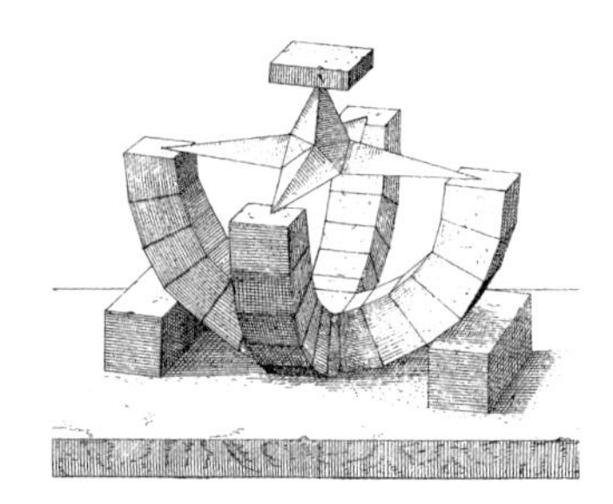

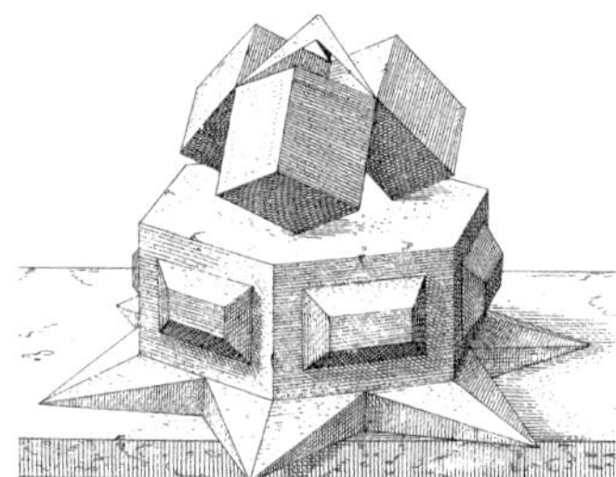
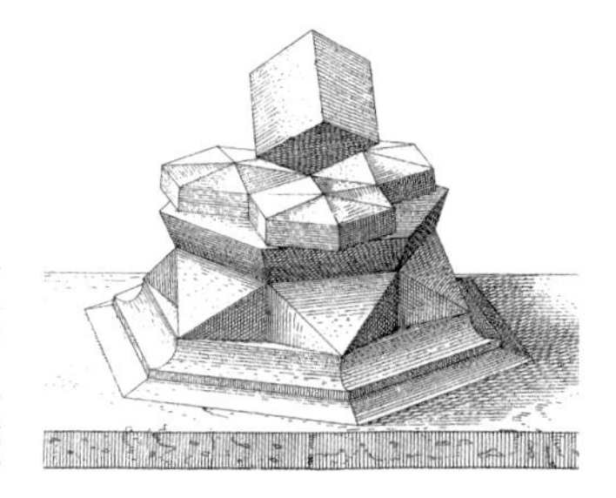

Details of pedestals from the figures in the second part of Perspectiva Corporum Regularium. *These figures reveal Jamnitzer's fascination with stereometric arrangements other than polyhedra. The first assemblage (top left) is taken from Jost Amman's portrait of Jamnitzer (see page 37), which provides a tantalising glimpse of the master's studio and his preoccupations.*

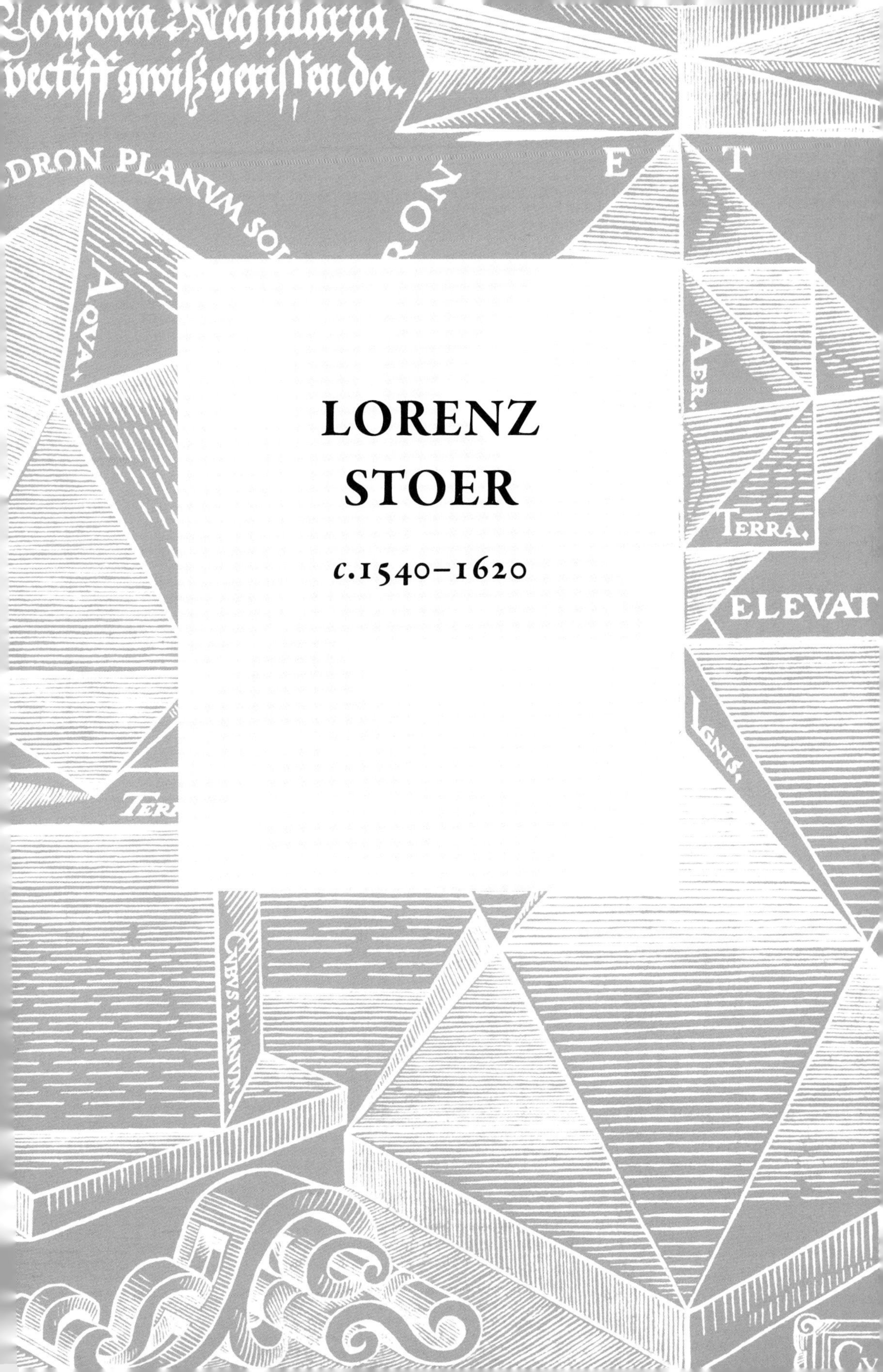

LORENZ STOER

*c.*1540–1620

Lorenz Stoer (*c.*1540–1620)

Geometria et Perspectiva, Nuremberg, 1567
Geometria et Perspectiva: Corpora Regulata et Irregulata, *c.*1562–99

Until relatively recently Lorenz Stoer was known only for the eleven woodcuts shown here. More recently, other drawings have come to light, including a folio of 336 delicate watercolours in the University Library in Munich that, according to the dates on some of them, seem to have been put together over a period of thirty years or more. Very little is known of this artist–craftsman's life other than that he was born and spent much of his early life in Nuremberg. No text accompanies the woodcut prints in the slender volume in which they appear, and no explanation has survived that might throw light on his general fascination with regular geometric figures.

Stoer's woodcuts in *Geometria et Perspectiva* consist of various fanciful combinations of regular and irregular figures, set in a somewhat haunted, ruined landscape. In the subtitle to this short book Stoer suggests that these drawings may be useful to cabinet-makers for *intarsia* (marquetry) decoration and to 'amateurs'. He later moved to Augsberg, a centre that specialised in this craft, which rather confirms this idea, but no direct adaptations of his work in this medium have survived, and his drawings are of rather higher quality than existing examples of inlaid panels. There is some evidence that printed drawings were used for this purpose at the time, but it is uncertain whether Stoer's designs were ever taken up.

Despite the titles of his book and folio manuscript, there is no attempt in either to teach perspective, in fact the perspective that he uses is not particular convincing. It seems clear though that Stoer's underlying motivation is the same as Dürer's before him, namely to elevate the standing of the arts and crafts (and the artists and craftsmen's social standing) through the adoption of mathematical and philosophical concepts.

Whatever else was happening in his life, Stoer continued with his depiction of geometric figures over a period of forty years. His persistence is both a tribute to his own dedication and to the enduring fascination of this genre.

Figure 1 from Geometria et Perspectiva, *Nuremberg, 1567.*

Figure 2 from Geometria et Perspectiva. *Nuremberg, 1567.*

Figure 3 from Geometria et Perspectiva, *Nuremberg, 1567.*

Figure 4 from Geometria et Perspectiva, *Nuremberg, 1567.*

Figure 5 from Geometria et Perspectiva, *Nuremberg, 1567.*

Figure 6 from Geometria et Perspectiva, *Nuremberg, 1567.*

Figure 7 from Geometria et Perspectiva, *Nuremberg, 1567.*

Figure 8 from Geometria et Perspectiva, *Nuremberg, 1567.*

Figure 9 from Geometria et Perspectiva, *Nuremberg, 1567.*

Figure 10 from Geometria et Perspectiva, *Nuremberg, 1567.*

Figure 11 from Geometria et Perspectiva, *Nuremberg, 1567.*

The title page of Lorenz Stoer's Geometria et Perspectiva, *Nuremberg, 1567. The subtitle indicates that these 'diverse designs of ruined buildings' might be useful to* intarsia *workers, and to amateurs. In the original the oval band is printed in light brown and contains the enigmatic epigram 'Who would do right by everyone? No one would even try'.*

From Geometria et Perspectiva: Corpora Regulata et Irregulata
(courtesy Harald Fischer Verlag, 2006).

Detail from opposite top left, Geometria et Perspectiva: Corpora Regulata et Irregulata *(courtesy Harald Fischer Verlag, 2006).*

From Geometria et Perspectiva: Corpora Regulata et Irregulata
(courtesy Harald Fischer Verlag, 2006).

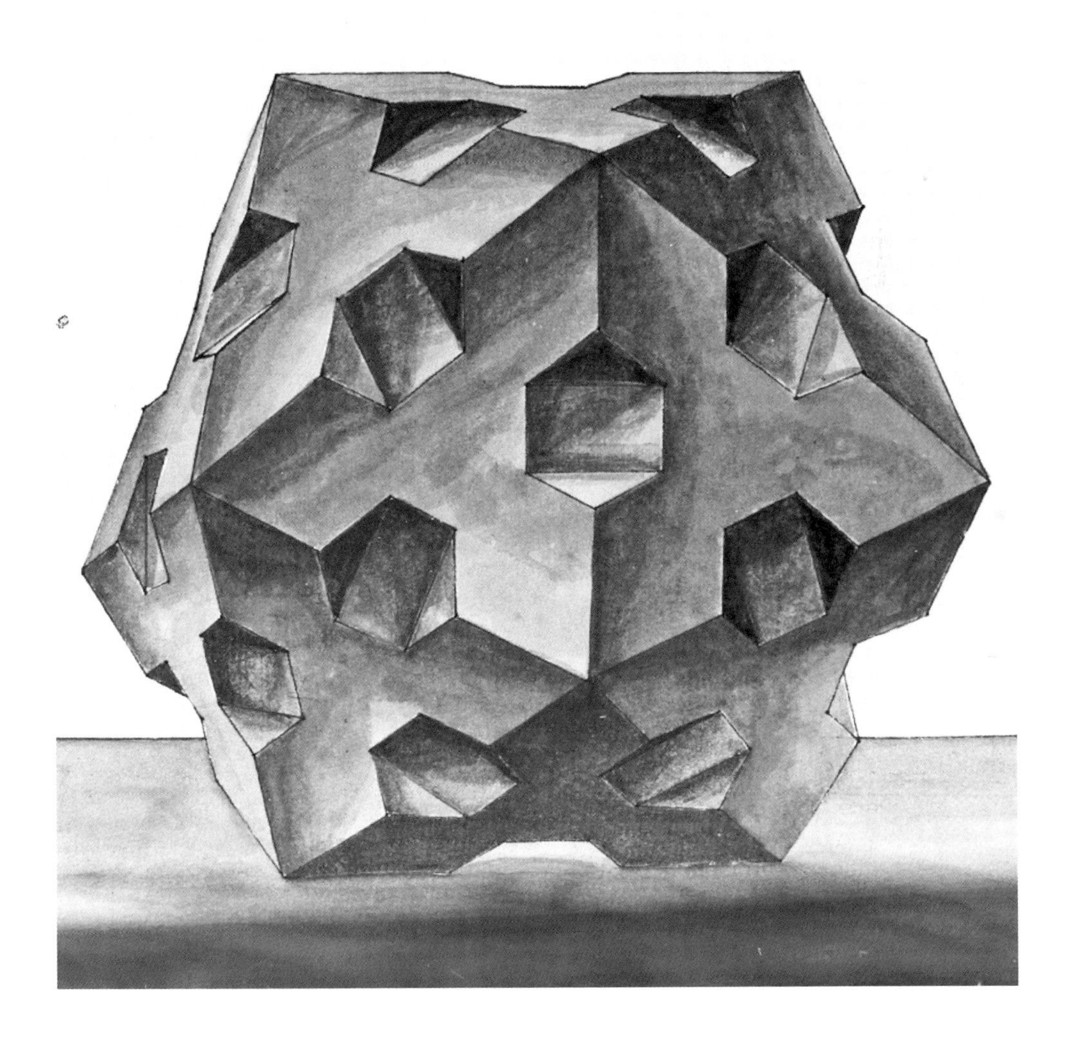

Detail from opposite top left, Geometria et Perspectiva: Corpora Regulata et Irregulata *(courtesy Harald Fischer Verlag, 2006).*

From Geometria et Perspectiva: Corpora Regulata et Irregulata
(courtesy Harald Fischer Verlag, 2006).

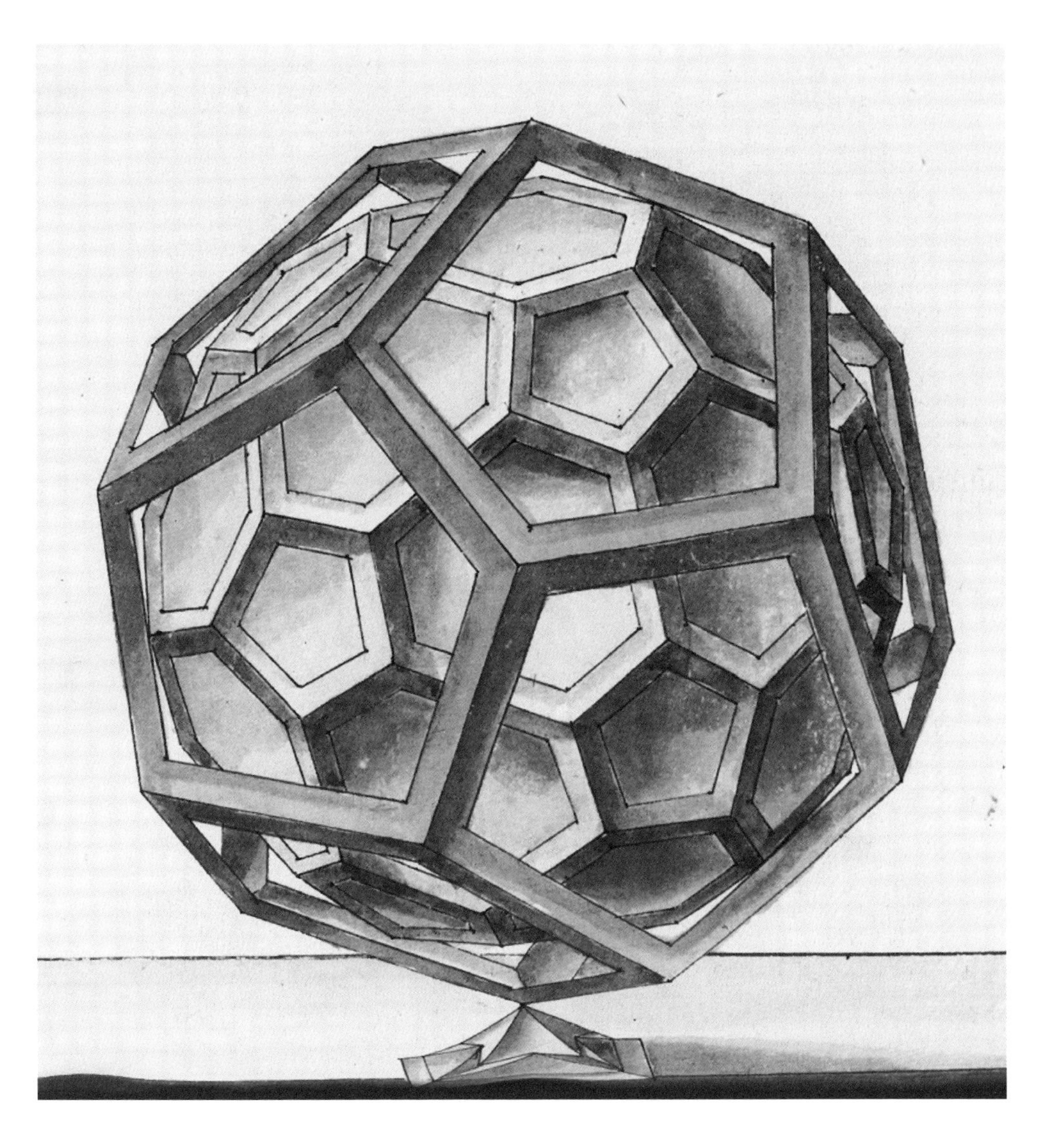

Detail from opposite top right, Geometria et Perspectiva: Corpora Regulata et Irregulata *(courtesy Harald Fischer Verlag, 2006).*

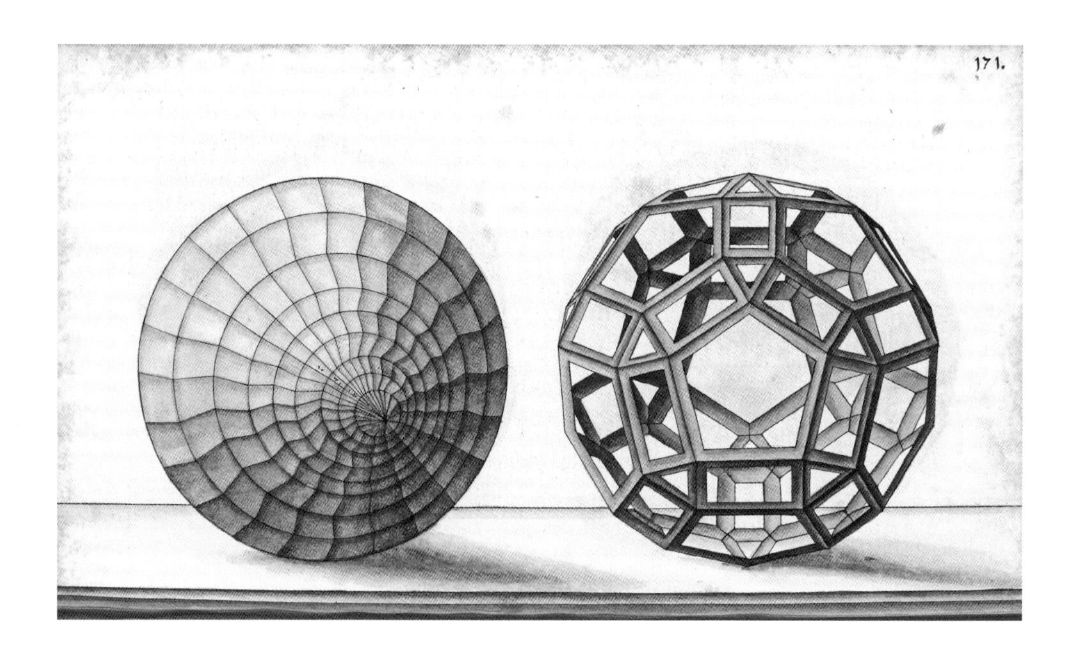

From Geometria et Perspectiva: Corpora Regulata et Irregulata
(courtesy Harald Fischer Verlag, 2006).

Detail from opposite top right, Geometria et Perspectiva: Corpora Regulata et Irregulata *(courtesy Harald Fischer Verlag, 2006).*

From Geometria et Perspectiva: Corpora Regulata et Irregulata
(courtesy Harald Fischer Verlag, 2006).

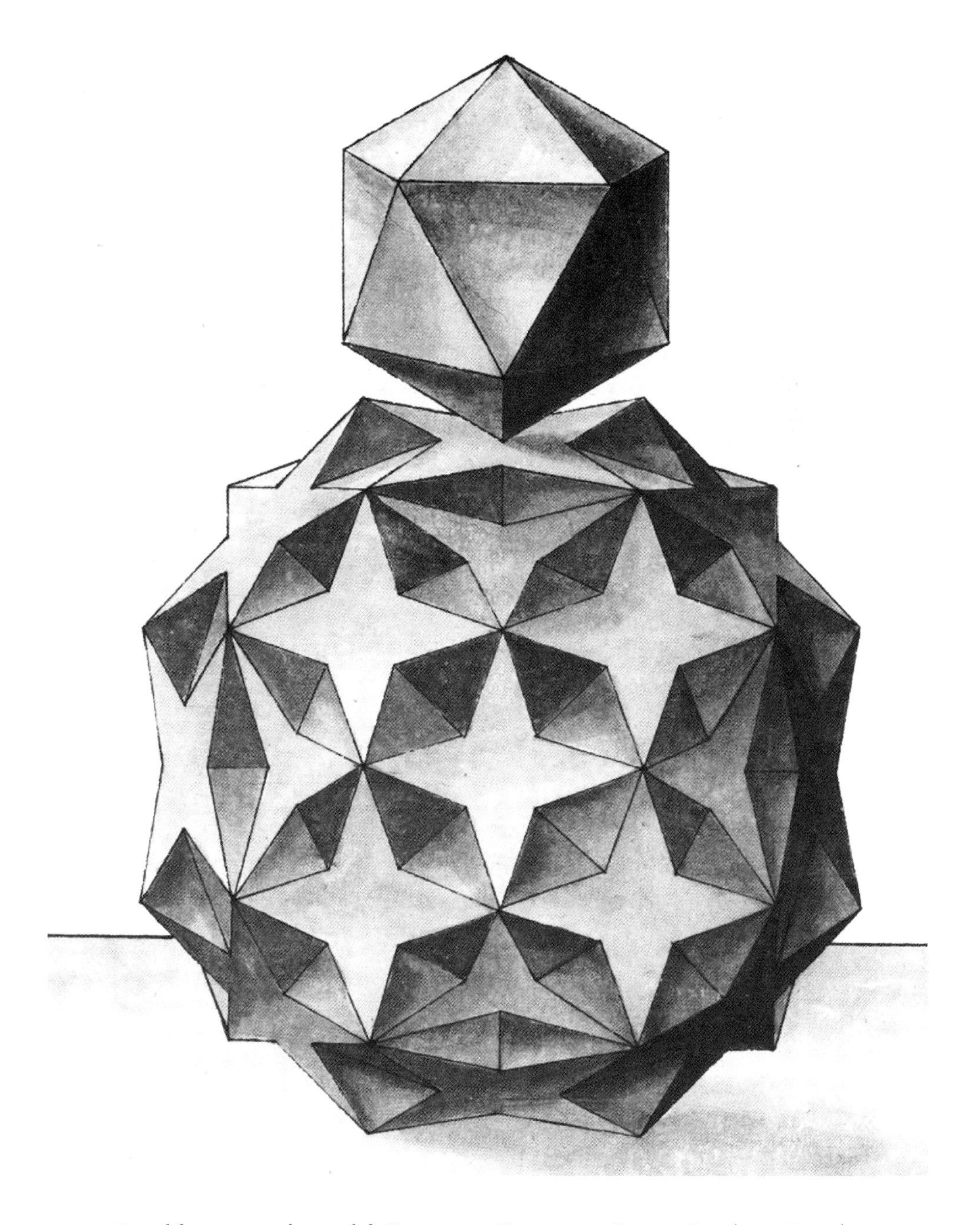

Detail from opposite bottom left, Geometria et Perspectiva: Corpora Regulata et Irregulata *(courtesy Harald Fischer Verlag, 2006).*

From Geometria et Perspectiva: Corpora Regulata et Irregulata
(courtesy Harald Fischer Verlag, 2006).

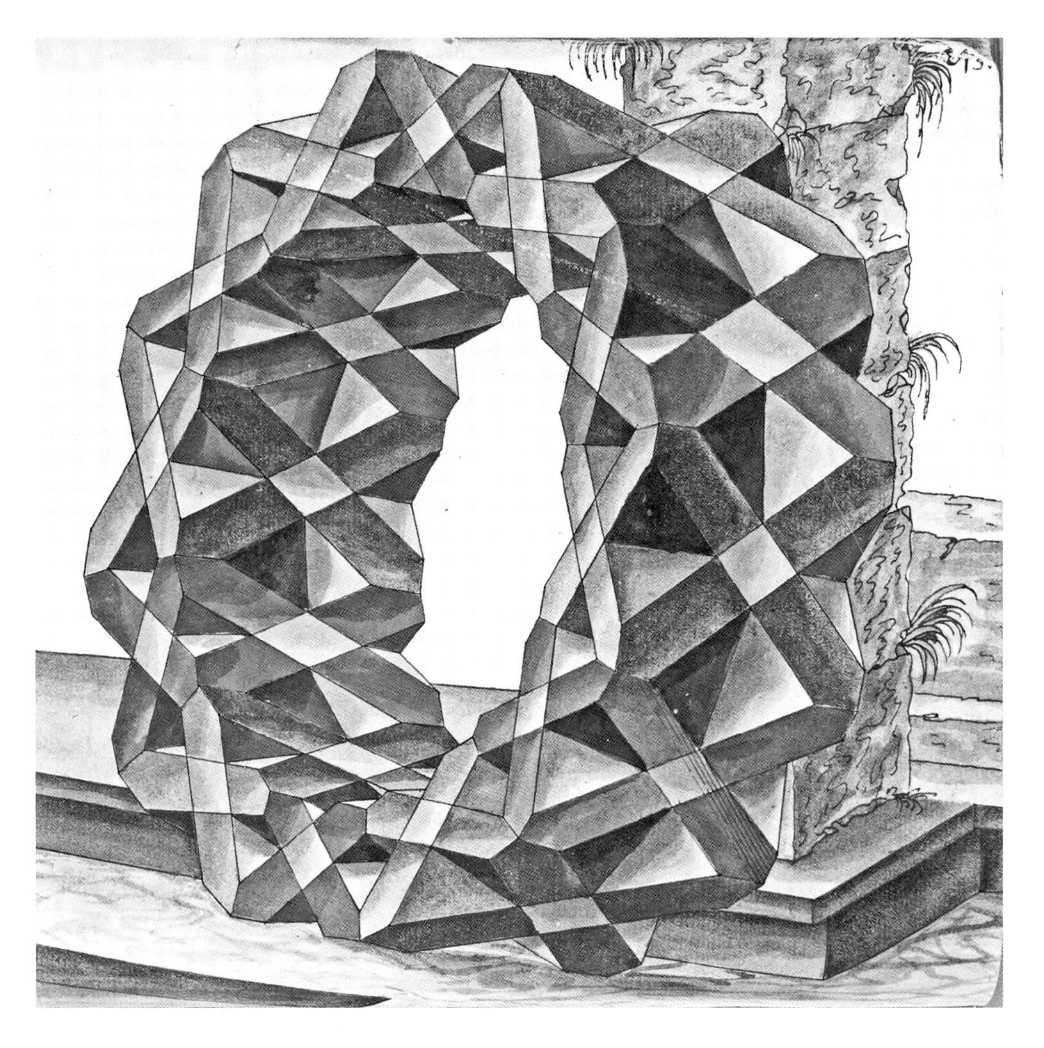

From Geometria et Perspectiva: Corpora Regulata et Irregulata
(courtesy Harald Fischer Verlag, 2006).

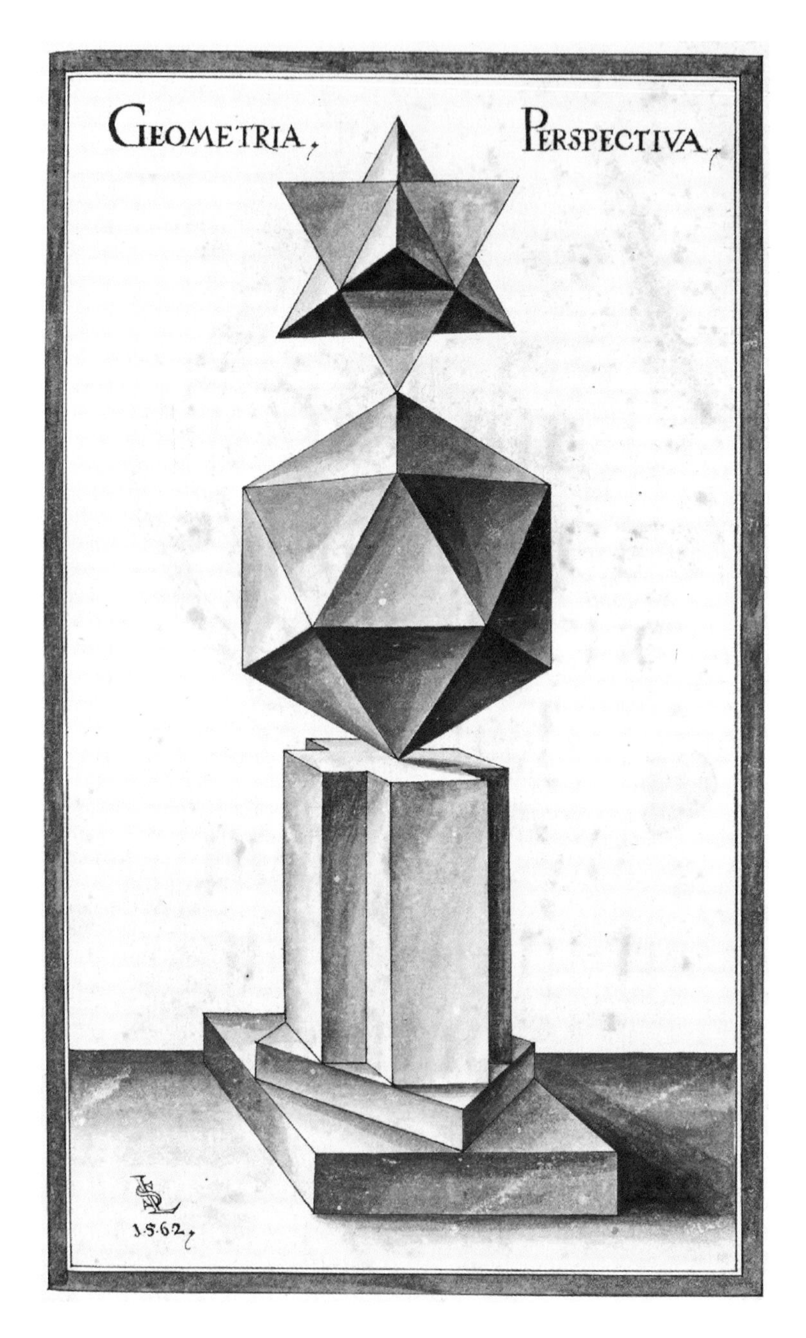

From Geometria et Perspectiva: Corpora Regulata et Irregulata *(courtesy Harald Fischer Verlag, 2006).*

From Geometria et Perspectiva: Corpora Regulata et Irregulata *(courtesy Harald Fischer Verlag, 2006).*

From Geometria et Perspectiva: Corpora Regulata et Irregulata *(courtesy Harald Fischer Verlag, 2006).*

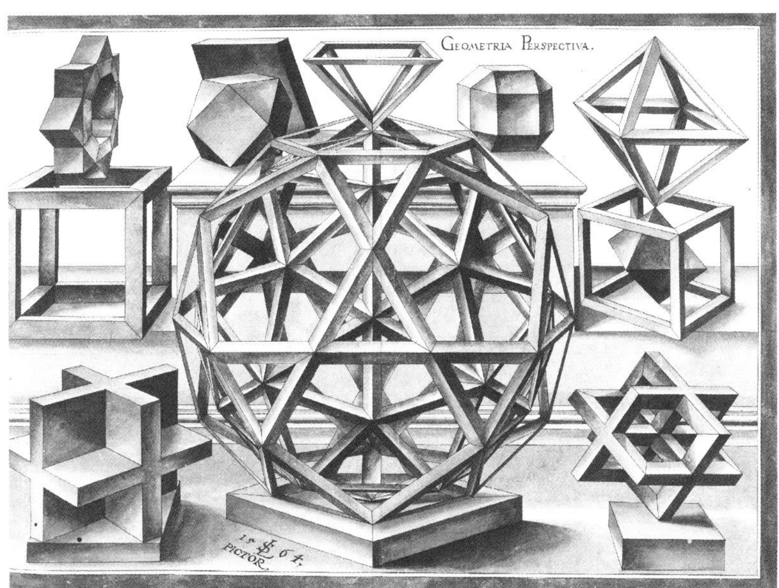

From Geometria et Perspectiva: Corpora Regulata et Irregulata
(courtesy Harald Fischer Verlag, 2006).

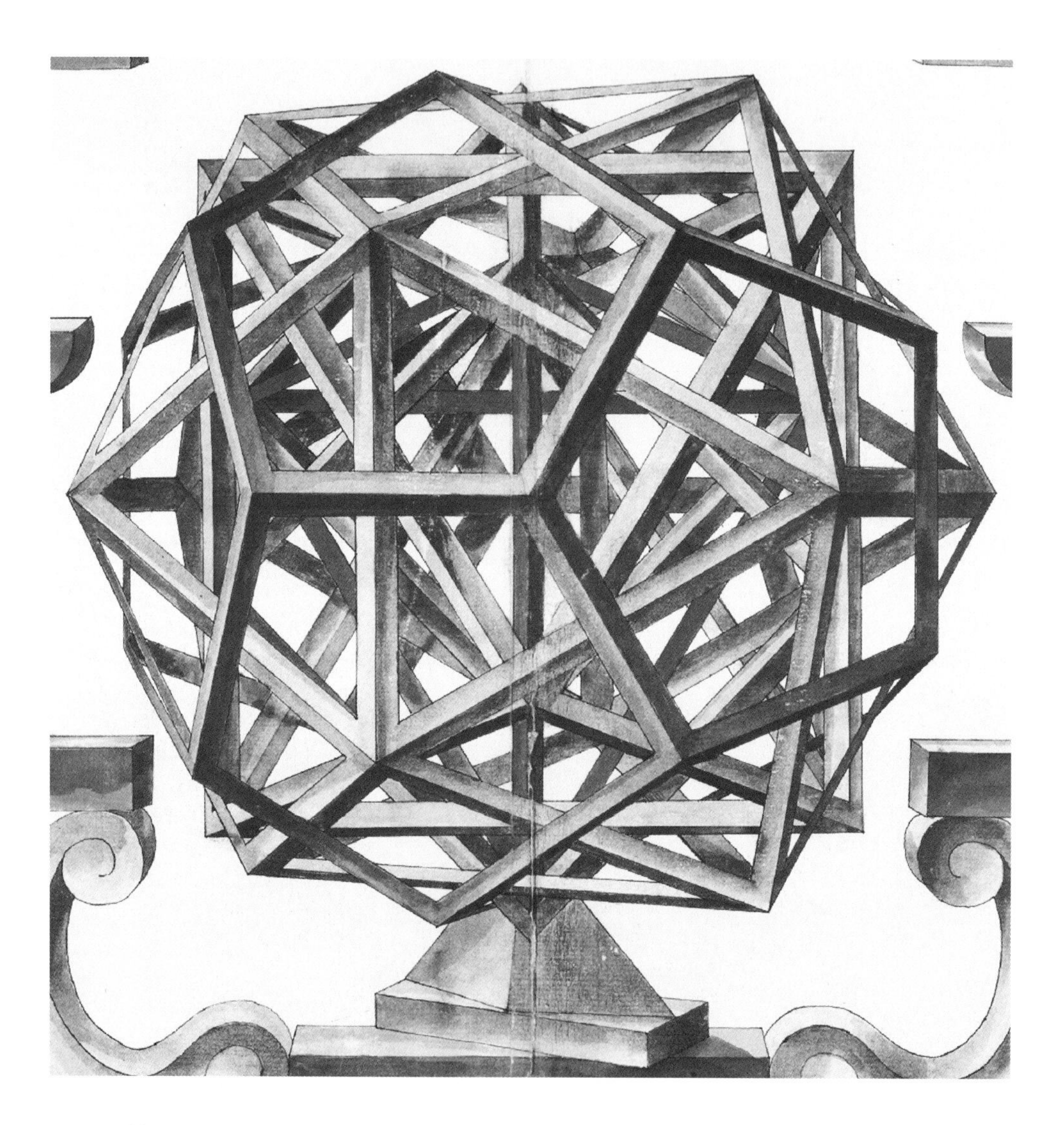

Detail from previous right-hand page top, Geometria et Perspectiva: Corpora Regulata et Irregulata *(courtesy Harald Fischer Verlag, 2006).*

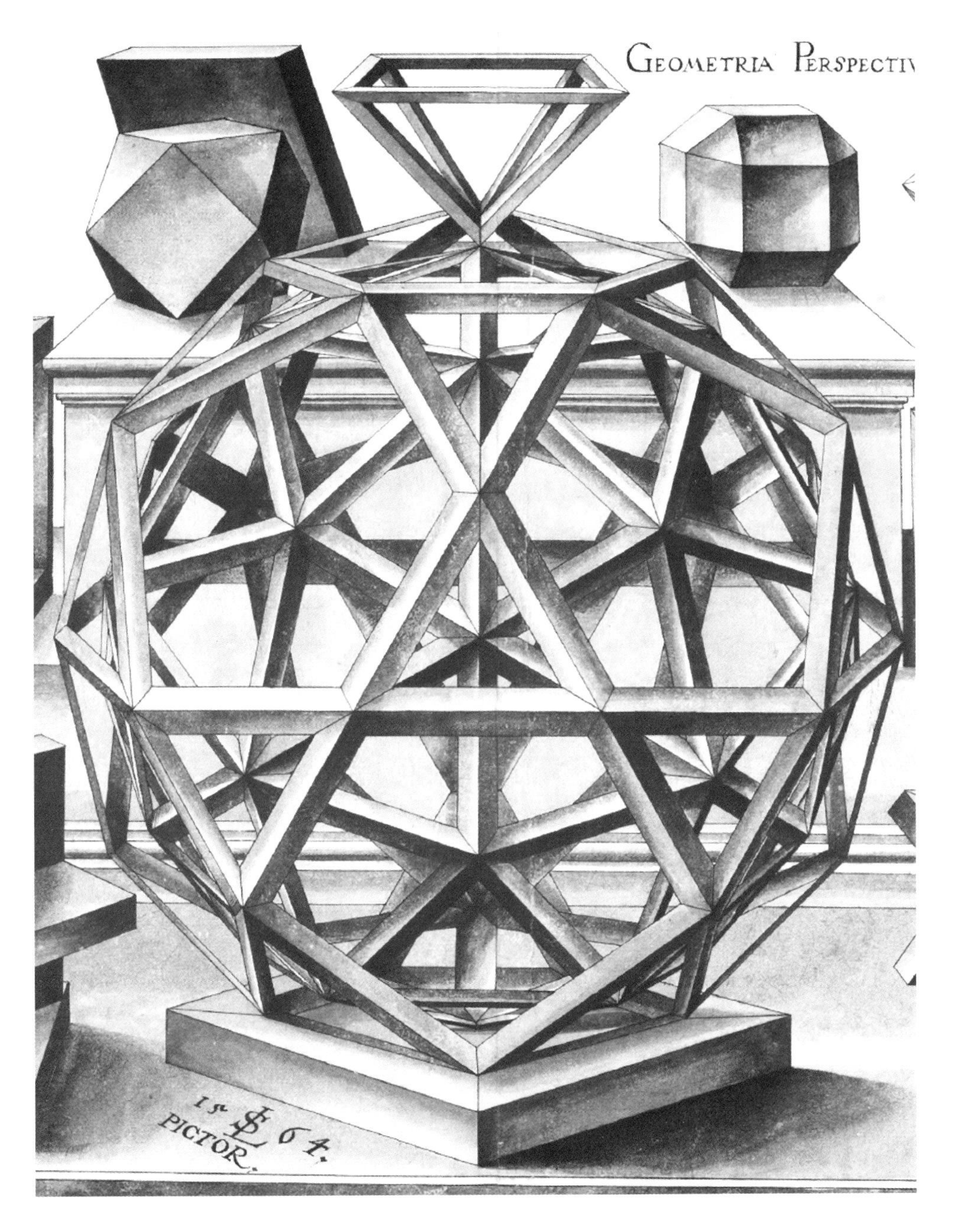

Detail from previous right-hand page bottom, Geometria et Perspectiva: Corpora Regulata et Irregulata *(courtesy Harald Fischer Verlag, 2006).*

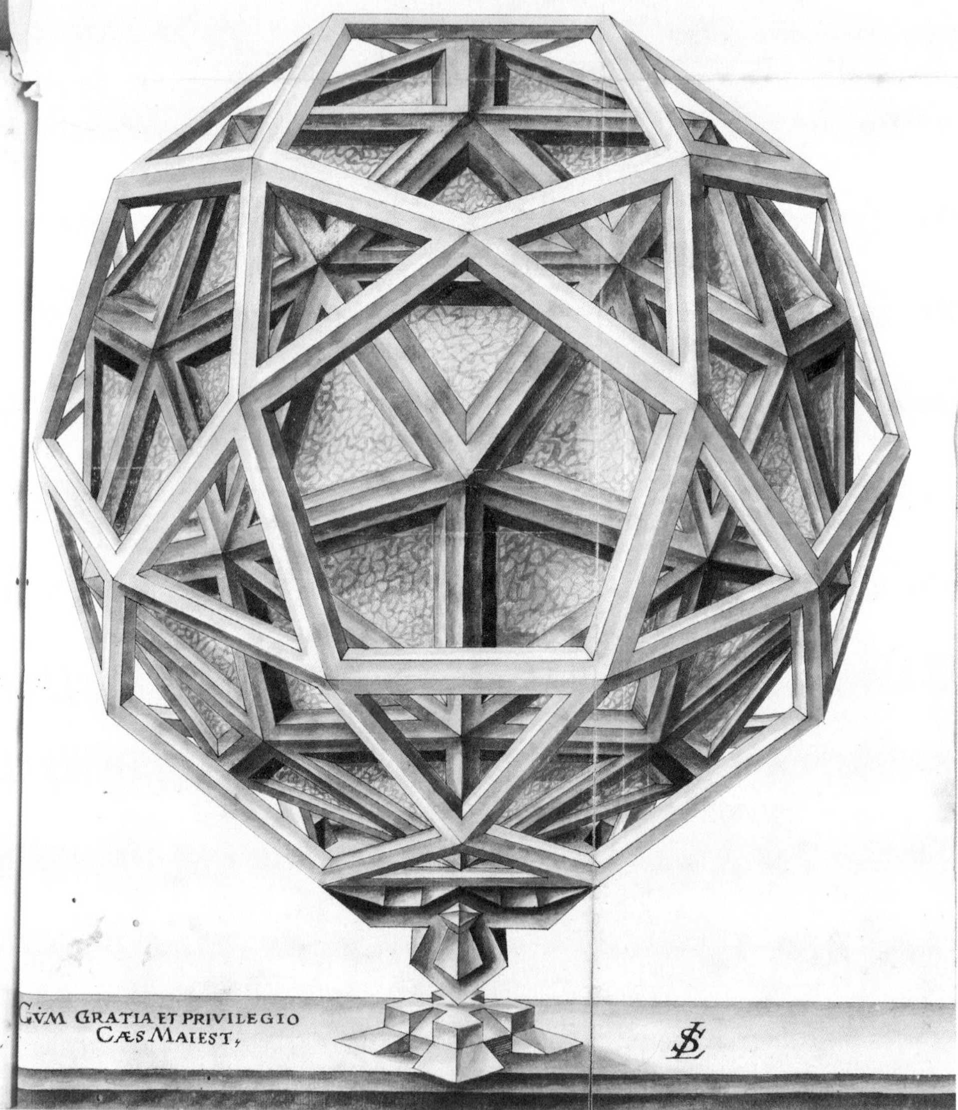

From Geometria et Perspectiva: Corpora Regulata et Irregulata
(courtesy Harald Fischer Verlag, 2006).

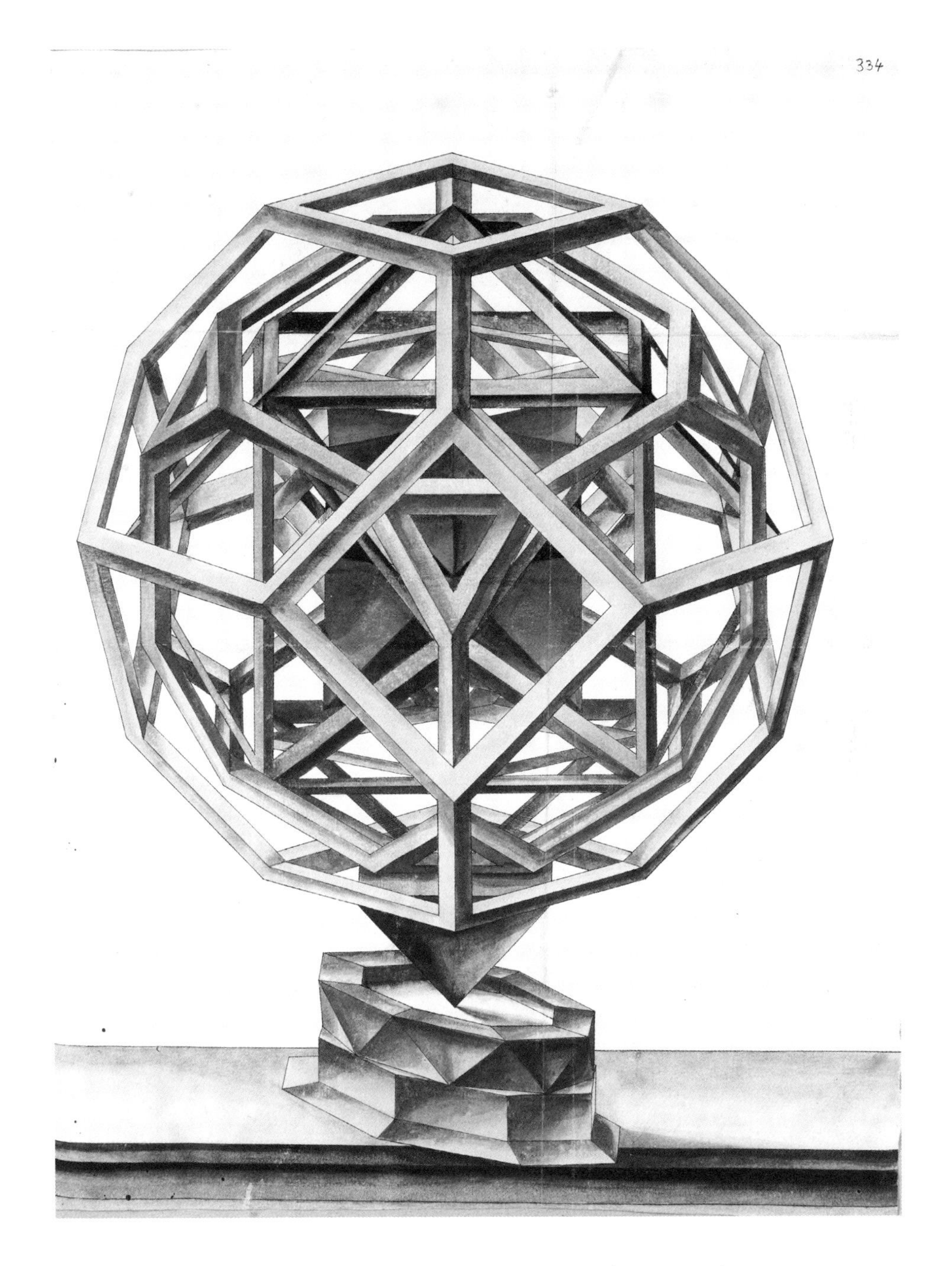

From Geometria et Perspectiva: Corpora Regulata et Irregulata
(courtesy Harald Fischer Verlag, 2006).

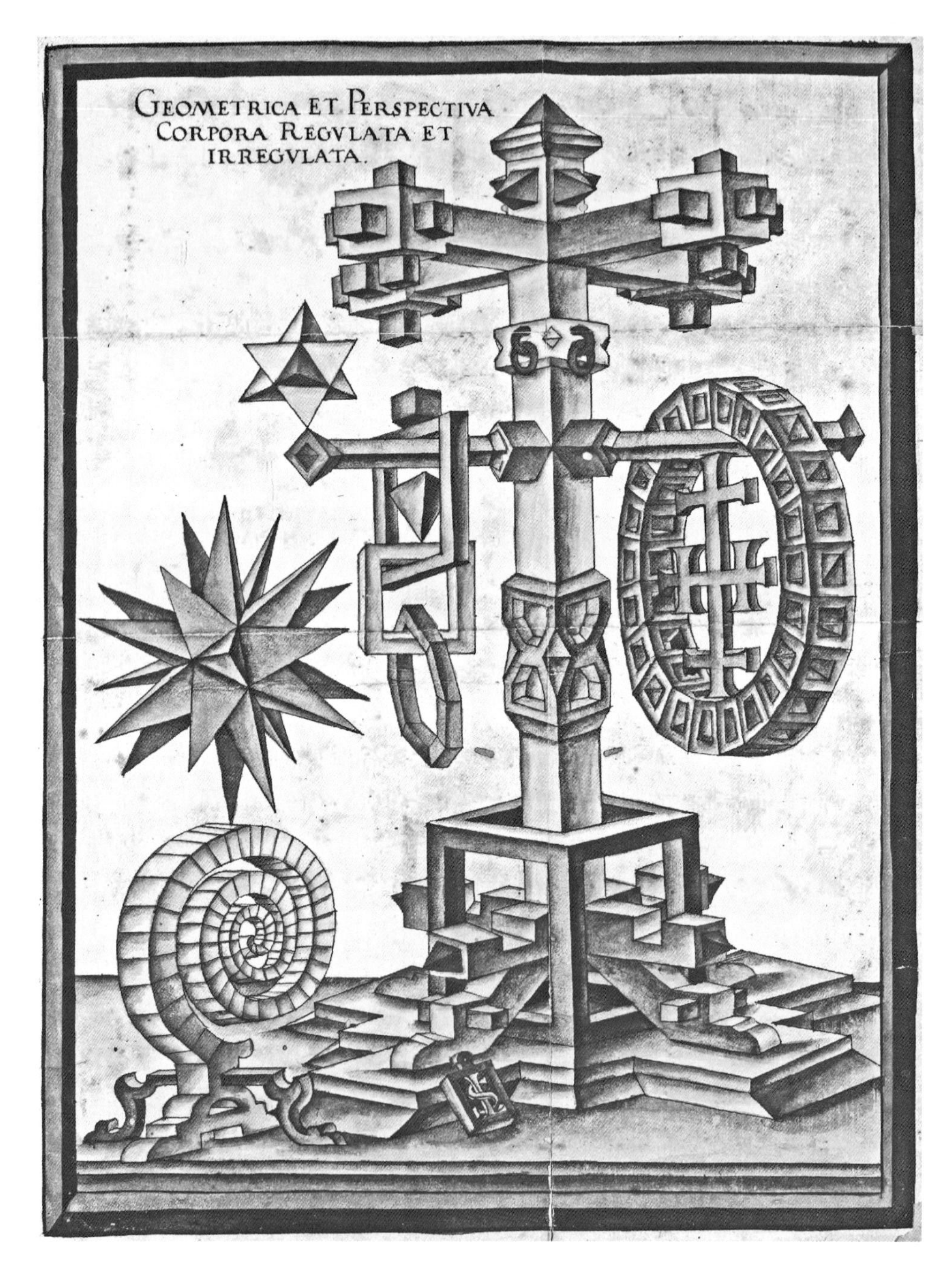

From Geometria et Perspectiva: Corpora Regulata et Irregulata *(courtesy Harald Fischer Verlag, 2006).*

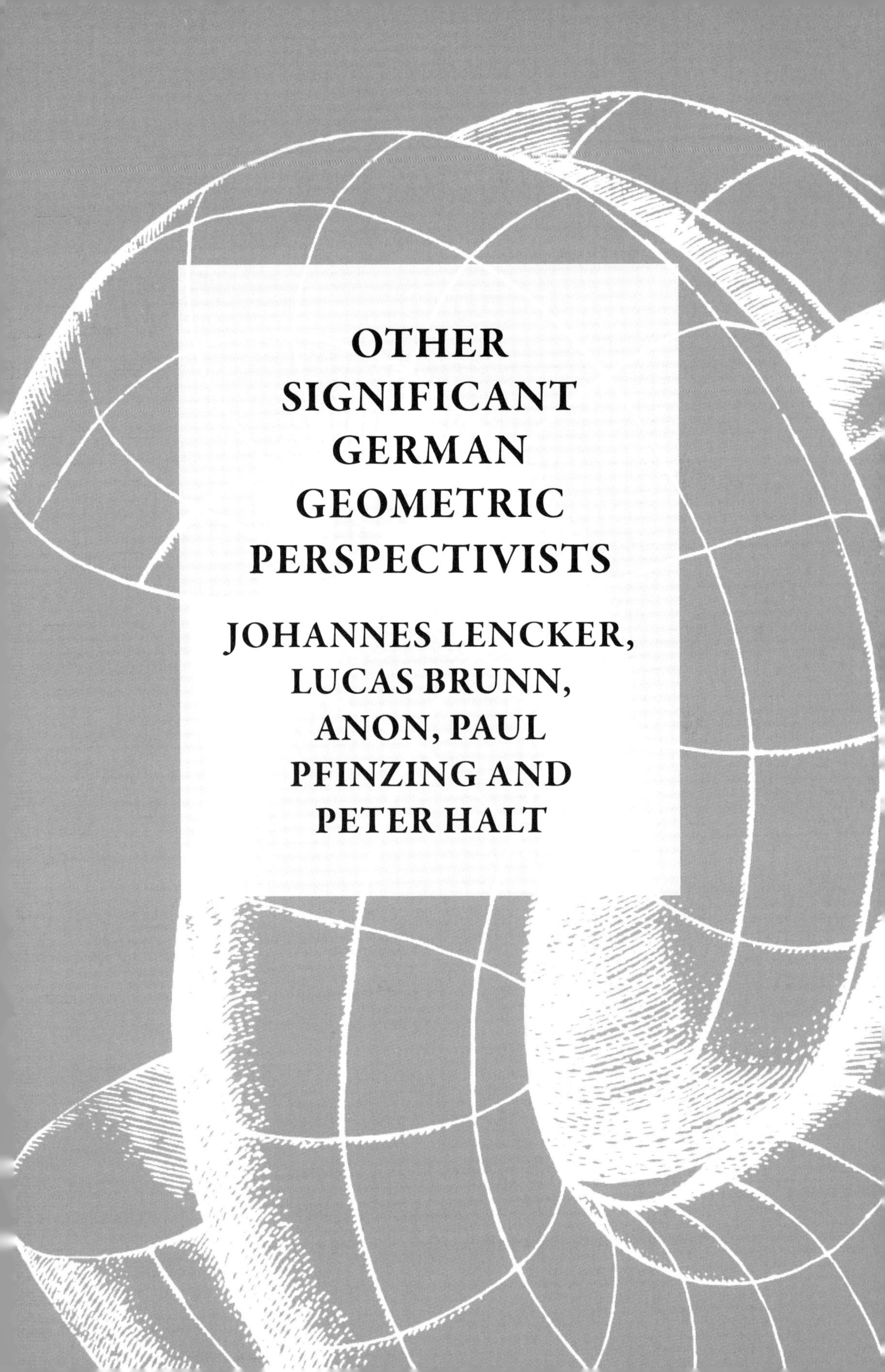

OTHER SIGNIFICANT GERMAN GEOMETRIC PERSPECTIVISTS

JOHANNES LENCKER, LUCAS BRUNN, ANON, PAUL PFINZING AND PETER HALT

Other significant German geometric perspectivists

Johannes Lencker (*c.*1551–85)

Perspectiva Literaria, Nuremberg, 1567
Perspectiva, Nuremberg, 1571

Consisting as it does of the letters of the entire alphabet in various perspectival postures, Lencker's *Perspectiva Literaria* must rank as one of the more curious examples of the geometric perspective genre, but it also has several interesting semi-regular forms that are relevant to this study of geometric fantasy. Lencker's use of letters in various attitudes to demonstrate perspective (and the application of his own perspective machine) was entirely original, although this theme was taken up again by Lucas Brunn, the curator of the Dresden Kunstkammer, in his own perspective treatise of 1613 (see opposite).

Lencker, like Jamnitzer, was trained as a goldsmith, and he also went on to become an important figure in the town politics of Nuremberg. Unfortunately not much else is known of life. His drawings of geometrical figures clearly owe something to Jamnitzer, and he is a better draughtman than Stoer, his figures are more freely drawn than either of these. Unlike Jamnitzer, there is no attempt to fit these drawings into any schema other than the alphabet itself. In fact he presents his illustrations as 'evidence in themselves' of perspective principles. It seems that, in common with Dürer, he had a good understanding of the basic principles of optics, and is known to have developed measuring and perspectival instruments, which he illustrates in a later work that is simply entitled *Perspectiva* (see page 55).

The *Literaria*, however, with its three-dimensional drawings of letters, is not accompanied by any explanation of his intentions. There were, of course, precedents for the proper forming of the letters of the alphabet in art–craft treatises; both Pacioli and Dürer dealt with them in their books, and they subsequently became a stock theme in this literature. Lencker, uniquely, brought perspective and lettering together, showing all the letters of the alphabet in a whole variety of positions. The book was meant to dazzle with its demonstration of drawing ability and knowledge of perspective; it was very popular when first published and manages to retain its appeal for the modern viewer.

Lencker's semi-regular figures, though limited in number, are confident and have a certain architectural quality. On a larger scale some of them would make fine public sculptures even today; the pity is that this artist produced so little work, or that so little has survived. Lencker, together with Jamnitzer, died of the plague that struck Nuremberg in 1585.

Lucas Brunn (1572–1628)

Praxis Perspectivae, Nuremberg, 1615

Lucas Brunn is known as the curator of the Dresden Kunstkammer, having been appointed as the Court Mathematician sometime before 1620. He later produced an German language edition of Euclid's *Elements* (Nuremberg, 1625). His use of letters to demonstrate how perspective drawings may be produced without the use of models, using a 'perspective machine' (see page 29), clearly follows on from Lencker's work in this area. Lencker himself had spent some time as a tutor in the Kunstkammer.

Anon (*c.*1565–1600)

Geometrische und Perspectivische Zeichnungen

The next set of geometrical drawings are from another folio, by an anonymous hand, containing 36 watercolours in all, and are broadly similar in style to the previous artists. Using pen and watercolour, these, like Stoer's, were apparently drawn over an extended period. Many are clearly derived from Jamnitzer and Lencker, others have an original eccentricity all of their own. An endearing, and distinctive, feature is the inclusion of small creatures of various kinds.

Jamnitzer's and Lencker's books had a broader appeal than previous perspective treatises, and established the genre – but Stoer's later work and that of this anonymous artist seem to have been more private productions. It is possible that they were commissioned, but more likely that they were simply drawn for personal satisfaction.

The series begins with drawings of Platonic solids, as a sort of declaration of intent, and goes on to explore similar themes to those of the previous artists, and clearly borrows from them. Indeed, the similarities between the range of subject matter of these drawings and those of the other artists featured in this book begs various questions that unfortunately can never be answered. How close were their relationships, and how familiar were they with each other's work? Under what circumstances were these illustrations produced? One would love to know more details of their day-to-day lives. What we can be sure of is that the calm, contemplative qualities of these images must have contrast strongly with what is known of the politically turbulent and pestilential backdrop of the times in which they were created. In Germany in the later sixteenth century, an artist might be forgiven in seeking refuge from the troubled world through the contemplation of eternal Platonic forms

Paul Pfinzing (1554–99)

Extract der Geometriae und Perspectivae, Nuremberg, 1598

Pfinzing was a printer, publisher and cartographer who produced a brilliant series of maps of Nuremberg in the 1580s. In 1598 he published his own geometric perspective treatise in a limited edition. This work was more clearly didactic those of Jamnitzer and his immediate followers, and presented various geometric constructs together with the tools of his trade – instruments for drawing, measuring and surveying.

Peter Halt (*fl.*1620–53)

Perspectivische Reiss Kunst

Little is known of this artist–craftsman other than that he was a stonemason by trade, and practised as an architect in Schorndorf. The *Perspectivische Reiss Kunst*, his only book in this genre, was obviously influenced by Jamnitzer. He may have also have known Lorenz Stoer personally, since both were in Augsberg in the early 1600s.

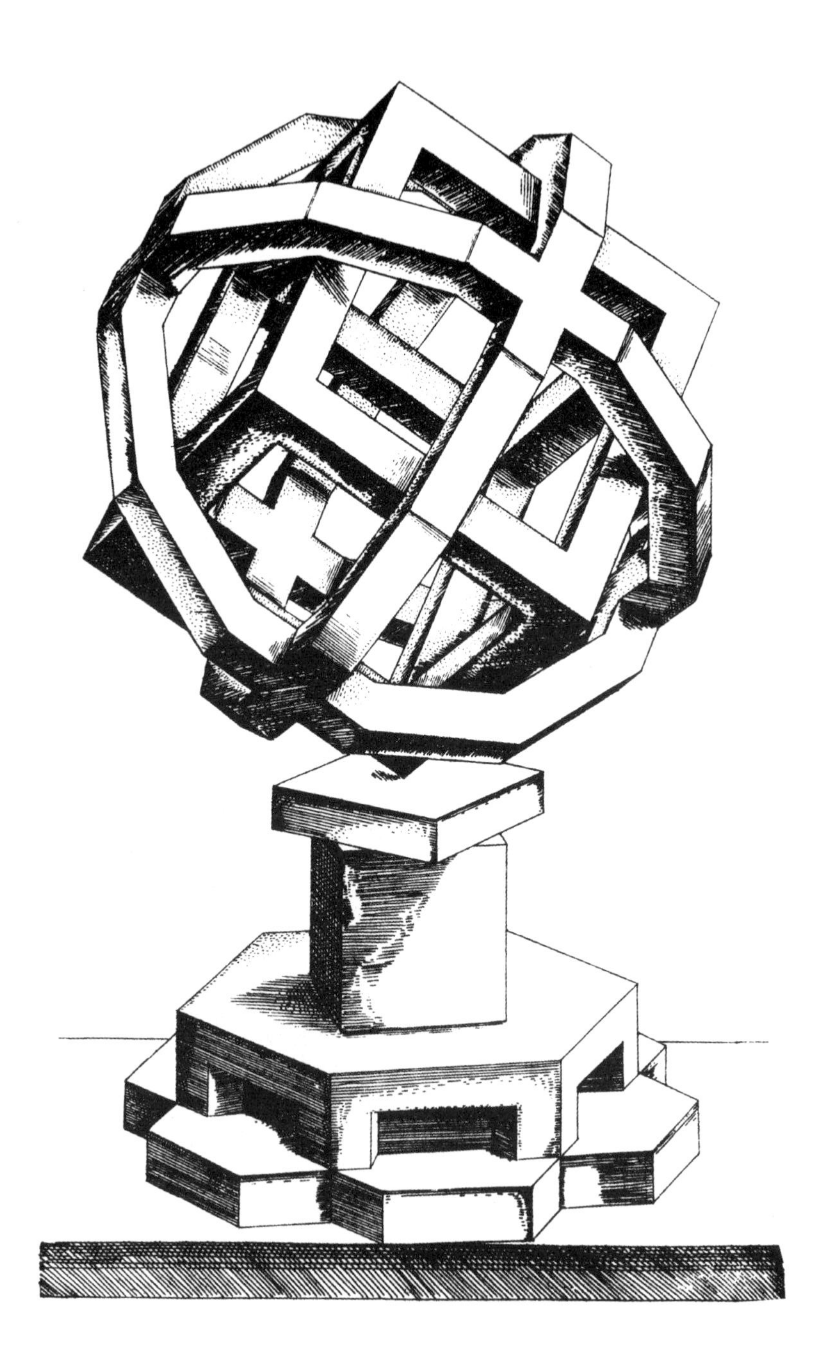

From Johannes Lencker's Perspectiva Literaria, *Nuremberg, 1567.*

From Johannes Lencker's Perspectiva Literaria, *Nuremberg, 1567.*

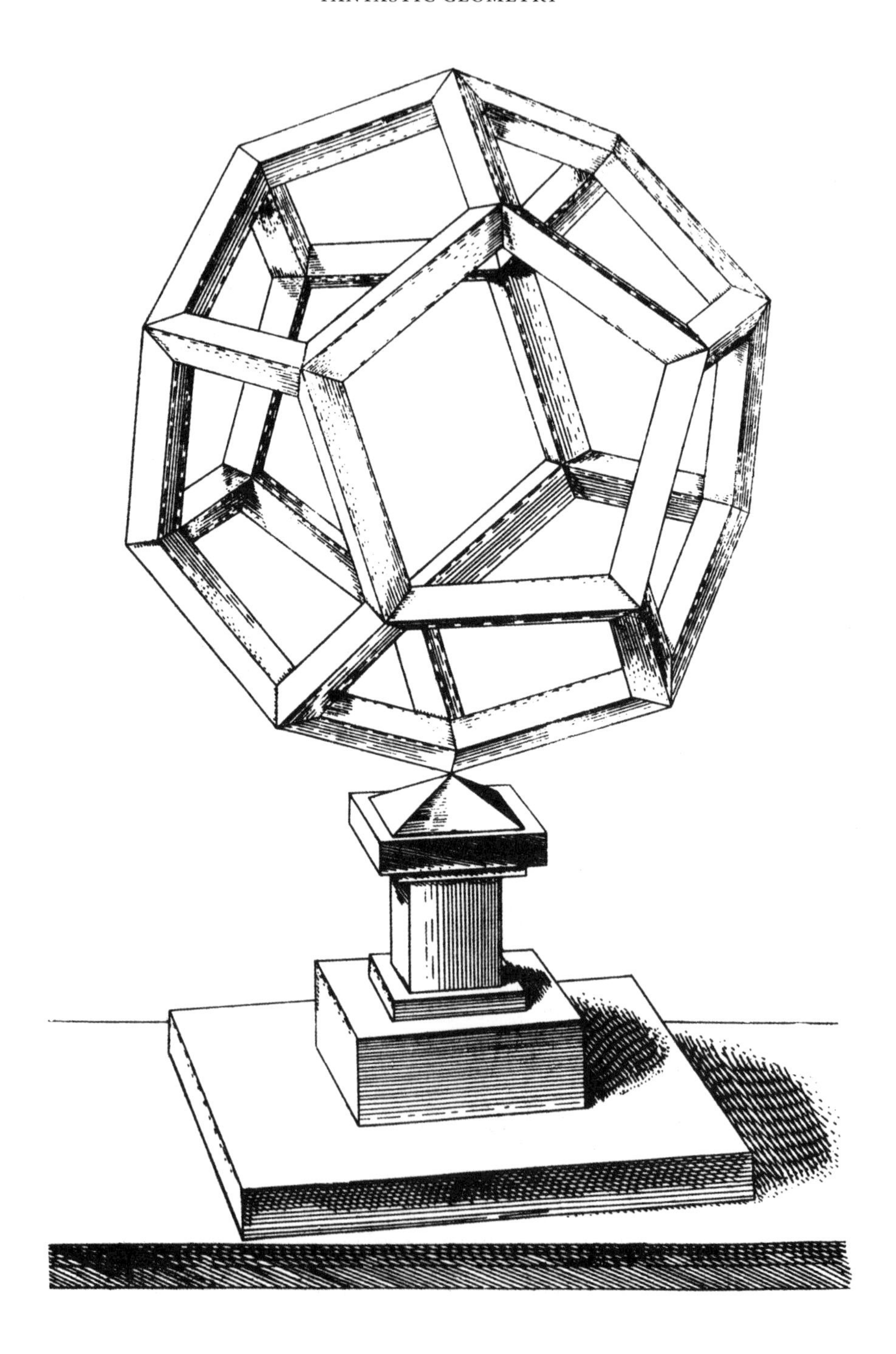

From Johannes Lencker's Perspectiva Literaria*, Nuremberg, 1567.*

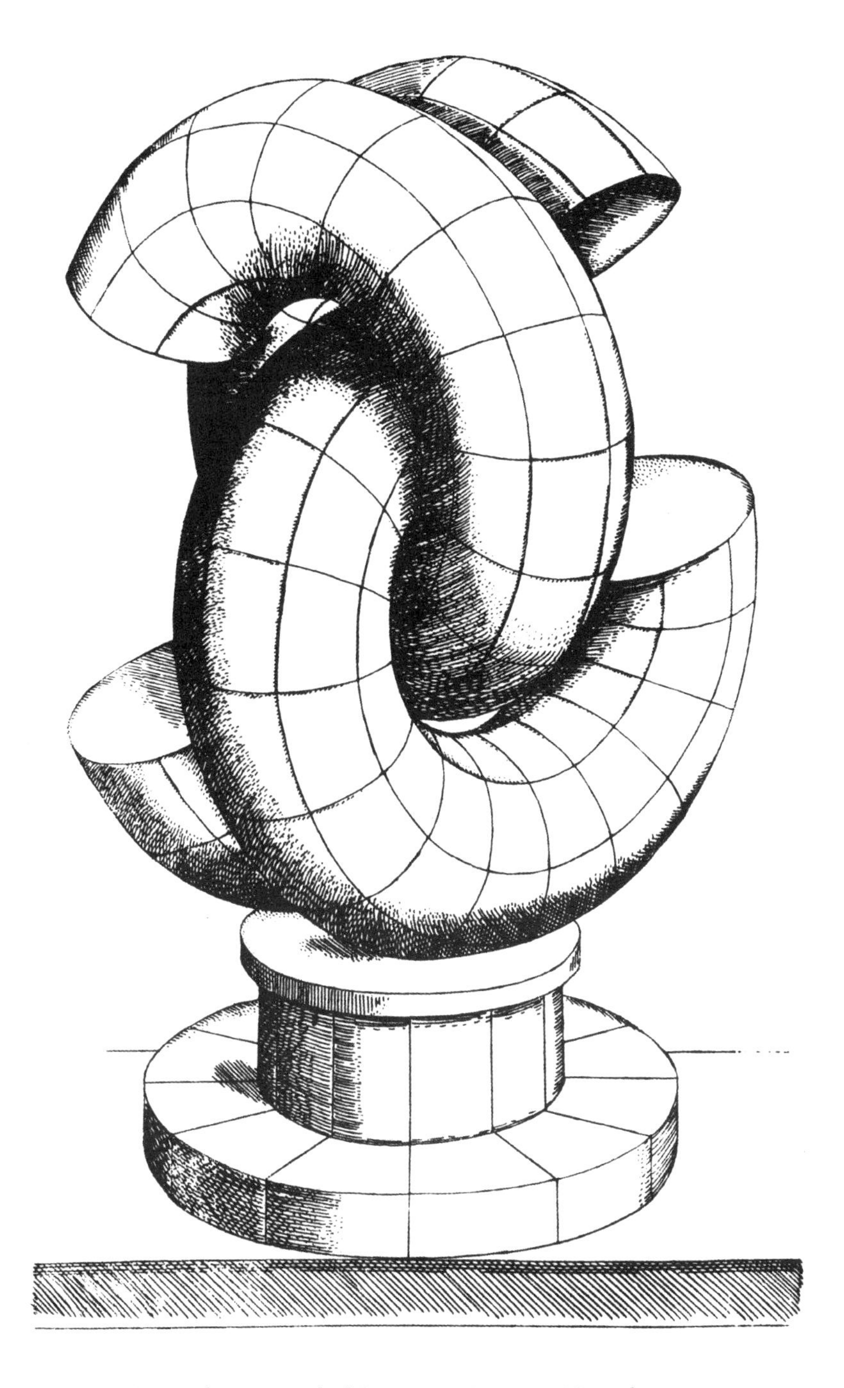

From Johannes Lencker's Perspectiva Literaria, *Nuremberg, 1567.*

From Johannes Lencker's Perspectiva Literaria, *Nuremberg, 1567.*

From Johannes Lencker's Perspectiva Literaria, *Nuremberg, 1567.*

PERSPECTIVA
Hierinnen auffs kürtzte
beschrieben/ mit exempeln eröffnet vnd an
tag gegeben wird/ ein newer besonder kurtzer/ doch gerechter vnnd
sehr leichter weg/ wie allerley ding/ es seyen Corpora/ Gebew/ oder
was möglich zuerdencken vnd in grund zulegen ist/ verzuckt oder
vnuerruckt/ ferner in die Perspectyf gebracht werden mag/ on einige vergebliche linie/ riß vñ puncten/ ꝛc. dergleichen weg bißhero noch
nit bekant gewesen/ Durch Hansen Lencker Burger
zu Nürmberg/ allen liebhabern guter künsten
zu ehren vnd gefallen publicirt.

Mit Röm. Key. May. freiheit/ auff sechs jar.
Gedruckt zu Nürmberg/ durch Dietrich Gerlatz.
M. D. LXXI.

The title page from Johannes Lencker's Perspectiva, *1571.*

From Johannes Lencker's Perspectiva Literaria, *Nuremberg, 1567.*

From Johannes Lencker's Perspectiva Literaria, *Nuremberg, 1567.*

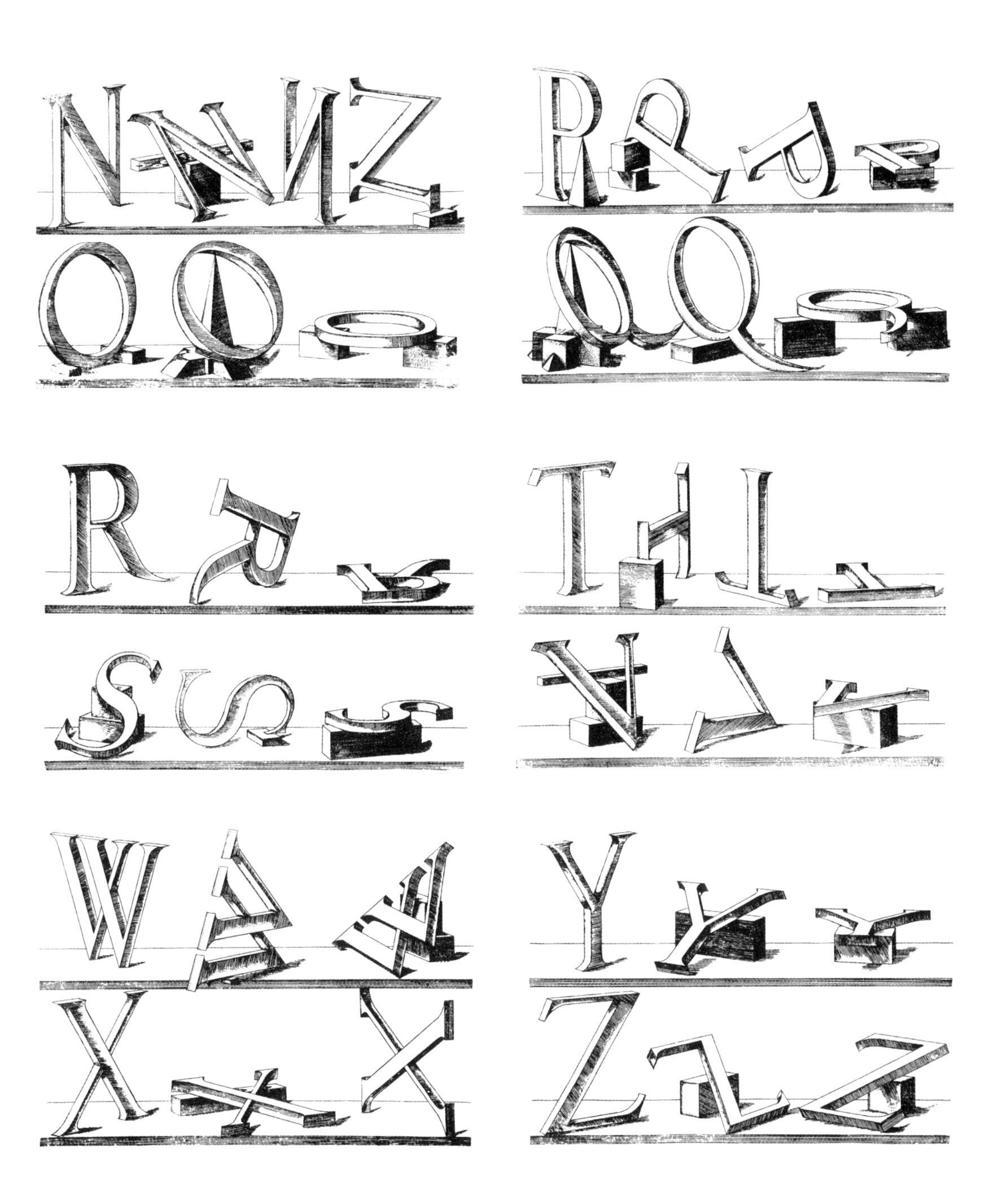

From Johannes Lencker's Perspectiva Literaria, *Nuremberg, 1567.*

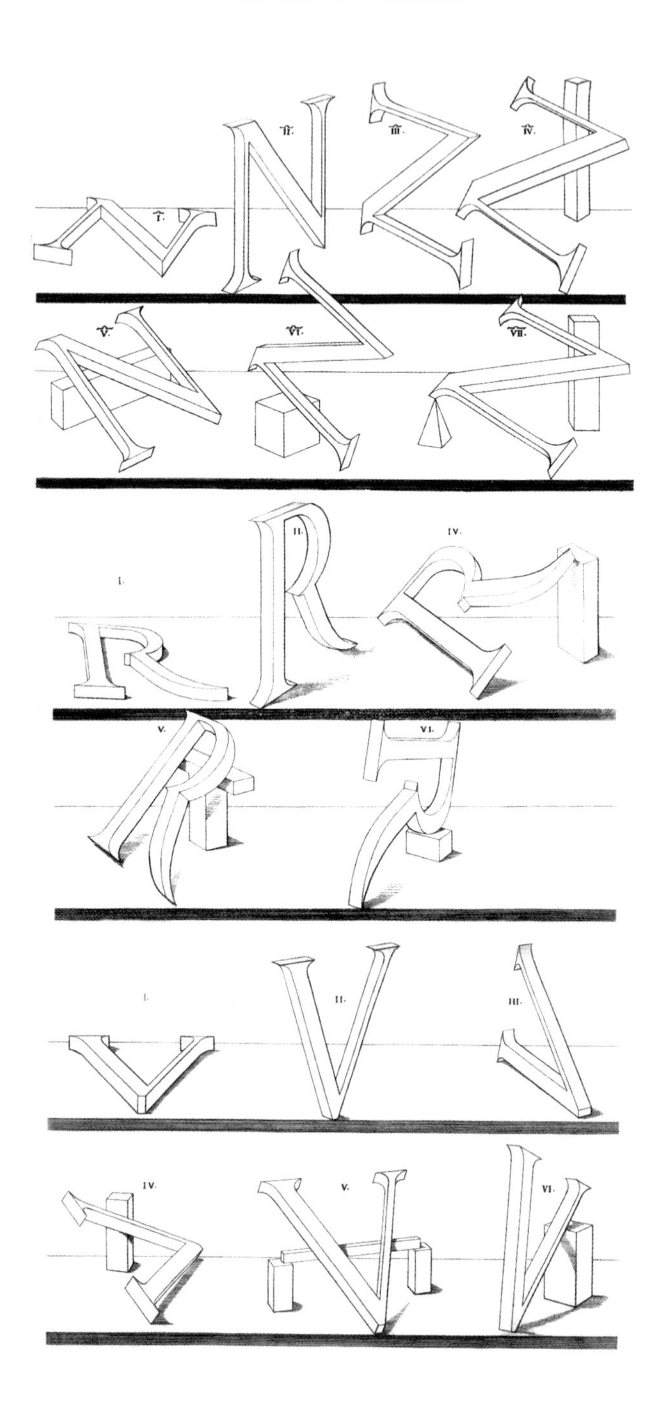

Lucas Brunn, Praxis Perspectivae, *Nuremberg, 1615.*

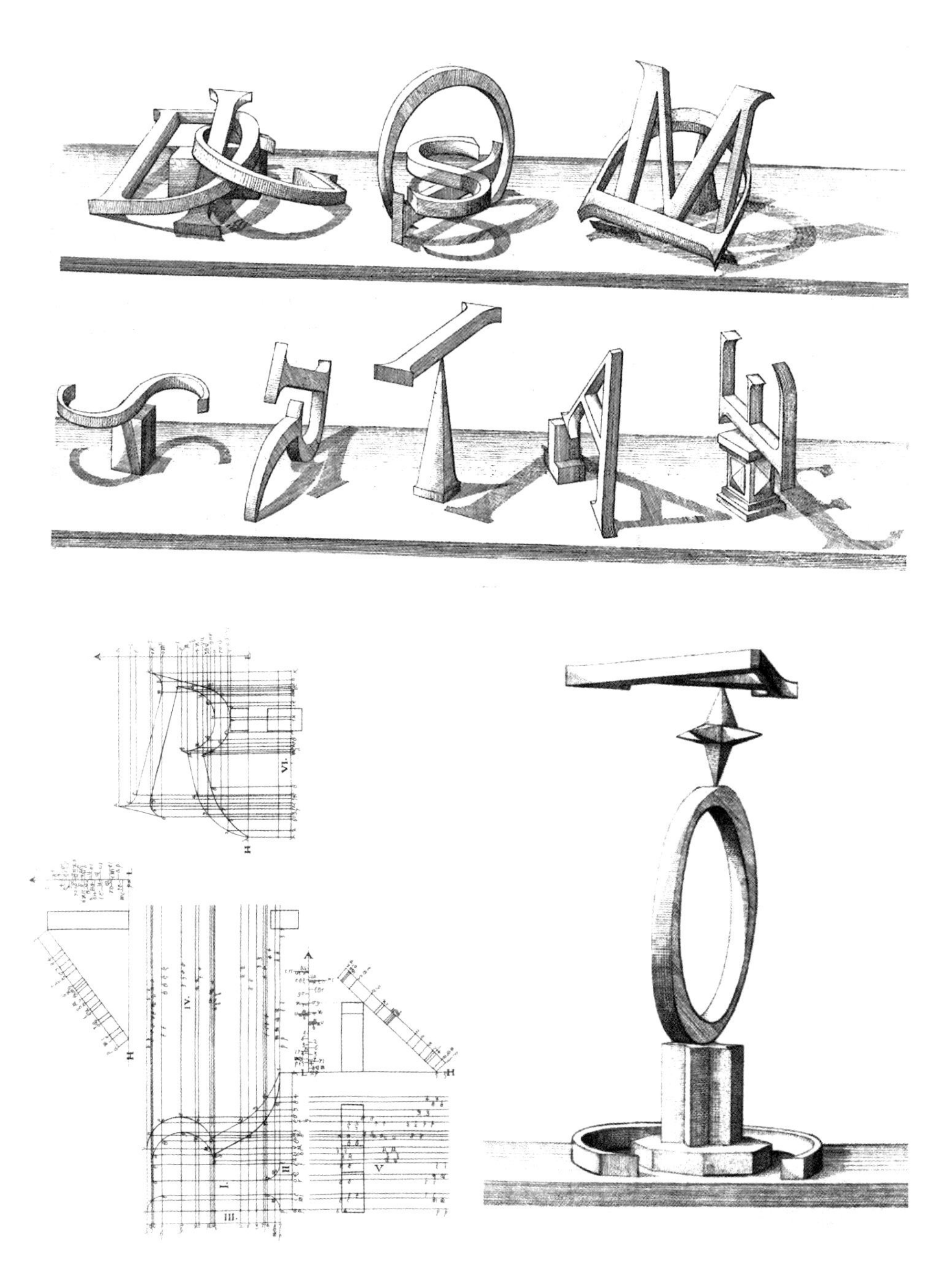

Lucas Brunn, who was at one time the curator of the Dresden Kunstkammer, and the inventor of the micrometer, devised a precision perspectograph (see page 29) which enabled him to draw accurate representations of cut-out models of the letters of the alphabet. In this he was following Johannes Lencker, who he almost certainly knew personally.

Anonymous artist (c.1545–1600): Cod. Guelf. 74.1 Aug. 20 (courtesy of Herzog August Bibliothek, Wolfenbuttel).

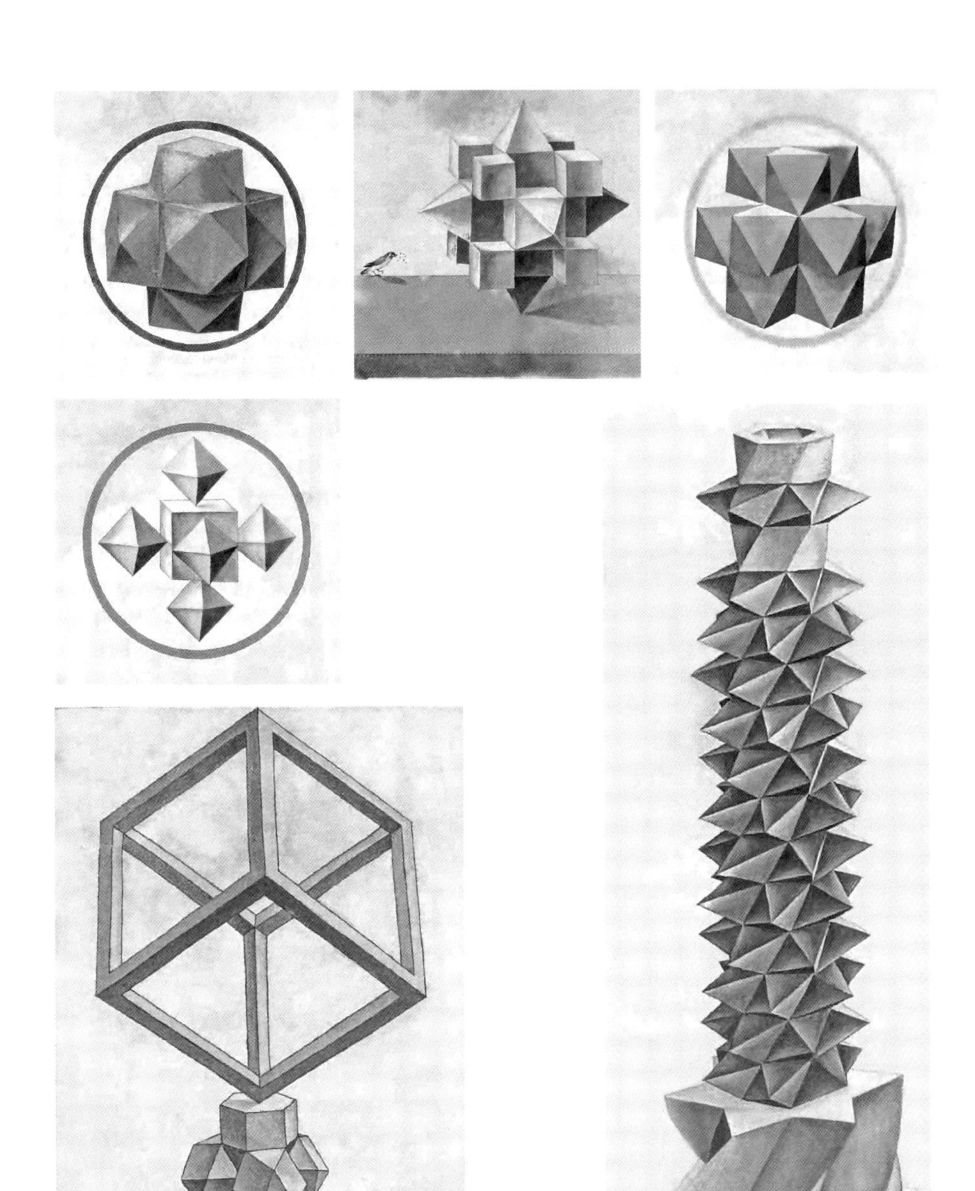

Anonymous artist (c.1545–1600): Cod. Guelf. 74.1 Aug. 20
(courtesy of Herzog August Bibliothek, Wolfenbuttel).

Anonymous artist (c.1545–1600): Cod. Guelf. 74.1 Aug. 20 (courtesy of Herzog August Bibliothek, Wolfenbuttel).

Anonymous artist (c.1545–1600): Cod. Guelf. 74.1 Aug. 20
(courtesy of Herzog August Bibliothek, Wolfenbuttel).

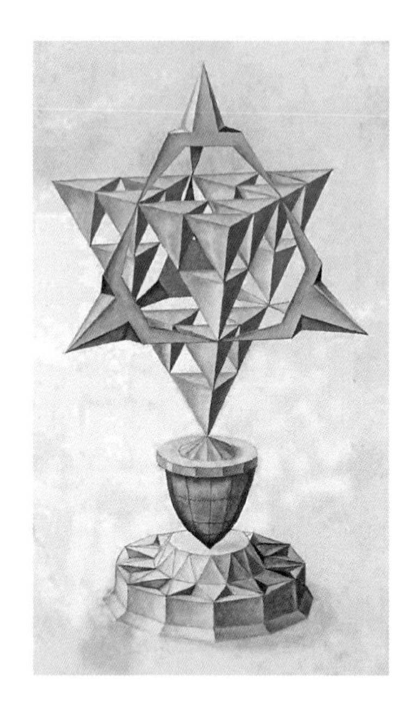

Anonymous artist (c.1545–1600): Cod. Guelf. 74.1 Aug. 20
(courtesy of Herzog August Bibliothek, Wolfenbuttel).

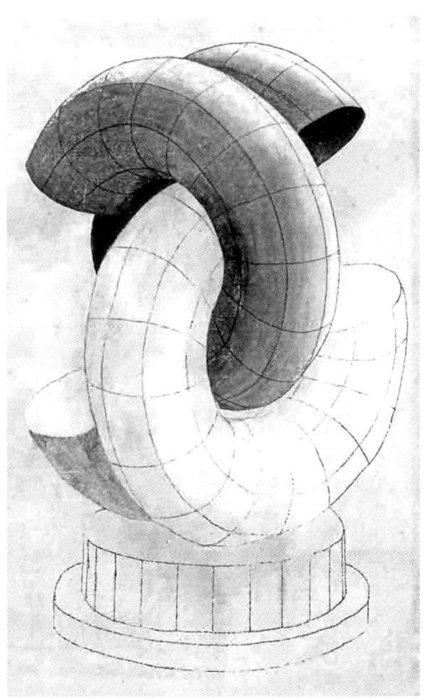

Anonymous artist (c.1545–1600): Cod. Guelf. 74.1 Aug. 20 (courtesy of Herzog August Bibliothek, Wolfenbuttel).

From Paul Pfinzing's Extract der Geometriae und Perspectivae, *Nuremberg, 1598.*

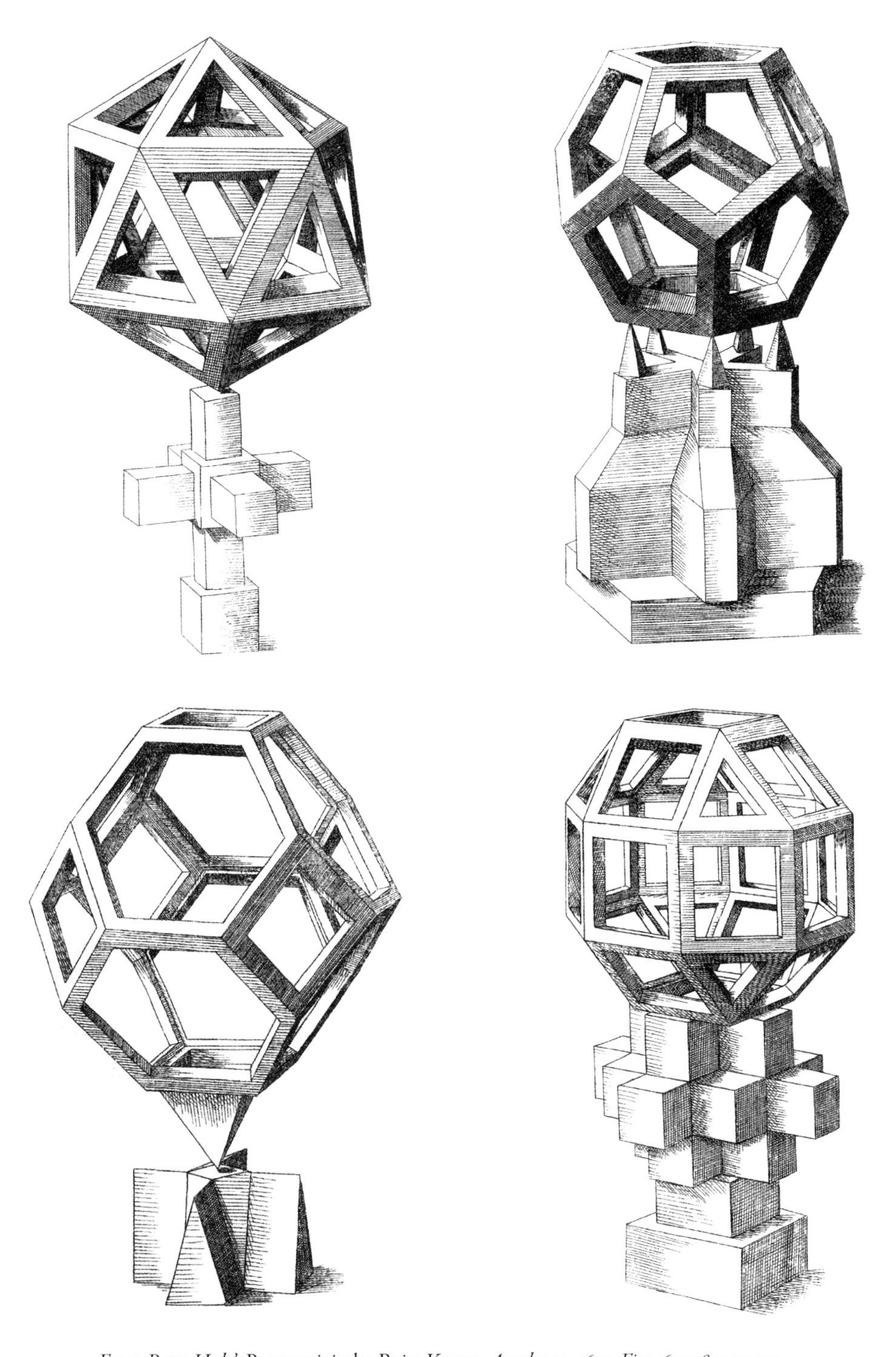

From Peter Halt's Perspectivische Reiss Kunst, *Augsburg, 1625. Figs. 69; 78; 101; 117.*

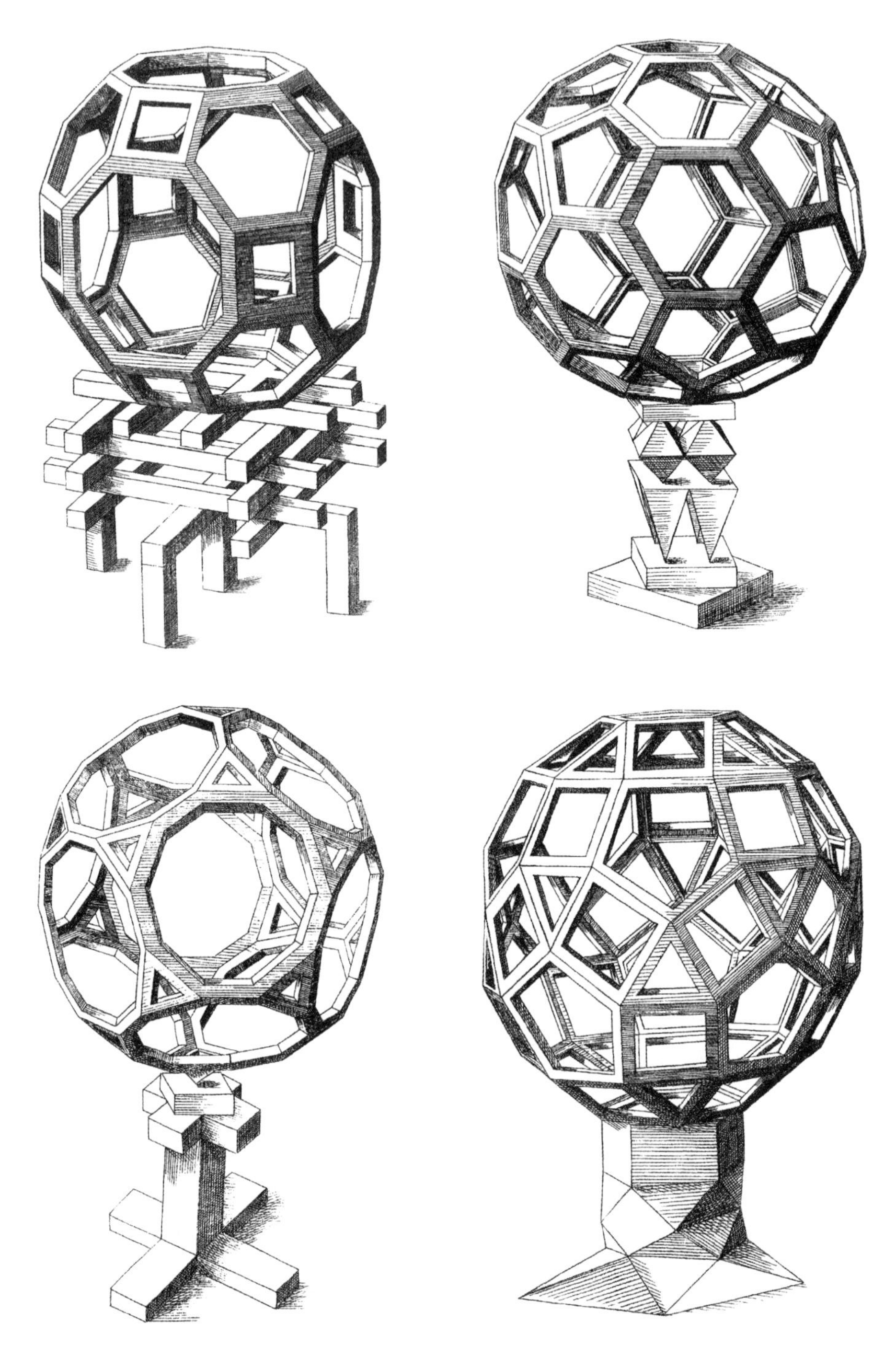

From Peter Halt's Perspectivische Reiss Kunst, *Augsburg, 1625. Figs. 130; 146; 150; 156.*

From Peter Halt's Perspectivische Reiss Kunst, *Augsburg, 1625. Figs. 90; 115; 72; 162.*

From Peter Halt's Perspectivische Reiss Kunst, *Augsburg, 1625. Figs. 40; 63; 95; 113; 122; 124; 126; 135; 155.*

From Peter Halt's Perspectivische Reiss Kunst, *Augsburg, 1625. Figs. 67; 88; 99; 111; 128; 143; 133; 161; 166.*

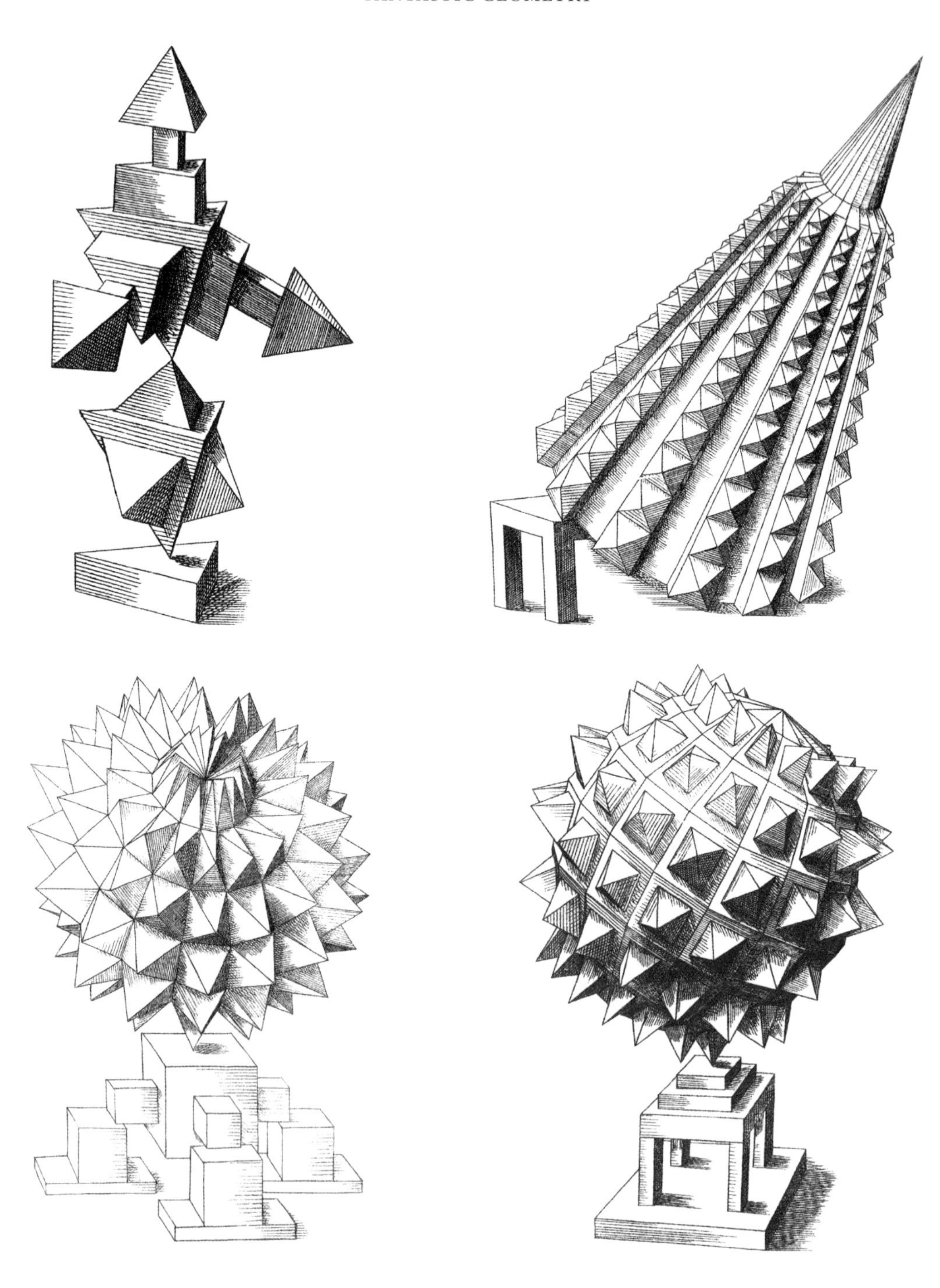

From Peter Halt's Perspectivische Reiss Kunst, *Augsburg, 1625. Figs. 33; 162; 169; 170.*

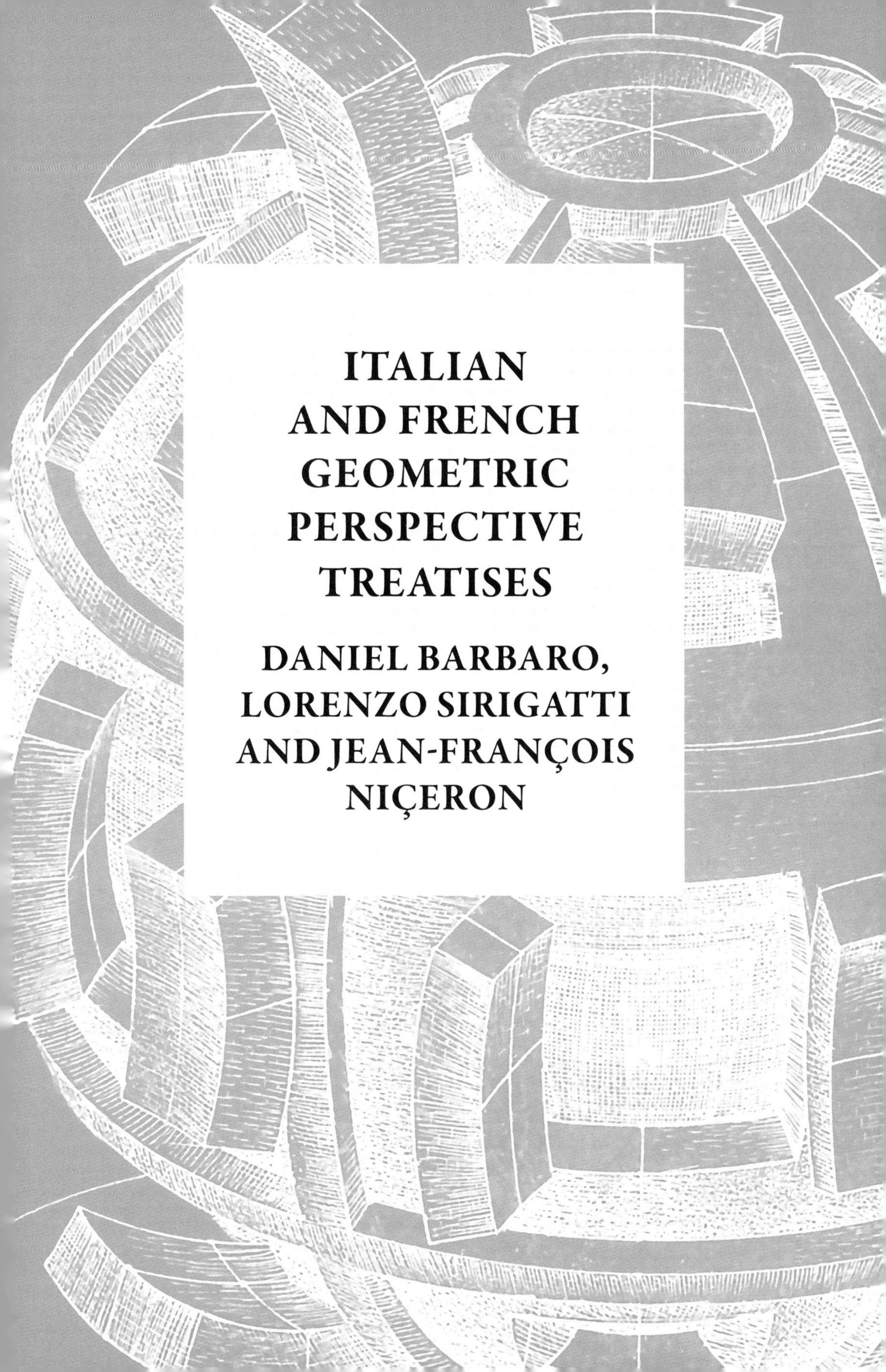

ITALIAN AND FRENCH GEOMETRIC PERSPECTIVE TREATISES

DANIEL BARBARO, LORENZO SIRIGATTI AND JEAN-FRANÇOIS NIÇERON

Italian and French geometric perspective treatises

Daniel Barbaro (1513–70)

La Pratica della Perspettiva, Venice, 1569

There can be little doubt that Daniel Barbaro qualifies for the term 'Renaissance man'. A Venetian aristocrat, diplomat and cardinal, he is best known for his translation of the ten books of Vitruvius, the Roman architect and engineer (for which Palladio provided the illustrations). His contribution to perspective literature, *La Pratica della Perspettiva*, also became very influential, and has an important place in the history of photography, being the first to describe the use of a lens in conjunction with a camera obscura.

(?) Martino da Udine (1470–1548)

Three prints

The source and artistic intention of these strange drawings, which bear the monograph 'P.P.', is obscure. They have an affinity with certain sketches by Uccello, Barbaro and Leonardo, and clearly demonstrate a competence and familiarity with the rules of perspective, but otherwise little is known about them. It has been suggested (by Arthur M. Hind) that the monogram 'P.P.' is that of Martino da Udine, who according to the art historian Georg K. Nagler worked in Ferrara and Udine. If so, other similar examples of this artists work have not survived, or have yet to be discovered.

Lorenzo Sirigatti *d.*1625

La Practica di Prospettiva, Venice, 1596

Sirigatti was a Florentine mathematician who is known to have lectured in Bologna. His work on perspective was very popular, running to eleven editions. However, like Jamnitzer's and Lencker's works, it is not really explanatory, although it impressed Galileo who is reputed to have seen it pre-publication (possibly Sirigatti's convincing images of shaded spheres inspired his own drawings of the surface of the moon?). Although there is little biographical detail, he is believed to have been appointed as a Bishop by Pope Sixtus Quintus 'for his many praise-worthy accomplishments'.

Jean-François Niçeron (1613–46)

La Perspective Curieuse, Paris, 1638

Jean-François Niçeron was a pupil of the Jesuit mathematician Friar Martin Mersenne (who was aware, and an active defender, of the ideas of Galileo, Kepler and Descartes). As well as being a capable mathematician Niçeron was an artist of some note, and through these combined interests was drawn into the problems of perspective, the techniques of anamorphic art and *trompe l'oeil* (in particular their practical applications in religious art). His *La Perspective Curieuse* is essentially an investigation into these subjects. The images of his presented here show his fine grasp of perspective, and his interest in the ways in which shadows were cast by complex bodies.

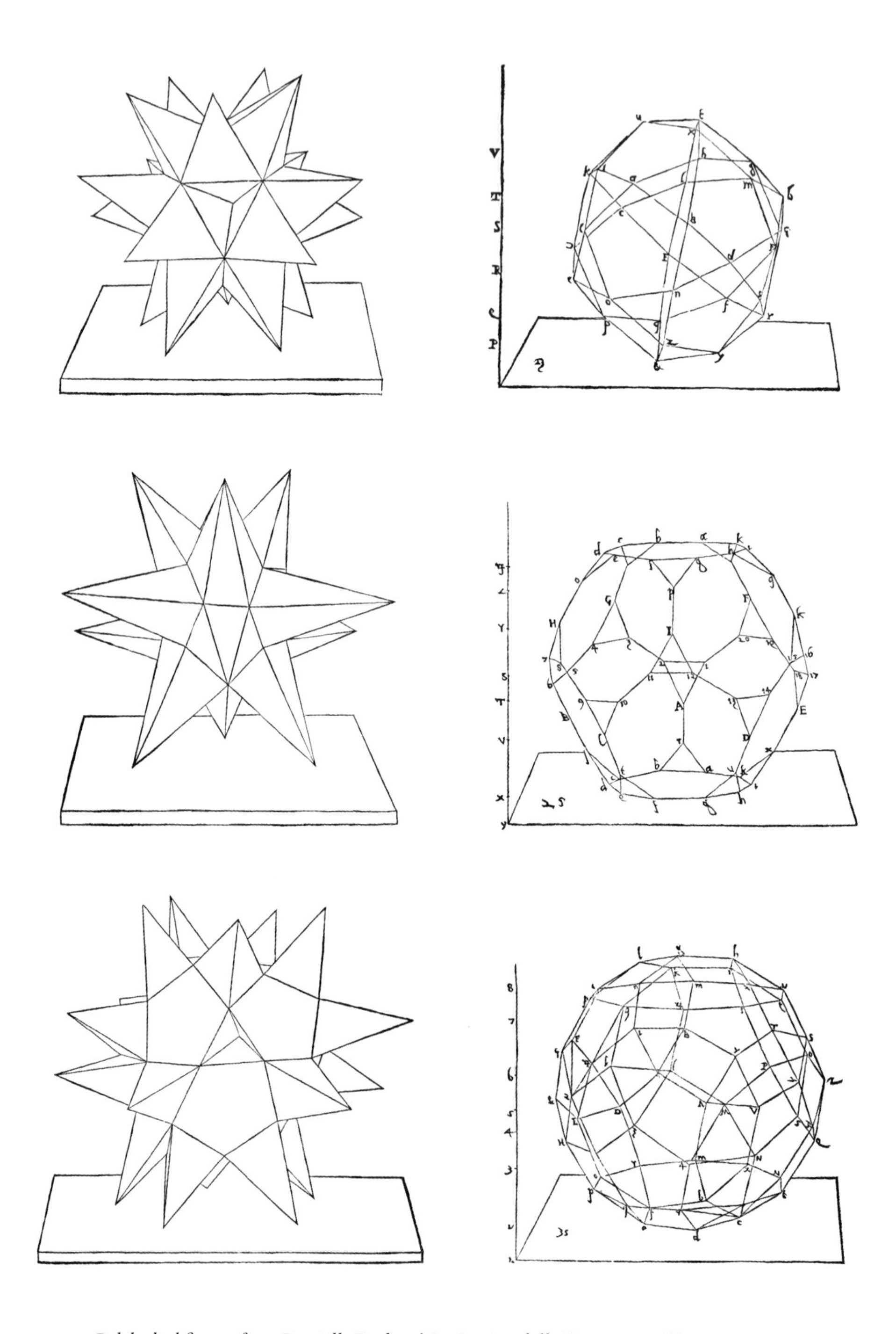

Polyhedral figures from Danielle Barbaro's La Pratica della Perspettiva, *Venice, 1569.*

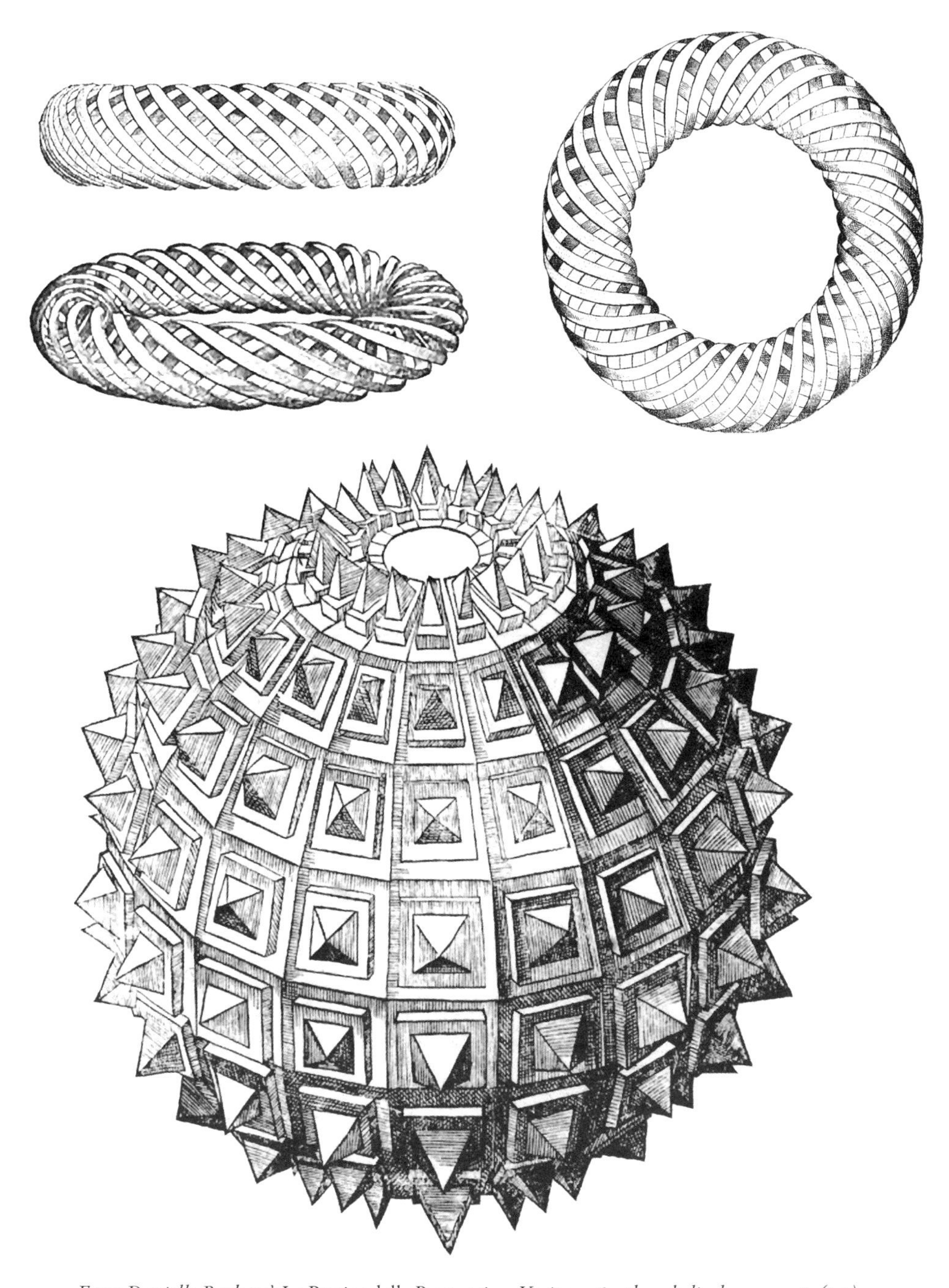

From Danielle Barbaro's La Pratica della Perspettiva, *Venice, 1569: three helical ornaments (top); a stellated spherical figure (bottom), clearly related to* mazzocchio *forms, which was, like them, an opportunity to demonstrate perspective skills and imagination. Barbaro's variants on the* mazzocchio *can be seen on page 271.*

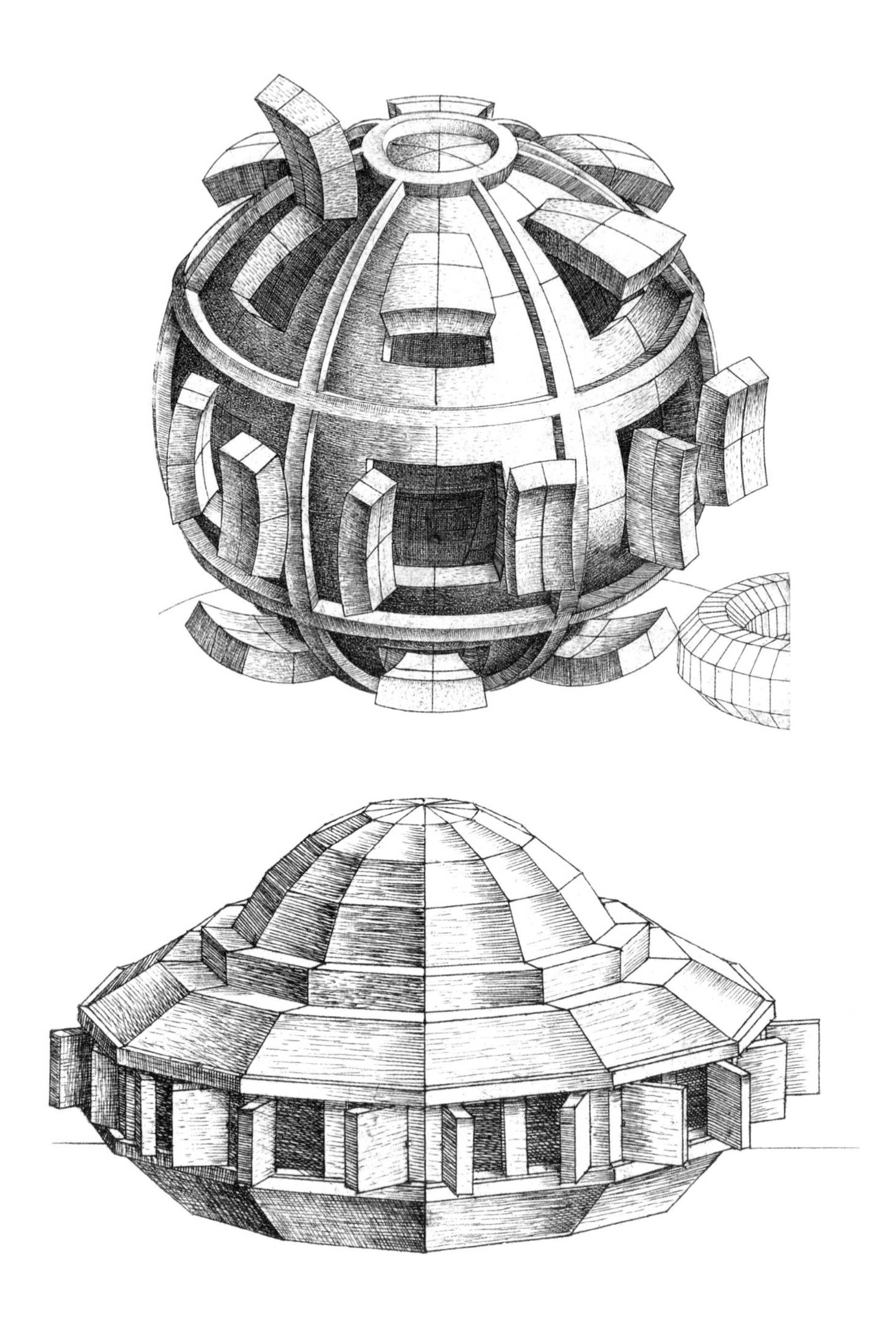

Monographed 'P.P.', attr. Martino da Udine (1470–1548), Fol. 1 (KK 5337) (top) (courtesy of the Kunst Historische Museum, Vienna). Monogrammist PP tätig um 1500 (bottom) (courtesy of the Hamburger Kunsthalle).

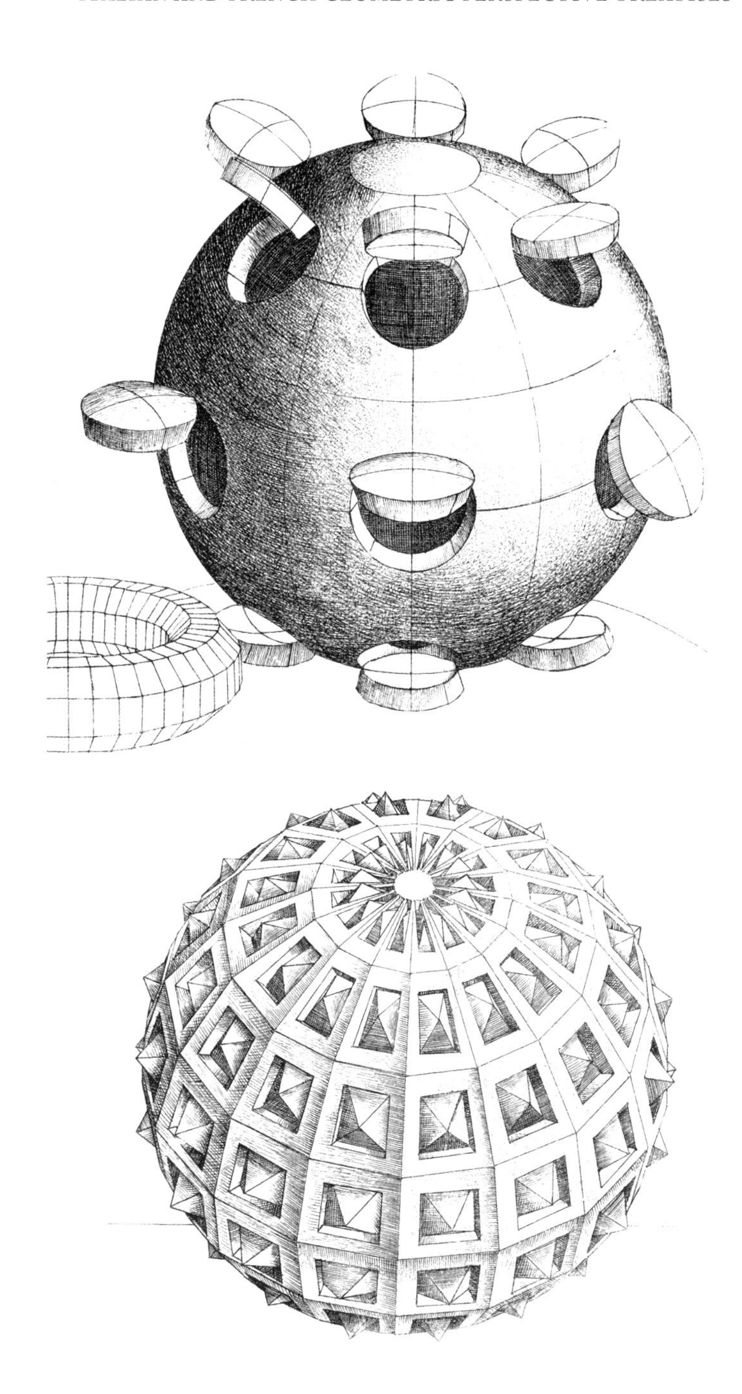

Monographed 'P.P.' : Attributed to Martino da Udine (1470–1548), Monogrammist PP tätig um 1500 (courtesy of the Hamburger Kunsthalle).

From La Practica di Prospettiva, *Lorenzo Sirigatti, Venice, 1596*
(courtesy of the Museo Galileo: Institute and Museum of the History of Science, Florence).

From La Practica di Prospettiva, *Lorenzo Sirigatti, Venice, 1596*
(courtesy of the Museo Galileo: Institute and Museum of the History of Science, Florence).

From La Practica di Prospettiva, *Lorenzo Sirigatti, Venice, 1596 (courtesy of the Museo Galileo: Institute and Museum of the History of Science, Florence).*

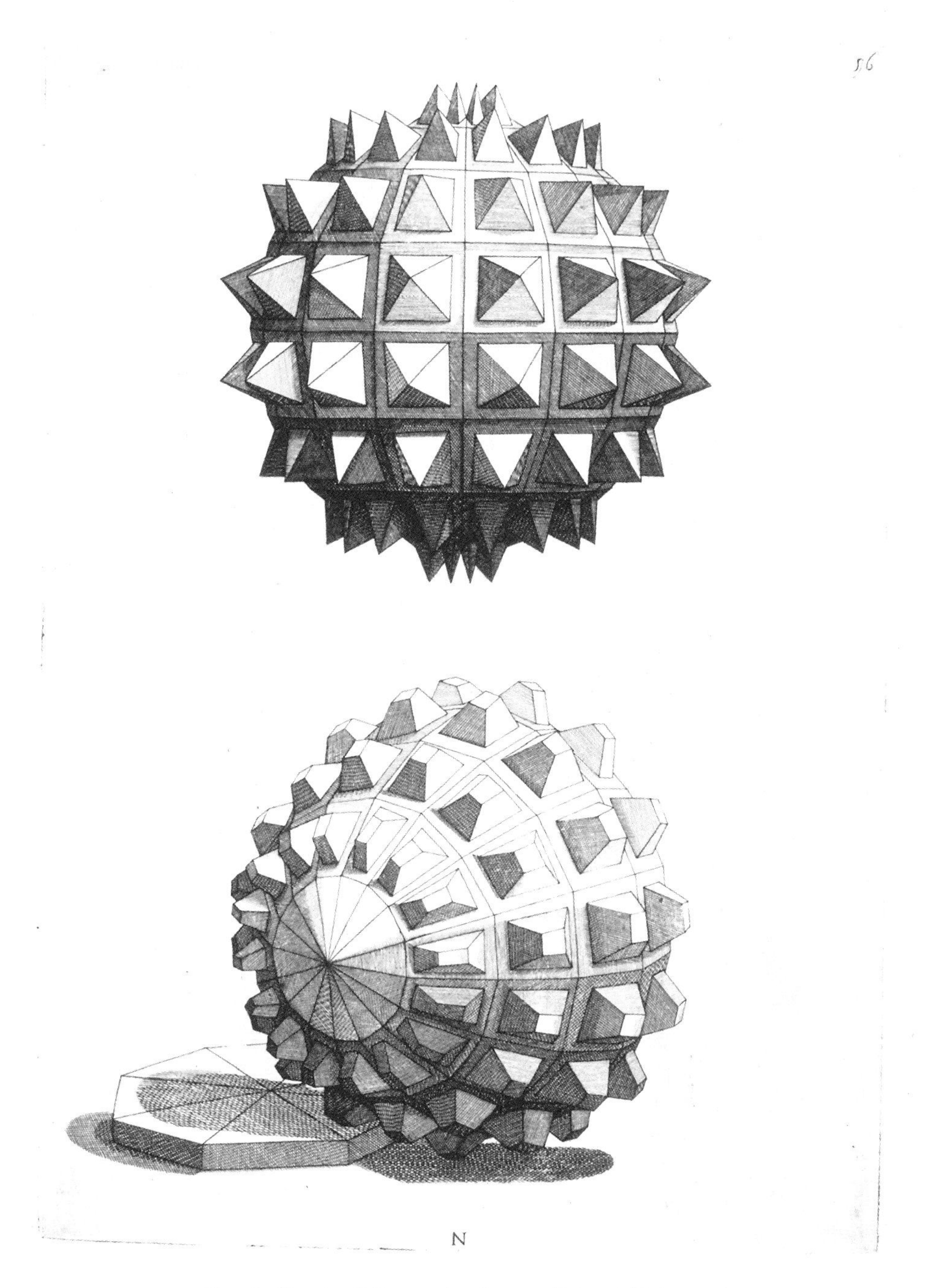

From La Practica di Prospettiva, *Lorenzo Sirigatti, Venice, 1596*
(courtesy of the Museo Galileo: Institute and Museum of the History of Science, Florence).

From La Practica di Prospettiva, *Lorenzo Sirigatti, Venice, 1596 (courtesy of the Museo Galileo: Institute and Museum of the History of Science, Florence).*

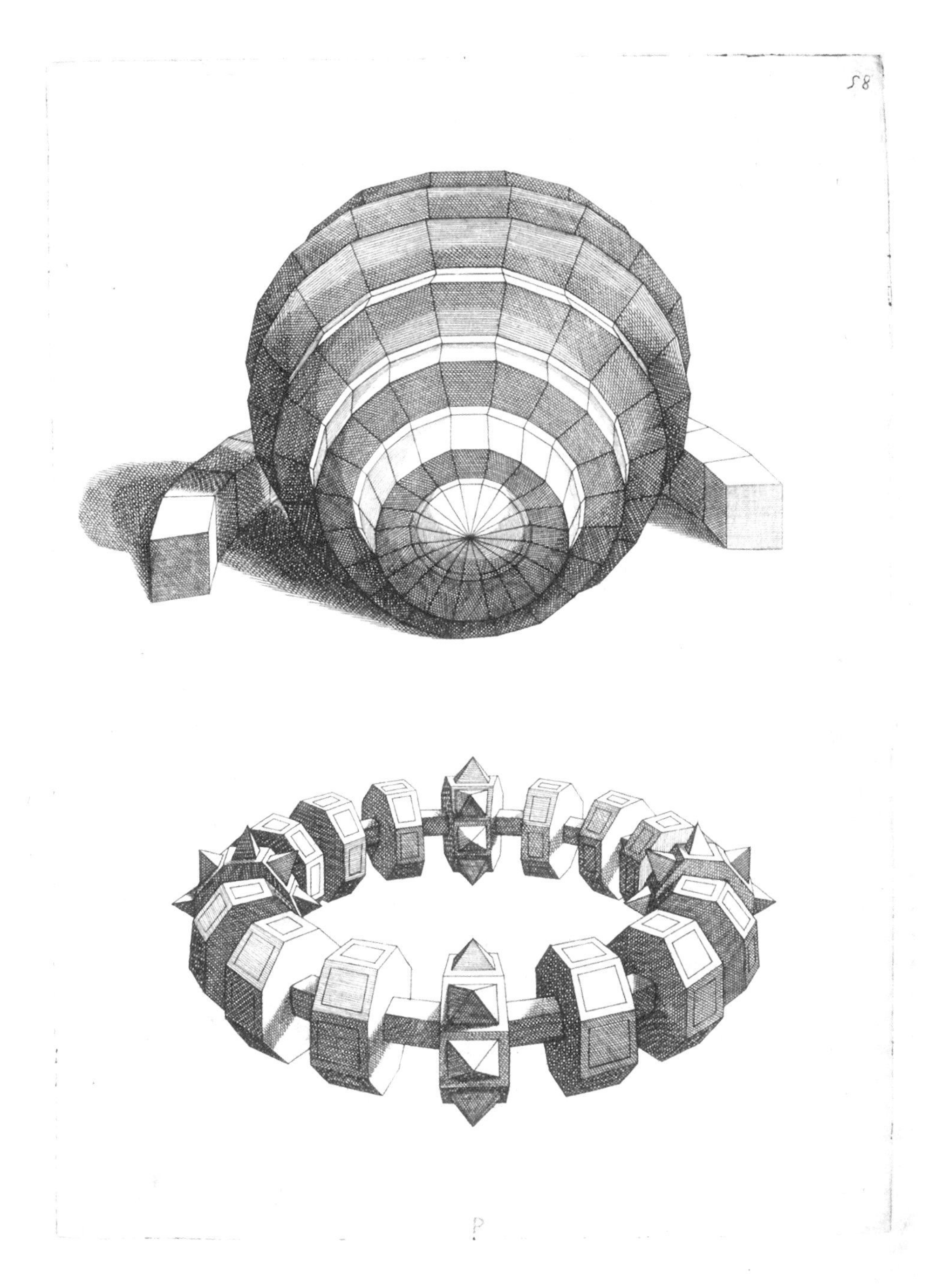

From La Practica di Prospettiva, *Lorenzo Sirigatti, Venice, 1596*
(courtesy of the Museo Galileo: Institute and Museum of the History of Science, Florence).

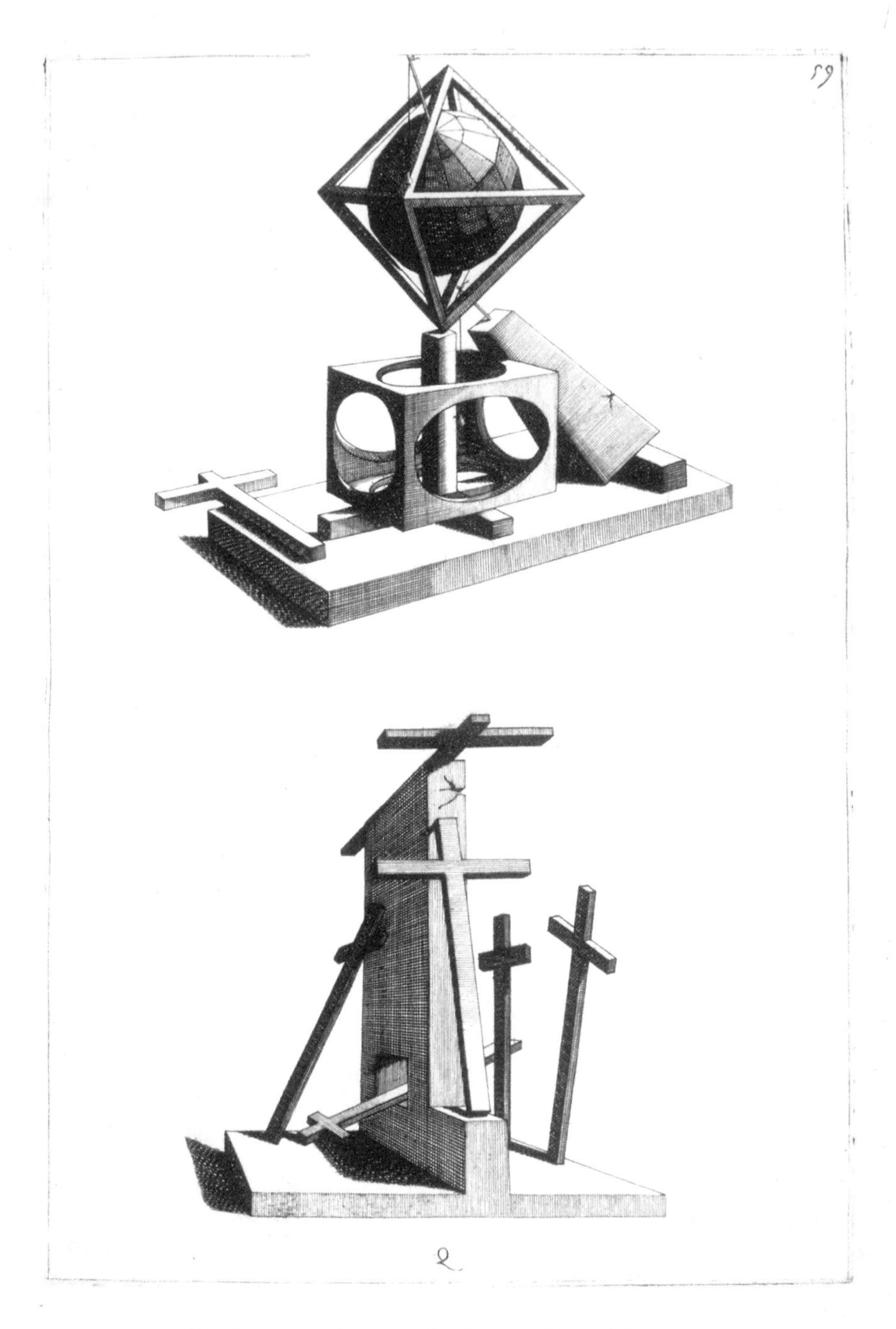

From La Practica di Prospettiva, *Lorenzo Sirigatti, Venice, 1596*
(courtesy of the Museo Galileo: Institute and Museum of the History of Science, Florence).

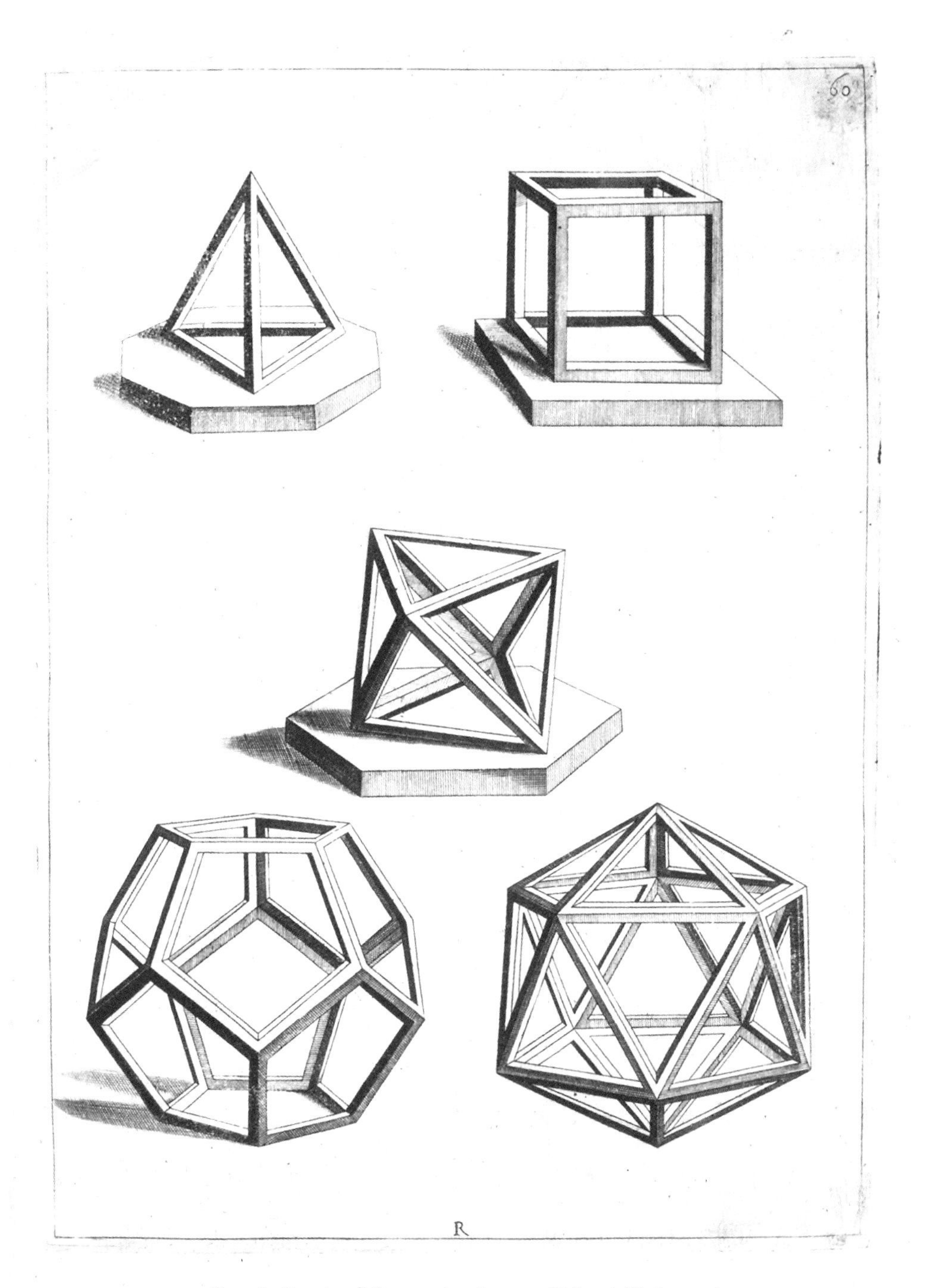

From La Practica di Prospettiva, *Lorenzo Sirigatti, Venice, 1596*
(courtesy of the Museo Galileo: Institute and Museum of the History of Science, Florence).

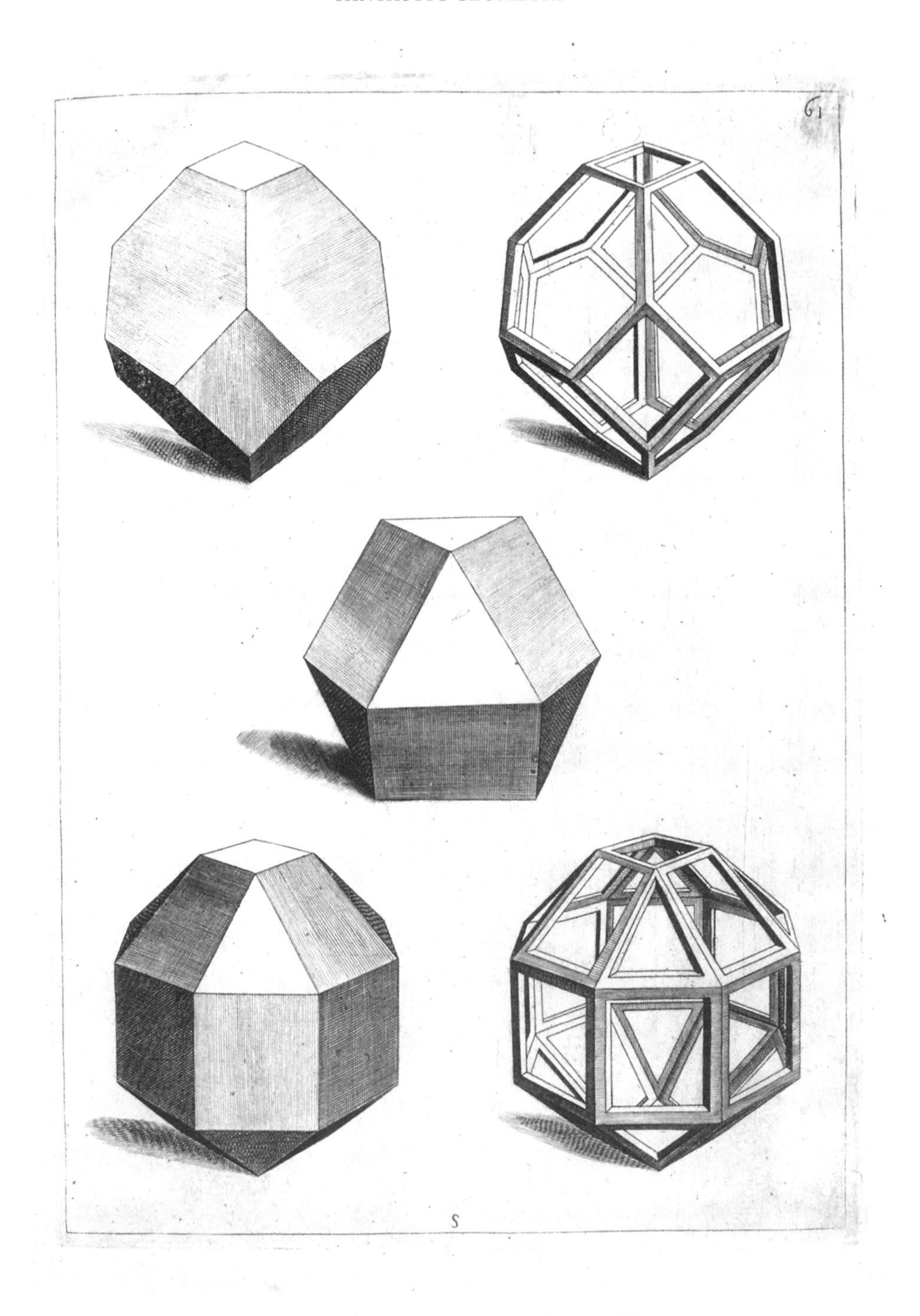

From La Practica di Prospettiva*, Lorenzo Sirigatti, Venice, 1596*
(courtesy of the Museo Galileo: Institute and Museum of the History of Science, Florence).

From La Practica di Prospettiva, *Lorenzo Sirigatti, Venice, 1596*
(courtesy of the Museo Galileo: Institute and Museum of the History of Science, Florence).

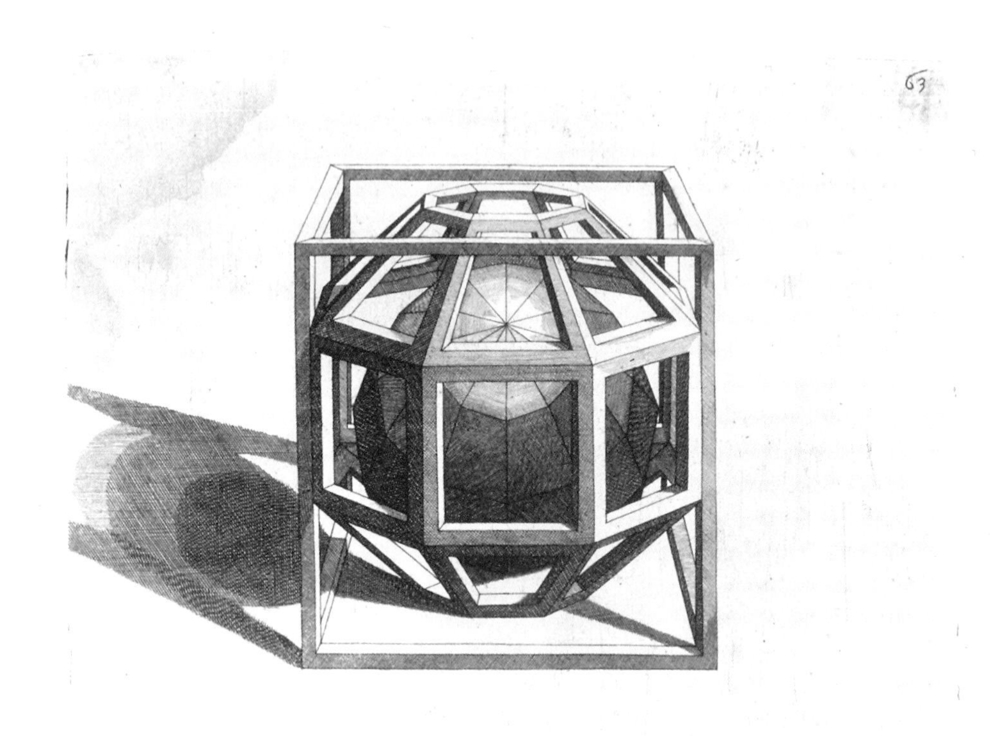

From La Practica di Prospettiva, *Lorenzo Sirigatti, Venice, 1596*
(courtesy of the Museo Galileo: Institute and Museum of the History of Science, Florence).

From La Practica di Prospettiva, *Lorenzo Sirigatti, Venice, 1596*
(courtesy of the Museo Galileo: Institute and Museum of the History of Science, Florence).

From La Practica di Prospettiva, *Lorenzo Sirigatti, Venice, 1596*
(courtesy of the Museo Galileo: Institute and Museum of the History of Science, Florence).

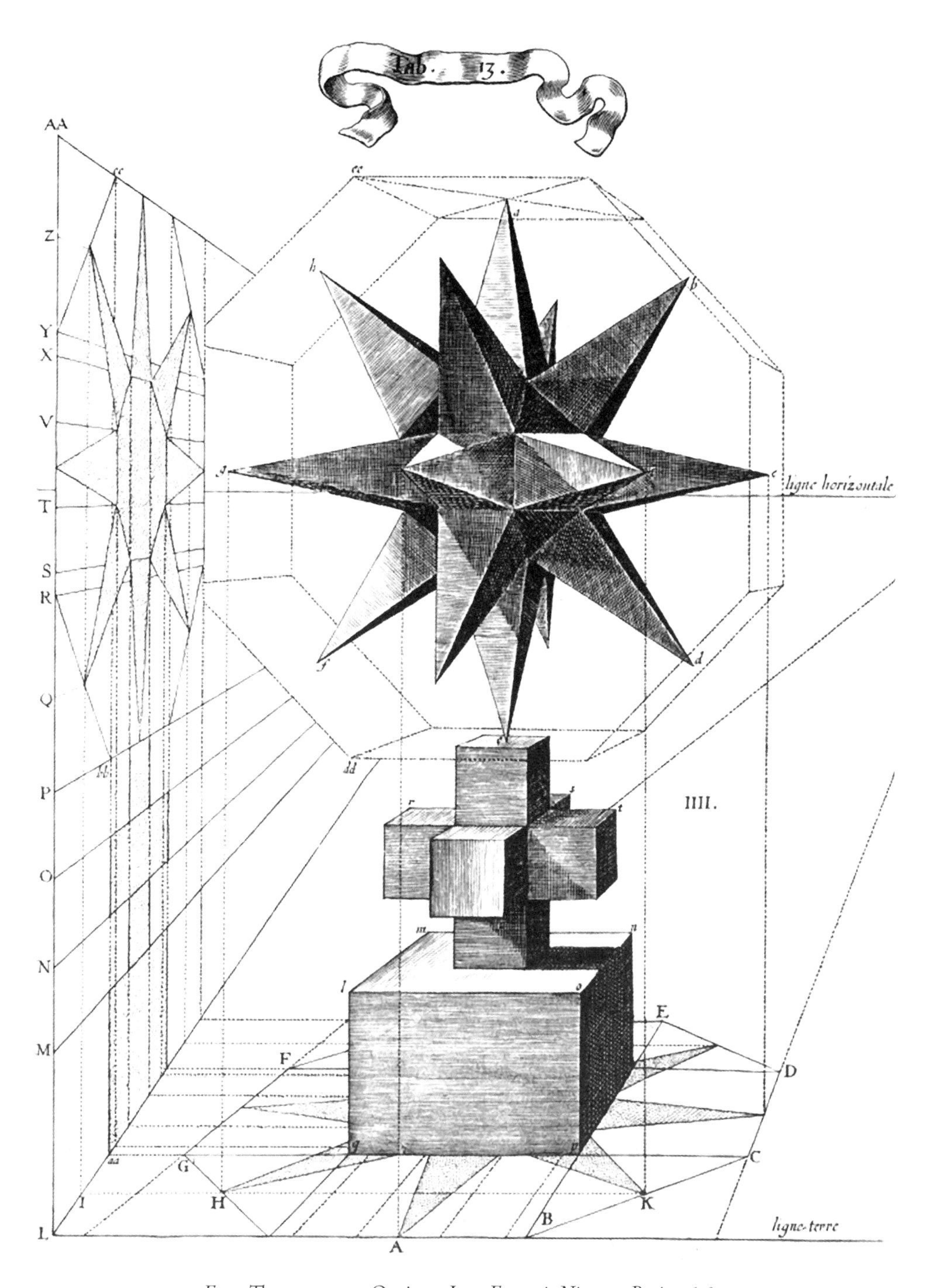

From Thaumaturgus Opticus, *Jean-François Niçeron, Paris, 1638.*

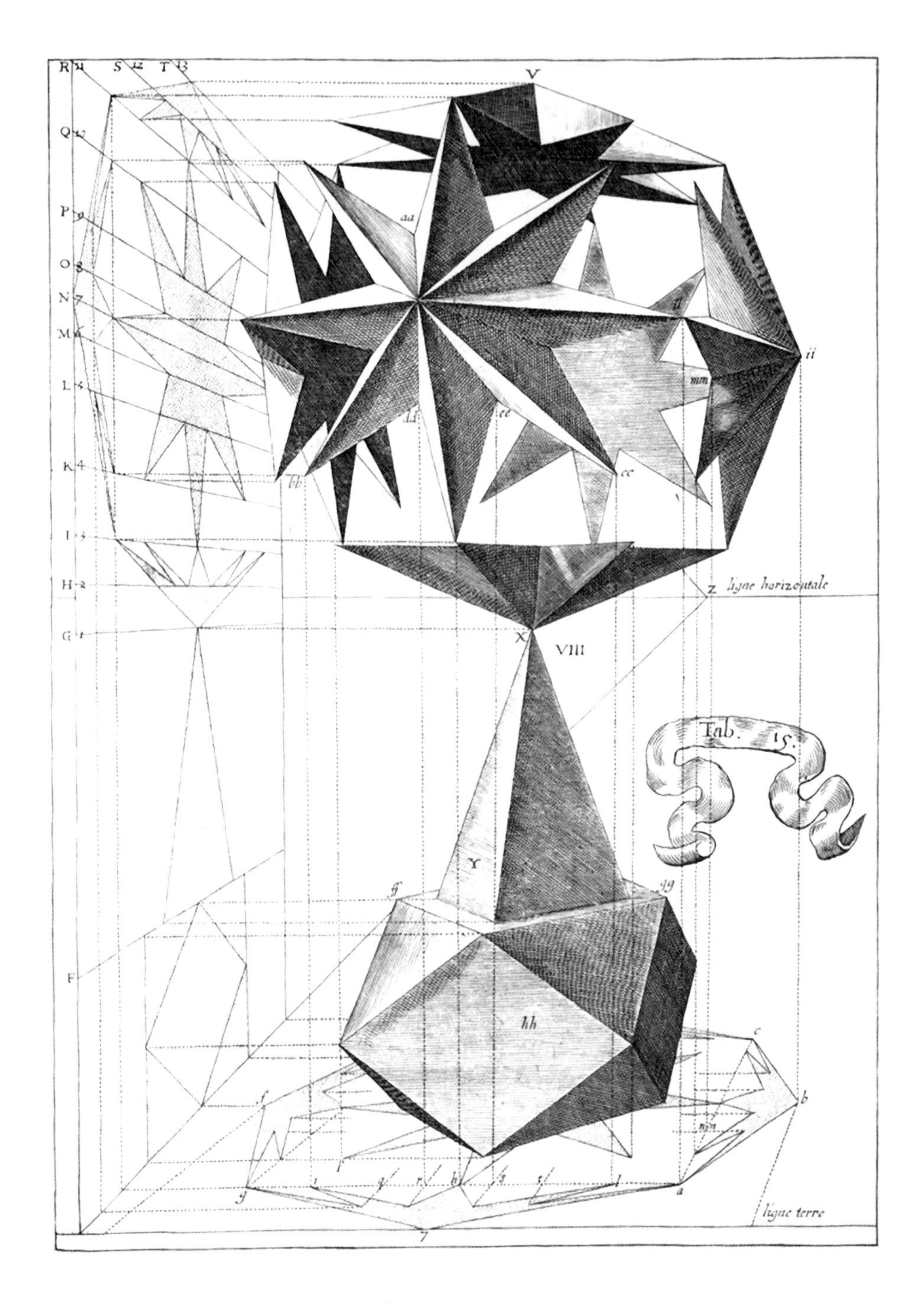

From Thaumaturgus Opticus, *Jean-François Niçeron, Paris, 1638.*

From Thaumaturgus Opticus, *Jean-François Niçeron, Paris, 1638.*

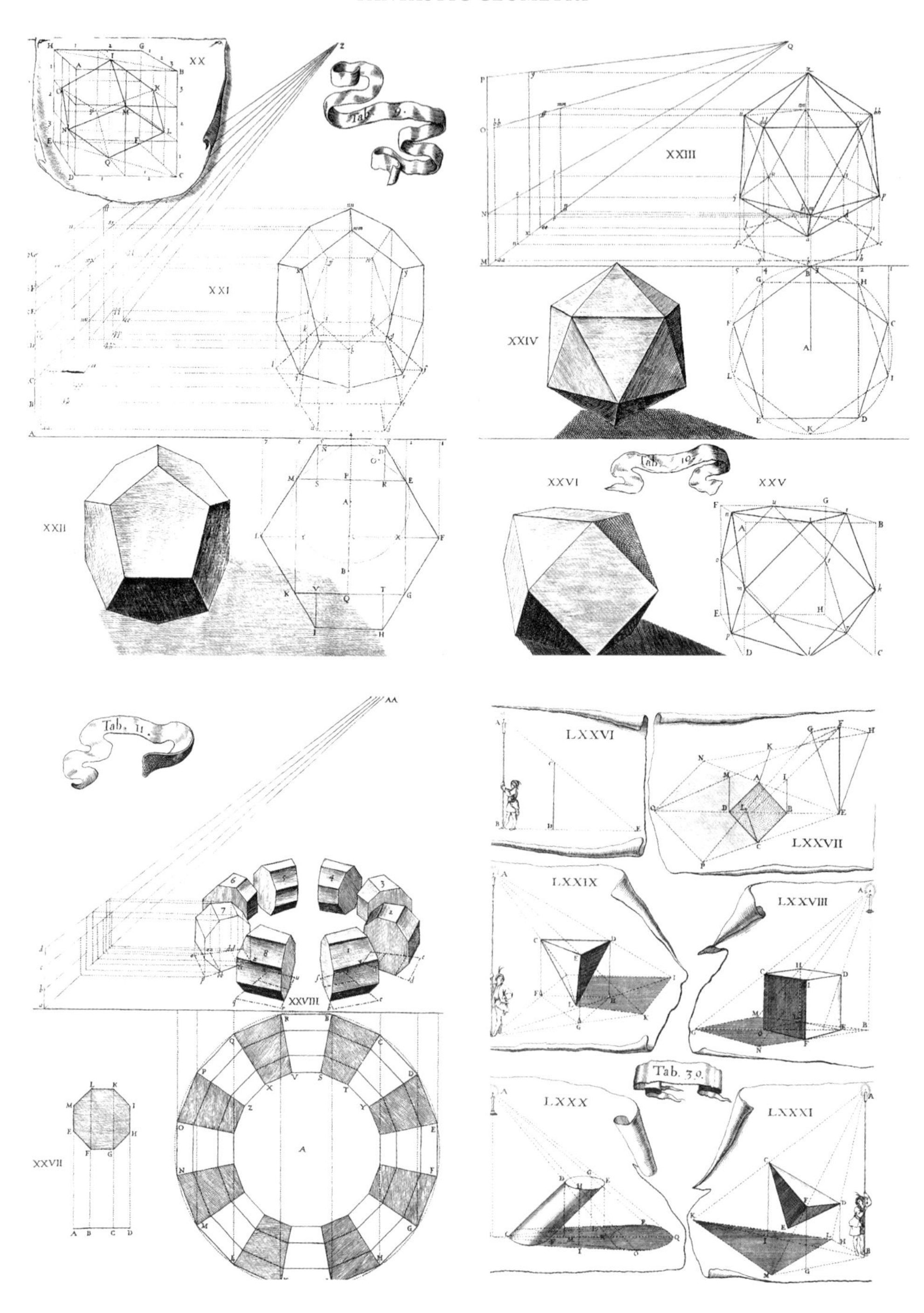

From Thaumaturgus Opticus, *Jean-François Niçeron, Paris, 1638.*

Addendum 1

Intarsia in Italy

Intarsia techniques, involving fine wood-inlay work, were part of the rich artistic heritage that came to Europe from the Islamic world via Spain (the term itself may derive from the Arabic *tarsi*, meaning mosaic or inlay). The Italian city of Siena, in particular, had a long association with the production of fine woodworking, and there are records of panels and doors being decorated in this way from as early as the fifteenth century. This tradition peaked around the time of the early Renaissance, with some of the finest work produced by such masters as Fra Giovanni of Verona (*c.*1433–1515), and Damiano da Bergamo (*c.*1490–1549), both of whose work clearly shares the preoccupations of fine artists at this time. Perspective and geometric motifs are common in Italian intarsia panels of the early sixteenth century, as is the use of *trompe l'oeil* effects. Interestingly, it seems fairly certain that Fra Giovanni used tracings of Leonardo's drawings of geometrical figures in some of his panels, and that they were regarded as appropriate subjects for religious meditation.

Intarsia panel from the Church of Santa Maria in Organo, Verona (c.1494–9), made by Fra Giovanni of Verona.

Intarsia panel from the Church of Santa Maria in Organo, Verona (c.1494–9), made by Fra Giovanni of Verona.

Intarsia panels from the Basilica of San Dominico (early 1500s), by Fra Damiano Zambelli (top). Intarsia panels from by the monastery of Monte Olivetto Maggiore, near Siena (c.1503–6), made by Fra Giovanni of Verona (bottom).

Addendum 2

Intarsia in Germany

During the Northern Renaissance, intarsia, together with its associated geometrical motifs and the use of *trompe l'oeil*, spread to Germany, to such centres as Nuremberg and Augsburg, where for a while it became extremely popular – indeed was almost a mania (*intarsienmanie*). By contrast with Italian intarsia, however, there were fewer religious connotations. It is known that German intarsia cabinet-makers, in common with their Italian counterparts, borrowed visual imagery from prints. Stoer's work was undoubtedly an influence, although there is little direct evidence of the use of his drawings, and certainly none at all of his famous *Geometria et Perspectiva* series (Nuremberg, 1567).

Intarsia writing desk, Augsburg, sixteenth century: Museum fur Angewandte Kunst, Frankfurt (top); Intarsia writing desk detail (bottom).

Intarsia writing desk, Nuremberg, sixteenth century: Museum fur Angewandte Kunst, Frankfurt (top); Detail of main panel (bottom).

Intarsia writing desk, Nuremberg, sixteenth century: Museum fur Angewandte Kunst, Frankfurt; left panel (top); right panel (bottom).

Addendum 3

The *mazzocchio*

The *mazzocchio* form, which became a stock item in geometric perspective treatises, began as a Florentine hat – or rather, as the supporting framework for this extravagant fashion item. Uccello drew a perspective version of a *mazzocchio* in brown ink and black wash, now in the Louvre (Fig. 1). Leonardo da Vinci made several drawings of this object in his notebooks (Fig. 2). They feature in both Wentzel Jamnitzer's and Johannes Lencker's books (Figs. 3–5). Peter Halt, in his *Perspectivische Reiss Kunst* (Figs 6–8), provides further variations on this motif, one of the few non-classical abstract figures employed in Renaissance geometric perspective treatises. In Lorenzo Sirigatti's *La Pratica di Prospettiva* it is adopted as a *leitmotif* (Figs. 9–11), and Danielle Barbaro presented a series of variants in his own perspective treatise *La Pratica della Perspetiva* (page 272).

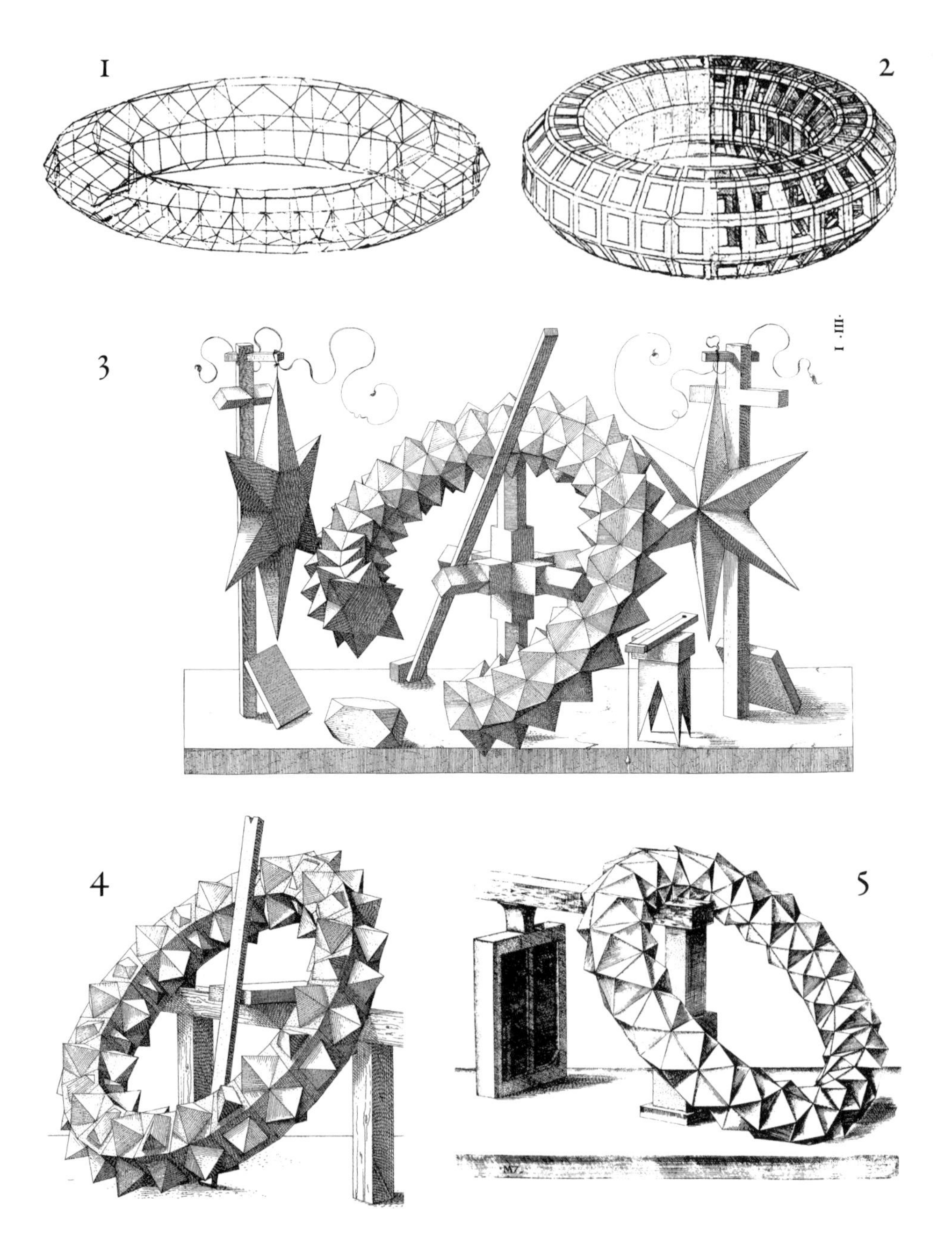

Mazzacchio

Uccello (top left); Leonardo (top right); Jamnitzer (centre and bottom left); Laencker (bottom right).

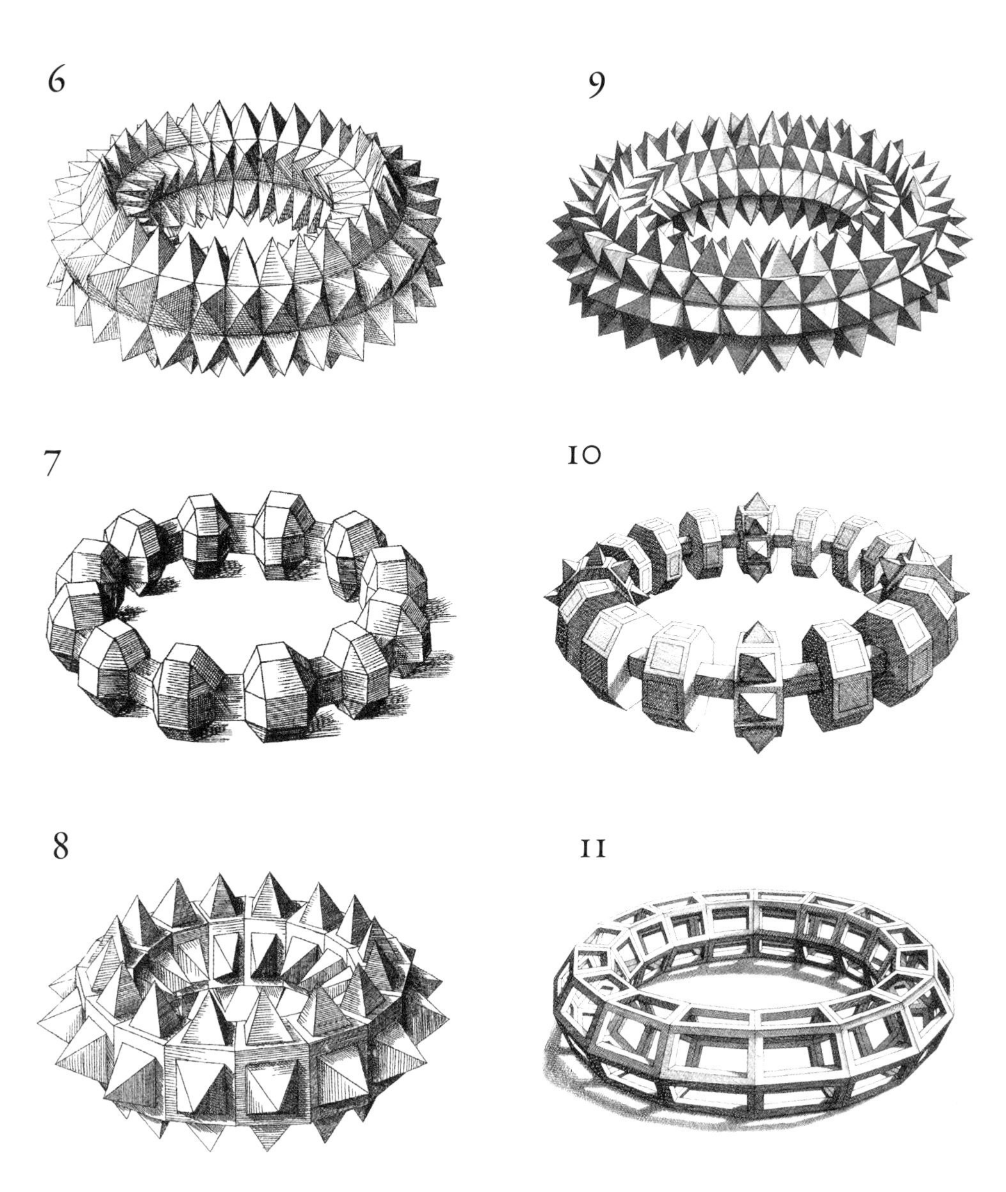

Mazzacchio
Peter Halt (left column), Sirigatti (right column).

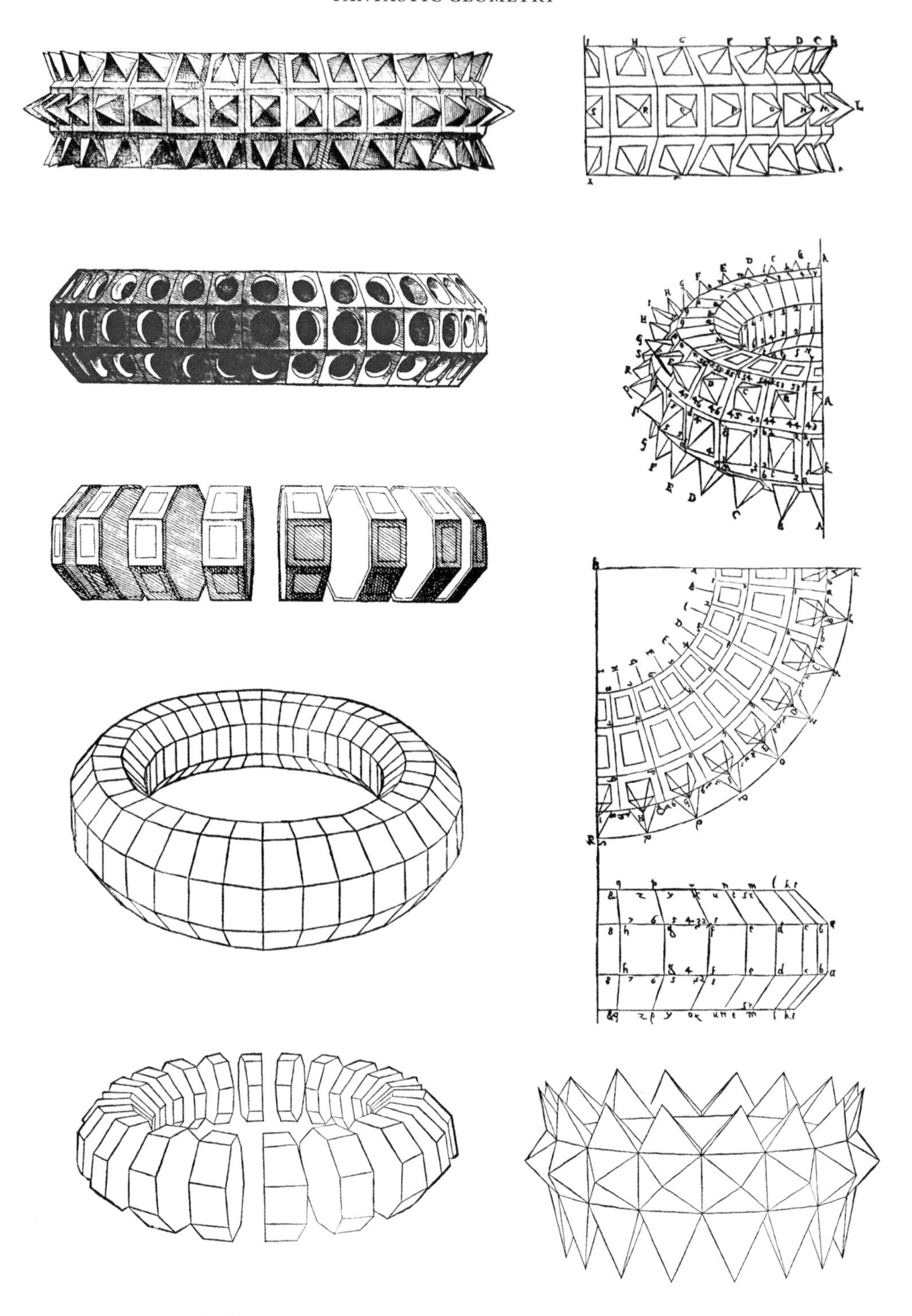

Mazzocchio figures from Danielle Barbaro's *La Pratica della Perspetiva*, Venice, 1569.

Addendum 4
The emblematic sphere

Spherical models for the purpose of astronomical and geographical calculation have existed since at least the time of Ptolomy – in fact the invention of the armillary sphere in particular is usually attributed to the Hellenistic astronomer Eratosthesnes in the second century BC. It would appear that from the very beginning these devices acquired an emblematic, as well as a practical, value. However, in practice they were often rather cumbersome. Ptolomy's own armillary sphere, with its seven interlocking rings, was almost impossible to manage, and centuries later Tycho Brahe gave up on his version for use in astronomical calculations. On the other hand, the armillary astrolabe was among those scientific instruments that Regiomontanus declared as 'nothing more useful' to uncover the relative motions of the celestial bodies without resorting to calculation.

Whatever their genuine practical value it is certain that, judging from their constant use as illustrations in scientific books from the late Middle Ages on, they also came to have an important emblematic value. Armillary spheres, in particular, are frequently found in portraits of astronomers, astrologers and mathematicians, and have often been used as an attribute of Astronomia, the personification of the art of astronomy, or Urania, its muse. Also employed by rulers as symbols of worldly dominion, armillary spheres have also been used to represent the contemplation of heaven (in saints' portraits and emblems), and of more rational notions of universality.

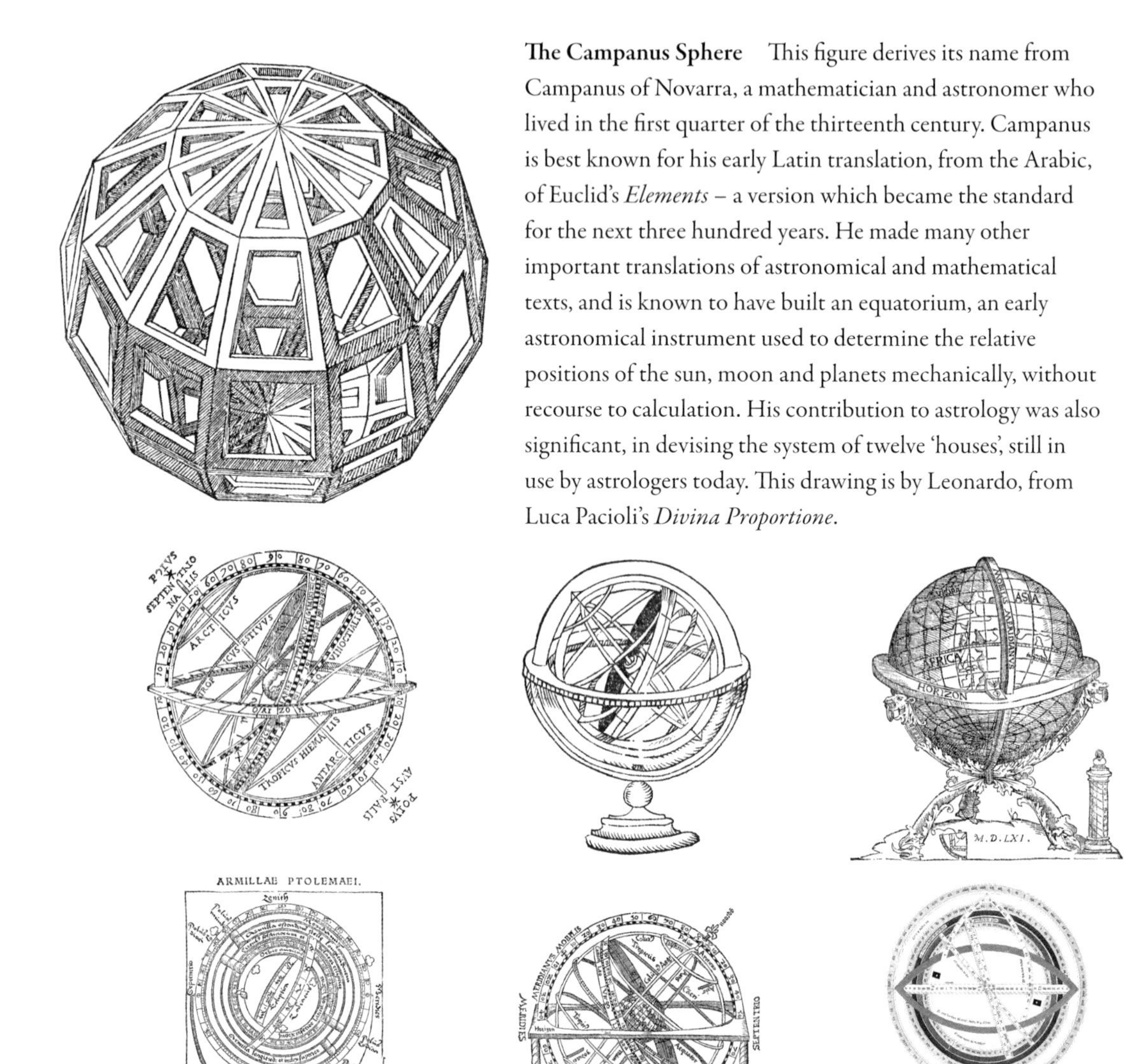

The Campanus Sphere This figure derives its name from Campanus of Novarra, a mathematician and astronomer who lived in the first quarter of the thirteenth century. Campanus is best known for his early Latin translation, from the Arabic, of Euclid's *Elements* – a version which became the standard for the next three hundred years. He made many other important translations of astronomical and mathematical texts, and is known to have built an equatorium, an early astronomical instrument used to determine the relative positions of the sun, moon and planets mechanically, without recourse to calculation. His contribution to astrology was also significant, in devising the system of twelve 'houses', still in use by astrologers today. This drawing is by Leonardo, from Luca Pacioli's *Divina Proportione*.

The Armillary Sphere An Armillary Sphere consists of a series of rings, representing celestial latitude and longitude, the ecliptic and equinoctial, etc, which form a framework centred on a central earth. It is essentially a spherical astrolabe, indicating the motion of the stars around the earth. This device was known to Hellenistic astronomers, and was taken up in the Islamic world, where it was further developed, and passed on to Europe as part of the great cultural bounty that gave rise to the Renaissance. Illustrated here are Armillary Spheres used as title pages to the works of Clavius, Kepler, Regiomomtanus, and Apianus (from his *Cosmographia*).

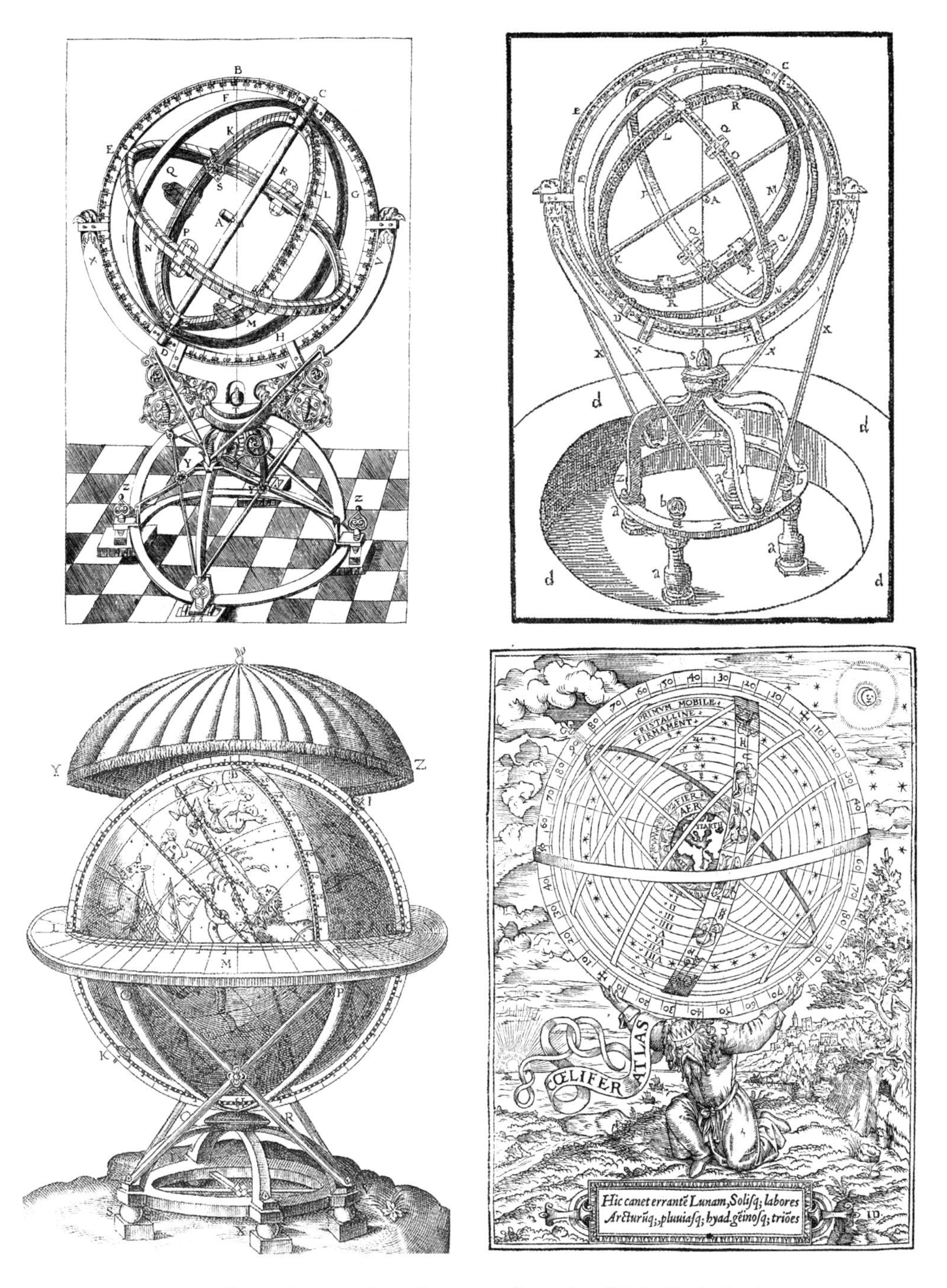

Armillary Spheres used as title pages in the works of Tycho Brahe (top).
Tycho's Celestial sphere (bottom left); Cunningham's Armillary (bottom right).

GEOMETRICAL PERSPECTIVE TREATISES AND OTHER RELEVANT PUBLICATIONS, ARRANGED BY DATE OF PUBLICATION

De Prospectiva pigendi, *c.*1470; Piero della Francesca (*c.*1410–92).

Libellus de Quinque Corporibus Regularibus, *c.*1480; Piero della Francesca (*c.*1410–92).

Euclid's *Elementa Geometriae*, Venice, 1482; Erhard Ratdolt (1442–1528).

De Divina Proportione, Venice, 1509; Luca Pacioli (1446–1517; Leonardo Da Vinci (1452–1519).

Underweysung der Messung mit dem Zirckel und Richscheyt, Nuremberg, 1525; Albrecht Dürer (1471–1528).

Vier Bucher von Menschlicher Proportion, Nuremberg, 1528; Albrecht Dürer (1471–1528).

Ein schön nützlich Buchlein, Nuremberg, 1531; Hieronymus Rodler (*d.*1539).

Ein aigentliche und grundliche anweysung in die Geometria, Nuremberg, 1543; Augustin Hirschvogel (1503–53).

Geometrische und Perspektivische Zeichnungen, Nuremberg?, *c.*1560; Anonymous (*c.*1565–1600).

Livres de Perspective, Paris, 1560; Jean Cousin (1490–1560).

Des Circles und Richtscheyts, Nuremberg, 1564; Heinrich Lautensack (1520–68).

Geometria et Perspectiva, Augsburg, 1567; Lorenz Stoer (*c.*1540–1620).

Perspectiva Literaria, Nuremberg, 1567, 1596; Johannes Lencker (1551?–85).

Perspectiva Corporum Regularium, Nuremberg, 1568; Wentzel Jamnitzer (1508–85).

La Pratica della Perspettiva, Venice, 1569; Daniel Barbaro (1513–70).

Perspectiva, Nuremberg, 1571; Johannes Lencker (1551?–85).

Leçons de Perspective Positive, Paris, 1576; Jaques Androuet du Cerceau (1549–84).

Mysterium Cosmographicum, Tubingen, 1596; 1621; Johannes Kepler (1571–1630).

La Practica di Prospettiva, Venice, 1596; Lorenzo Sirigatti, *d.*1625.

Extract der Geometriae und Perspectivae, Nuremberg, 1598; Paul Pfinzing (1554–99).

Perspective, Amsterdam, 1604; Jan Vredeman de Vries (1527– *c.*1607).

Strena seu de Niva Sexangula, Frankfurt, 1611: Johannes Kepler (1571–1630).

Praxis Perspective, Leipzig, 1615; Lucas Brunn (1572–1628).

Harmonices Mundi, Frankfurt, 1619: Johannes Kepler (1571–1630).

Prospettiva Pratica, Florence, 1625; Pietro Accolti (1579–1642).

Perspectivische Reiss Kunst, Augsburg, 1625, Peter Halt (uncertain).

La Perspective Curieuse, Paris, 1638; Jean-François Niçeron (1613–46).

La Perspective Pratique, Paris, 1642; Pierre le Dubreuil (1602–70).

Aerarium Philosophiaae Mathematicae, Rome, 1648; Mario Bettini (1582–1657).

Perspectiva pictorum et Architectoerum, Augsburg, 1693; Andrea Pozzo (1642–1709).

Linear Perspective, London, 1715; Brook Taylor (1685–1731).

Lucidum Prospectivae Speculum, Augsburg, 1727; Paul Heinecken (1680–1746).

BIBLIOGRAPHY

Anderson, Kirsti, *The geometry of an Art: the history of the mathematical theory of perspective*; Springer, NY, 2007.

Bedini, Silvio, 'The Perspective Machine of Wentzel Jamnitzer', *Technology and Culture*, April 1968, Volume 9, Number 2.

Cromwell, Peter R., *Polyhedra*; Cambridge University Press, 2004.

Gluch, Sibylle, *The Craft's Use of Geometry in Sixteenth Century Germany*, University of Dresden, 2007.

Hart, George W., *Polyhedra and Art through History*, www.georgehart.com.

Kemp, Martin, *The Science of Art: optical themes in western art*; Yale University Press, 1990.

Pfaff, Dorothea, *Lorenz Stoer: Geometria et Perspectiva*; LMU Publikatione.

Richter, Fleur, *Die Ästhetik geometrischer Körper in der Renaissance*, Verlag Gerd Hatje, 1995.

Smith, Jeffry Chipps, 'Nuremberg and the Topologies of Expectation', *Journal of the Northern Renaissance*, Spring, 2009.

Schreiber,P., 'A New Hypothesis on Dürer's Enigmatic Polyhedron in his Copper Engraving Melencolia', *Historia Math*, 26, 369–77, 1999.

Sutton, Daud, *Platonic and Archimedean Solids*, Walker & Company, 2002.

Van den Broeke, Albert and Ruttkay, Zsofia, *A Closer Look at Jamnitzer's Polyhedra*, University of Twente.

Various, *The Sources and Literature of Perspective*, www.sumscorp.com.

Veltman, Kim H, *Geometric Games: A History of the Not So Regular Solids*, 1990.

Wood, Christopher S., *The Perspective Treatise in Ruins: Studies in the History of Art, Symposium Papers XXXVI*, Washington Nat. Gall. of Art, CASVA, 2003 (republished with CD-ROM edition of Lorenz Stoer's *Geometria et Perpectiva*, Harald Fischer Verlag, Erlangen, 2006).

ACKNOWLEDGEMENTS

The author would like to thank the following:

Daud Sutton for permission to use his drawings of the Platonic and Archimedean solids, taken from his book of the same name, published by Wooden Books in 2002.

Herzog August Bibliothek, Wofenbuttel, for permission to use the illustrations by an anonymous artist, ref. Cod Guelf. 71.1, Aug. 2 o.

Museo Galileo (Institute and Museum of the History of Science), Florence, for permission to use the Lorenzo Sirigatti drawings from *La Pratica i Prospettiva*.

Harald Fischer Verlag, Erlangen, for permission to use Lorenz Stoer's illustrations from *Geometria et Perspective: Corpora Regulate et Irregulata*.

Staatliche Graphische Sammlung, Munchen, for permission to use illustrations by Lorenz Stoer.

Rijksmuseum, Amsterdam, for permisson to use illustrations by Wenzel Jamnitzer.

Stadtbibliothek, Nuremberg, for permission to use illustrations by Albrecht Dürer.

Museum fur Angewandte Kunst, Köln, for permission to use photographs of an Intarsia Kabinett.

Museum fur Angewandte Kunst, Frankfurt, for permission to use drawings of Intarsia.

Hamburger Kunsthalle, for permission to use a print by 'Monogramme P.P.'

Kunsthistorisches Museum, Wien, for permission to use a print by 'Monogramme P.P.'

INDEX